MAT 011
BEGINNING ALGEBRA

2010–2011

Custom Edition for Montgomery County Community College
2002 AMATYC Input Award Winner

DR. ROSEANNE HOFFMAN • WALTER R. HUNTER • SUSAN K. YANKOSKY

Learning Solutions

New York Boston San Francisco
London Toronto Sydney Tokyo Singapore Madrid
Mexico City Munich Paris Cape Town Hong Kong Montreal

Cover Art: TO COME FROM CREATIVE

Pearson Learning Solutions, 501 Boylston Street, Suite 900, Boston, MA 02116
A Pearson Education Company
www.pearsoned.com

Printed in the United States of America

1 2 3 4 5 6 7 8 9 10 V312 15 14 13 12 11 10

000200010270580451

WH

ISBN 10: 0-558-70309-7
ISBN 13: 978-0-558-70309-7

Montgomery County
Community College

To MAT 011 Students:

When I was in fourth grade, I watched my father receive his bachelor's degree, in a very ornate ceremony that I was unfamiliar with at the time, at a large civic center in Baltimore. I remember being fixated on the pomp and circumstance. My father's achievement was marked by years of studying, sometimes with me, at the kitchen table. He balanced work, family and school and his persistence and achievement helped transform his family in ways he could not imagine at the time. I'm certain that his dedication and commitment to learning influenced my career choice and passion for shaping our community college into one that places student success above all else. I believe in the transformational power of education. I'm sure you do too. Perhaps that is one reason you are enrolled at Montgomery County Community College.

Our College places its singular focus on increasing student success especially for students enrolled in preparatory math courses like this one. That's why our College is one of fewer than 100 community colleges in the country that is part of the Achieving the Dream initiative, an initiative designed to help colleges to help more students to reach their educational goals. National research from Achieving the Dream colleges shows that this course is one of the most important postsecondary classes you will ever enroll in. This course is a "gateway" course which means that your success here could predict success in subsequent collegiate courses (math and non-math), success in attaining your associate degree, and success upon transfer should that be your chosen path.

Our College is filled with resources that will support your success. Just ask! This textbook was written by our terrific math faculty members, along with assistance from an ORI 100 instructor. The book was carefully designed to support you through challenging math concepts. Our Learning Assistance Center is filled with resources for you to further practice the concepts you learn in the classroom. Our Student Success Center is home to academic advisors and counselors that are here to coach you when you need an extra hand. And, your faculty is also ever present to support and encourage you inside and outside the classroom.

Yes, I believe in the transformational power of education. My father didn't stop after he earned his bachelor's degree. He continued on and later earned a master's degree. He makes a habit of learning. Even in retirement, my father is still in school, taking a hybrid anatomy and physiology course to secure a certificate and second career in medical coding. A commitment to continuous learning has transformed my father and my family.

With this course, commit to making a habit of learning. Success here is one of the first steps toward your individual transformation, a transformation that will reap benefits you never dreamed of.

Here's to achieving **your** dream,

Karen A. Stout

Karen A. Stout
President

TABLE OF CONTENTS

MATH 011 INTRODUCTION

"I can't do math!!" " I have a calculator. Why do I need to know the multiplication tables?" "I've been working for 25 years and algebra has never come up on the job."

"I didn't take the placement test seriously. This is ridiculous to have to take non-credit math classes and waste all this time and money."

"Some people are born mathematicians and some aren't." "Computers will do all of the math I need."

As you sit in your Math 011 class this first week, you probably will hear some of the above comments being made by your classmates. You may even be uttering some of them yourself. (Interestingly enough, a student bragging about not being able to read is rare indeed.)

Please understand that placement into a non-credit course is not a punishment; it is a sincere effort on the part of the College to help you begin your math requirements at a place where you can succeed. If you are convinced that the placement results are not a true indication of your abilities, then please take a re-test. (The re-test should be taken before the first day of the semester.) However, if the re-test confirms your initial results, please return to class with a positive attitude and a willingness to work.

What would be a **true** tragedy would be to pay for the same class twice! Remember: You must earn a C to move to the next level.

Health Club Metaphor

When one joins a health club, the goal is usually a very positive one: to lose weight, to get in shape, to improve cardio-vascular health, or to look good in a bathing suit. However, good intentions and membership fees are just the easy first steps. Success depends on determination and hard work—going to work out when one does not really feel like it, doing more repetitions than are comfortable, giving up other, more enjoyable, activities to adhere to the workout routine.

No one would dispute the fact that results depend upon the individual. No health club, no personal trainer can do the sweating for the person, no matter who he or she may be.

You have just joined Club Math; your success or failure is in your own hands. Many aids are available to you, but ultimately you are the determining factor. Math muscle or math flab—you decide.

TEXTBOOK USE

This Math 011 textbook is designed to reflect an applications approach to algebra. That is, you will be required to get very involved in each class and in each assignment. Individual sections contain an overview section, class work, group work, and exercise sections. The preview section should be read by the student either before or after the section is covered by the instructor. The class work section will be done with the instructor as a guide, the group work section with the assistance of classmates, and the exercises completed at home, with a study group, or with a tutor.

Each chapter ends with a review section for an exam. This can be handled in an individual or group situation. (Groups are wonderful review tools. Ask your instructor for suggestions on forming study groups.)

The textbook is designed as a workbook. You should take notes in the class work sections. There is not enough space provided in the book to adequately do the exercises. Homework exercises should be done on separate paper from a loose leaf note book. This allows you to do the same problems again and again. Such repetition can be very helpful when reviewing for a test.

PRACTICAL SUGGESTIONS FOR MATH SUCCESS

1. **Attend class faithfully** (Everyone has illnesses and family emergencies; work around them. You can rarely make up material missed in a class session.)

2. Believe you can be successful even if math has not been a strength in the past. **Positive thinking does work**.

3. **Read** the pages assigned before attending class. Even if you don't understand the material, just seeing it begins a circuitry in the brain for future development and expansion.

4. Be aware of your **learning style** and techniques you can use to manipulate the material to your best learning advantage

5. Do some type of math work **every day**. The learning curve drops dramatically with even a one-day hiatus.

6. Plan on **short, frequent math sessions**. Twenty minutes is enough at the beginning. (Set a quiet timer and reward yourself with a pleasant activity after each session). Three periods a day is ideal.

7. Your math professor is an expert; use his or her talents both inside and outside of the classroom. Learn your instructor's name and office location. Visit during **office hours** to ask questions and clarify difficult problems.

8. Use lined paper for all problem solving; write on only one side and allow plenty of white space between numbers. Store your homework in a three ring binder. It is imperative to keep information very **organized**.

9. Create **note cards** for important formulas, key definitions and rules. They will be a great reference when studying for a test and/or doing your homework. Write the page number on each card so you can refer back to the book.

10. Don't write on handouts unless you make copies first. Again, these can be reused as study tools for exams. ***If handouts are used in class, ask your instructor for 2 copies.***

11. We often learn more from our failures than from our successes. **Don't get discouraged** if it seems to be difficult. Most worthwhile human endeavors are.

12. Don't be embarrassed to **ask questions** in class if you need clarification on homework or on the lecture. The only stupid question is the one that goes unasked.

13. **Repetition** is important; keep working on problems until they become very familiar to you. The process is important, not the numbers.

14. **Reading and Writing Mathematics Exercises** may appeal to students whose learning styles require a different approach than is being offered in the classroom. If you are having difficulties with the Practice Exercises, attempt the Reading and Writing Exercises first. Often reviewing the material in a different manner will result in better comprehension. Experiment – see what works for your unique learning style

Creating a Weekly Planner

New students must learn to budget their time in order to be successful in college. Follow the steps below to create your own weekly planner. You should do this every week.

1. Make extra copies of page v.

2. Fill in your class times; include travel time to and from school.

3. Fill in your work schedule; include travel time to and from work.

4. Fill in other weekly activities. (sports, clubs, etc.) Include travel time.

5. Fill in important school dates, such as tests and due dates for papers. Use a red pencil to denote their importance.

6. Schedule four to six hours a week to study for your math course. Do not use more than half hour blocks.

7. Schedule study time for the rest of your courses. For each course, you should schedule between four and six hours.

8. Make sure you have time to eat, sleep, and socialize.

NAME ______________________________ WEEK OF ____________________

WEEKLY PLANNER

	Sunday	Monday	Tuesday	Wednesday	Thursday	Friday	Saturday
Morning							
7:00							
7:30							
8:00							
8:30							
9:00							
9:30							
10:00							
10:30							
11:00							
11:30							
Afternoon							
12:00							
12:30							
1:00							
1:30							
2:00							
2:30							
3:00							
3:30							
4:00							
4:30							
Evening							
5:00							
5:30							
6:00							
6:30							
7:00							
7:30							
8:00							
8:30							
9:00							
9:30							
10:00							
10:30							
11:00							
11:30							

Montgomery County Community College

Learning Assistance Labs

Central Campus (Blue Bell, PA) – 215.641.6452 – College Hall Room 320
West Campus (Pottstown, PA) – 215.718.1945 – Room 159

The Learning Assistance Labs (LALs) of Montgomery County Community College provide academic support services for all MCCC students. Assistance is available for most courses offered at the college and all services are free. The purpose of the Labs is to assist all students in the pursuit of academic success. **Students enrolled in MAT 011 (Beginning Algebra) can get assistance with course topics by utilizing one or more of the following services:**

One-on-One Tutoring – Students sit with a tutor to discuss course material, review homework problems, and prepare for tests. Students should attend class and attempt assigned problems before visiting the lab for tutoring. No appointment is required. Students come to the lab, sign in, and ask to see a MAT 011 tutor. Students are usually served within 30 minutes of visiting the lab if not immediately.

Small Group Tutoring – Students sit with a tutor and other MAT 011 students to discuss course material, review homework problems, and prepare for tests. Students should attend class and attempt assigned problems before attending a group tutoring session. Contact LAL Central and LAL West respectively for details and schedules.

On-line Tutoring – Students log on to the MAT 011 tutoring site, post questions for the tutor, and check back for a response within 24 hours. To register for On-line Tutoring, contact LAL Central (215-641-6452). All MCCC students (Central, West, and Distance) may use this service.

Supplemental Instruction in the Developmental Studies Lab at Central Campus – Students may use special computer software to practice topics and problems covered in the classroom. Call the DSL (215-641-6693) for details.

Hours – Central Campus (Blue Bell)

Fall and Spring Terms

Monday through Thursday
7:30 a.m. to 9:30 p.m.
Friday
7:30 a.m. to 5:00 p.m.
Saturday
10:00 a.m. to 4:00 p.m.
Sunday
1:00 p.m. to 5:00 p.m.

Summer Sessions

Monday through Thursday
8:00 a.m. to 9:30 p.m.
Friday
8:00 a.m. to 5:00 p.m.
Saturday
10:00 a.m. to 4:00 p.m.

Hours - West Campus (Pottstown)

Fall and Spring Terms

Monday through Thursday
8:00 a.m. to 9:00 p.m.
Friday
8:00 a.m. to 5:00 p.m.
Saturday
9:00 a.m. to noon

Summer Sessions

Monday through Thursday
8:00 a.m. to 9:00 p.m.
Friday
8:00 a.m. to 5:00 p.m.

ELECTRONIC STUDENT RESOURCES

Arrays of technology tools were designed to accompany the newly created textbook. Animated ToolBook modules made available on a CD provide a different learning style that is appropriate for many students. A web page was developed with Power Point lectures, SmartBoard lectures with audio, and sample tests.

Web Page

The electronic resources include the following:

- Smartboard lectures with audio on all Class Work
- Class Work notes
- Solutions Manual for homework exercises
- Sample Tests
- Flash Modules on important topics in the course.
- Power Point lectures
- Calculator Supplement
- Course Outline

Ask your teacher on how to find the web page.

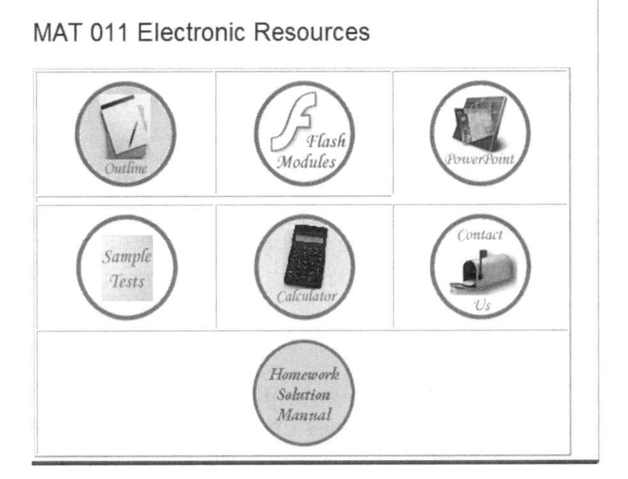

ToolBook Modules

Eleven ToolBook modules were written to accompany a context based elementary algebra course. The modules are interactive, animated, audio enriched lessons. The goal of the ToolBook modules is to use another medium to present elementary algebra topics. One page from one of the eleven modules included here is just a static page. This page does not show or capture the animation, the sound, nor the interactivity required by the student. The sound is a value-added feature for English as a second language (ESL) and for on-line students. Ask your instructor for a CD.

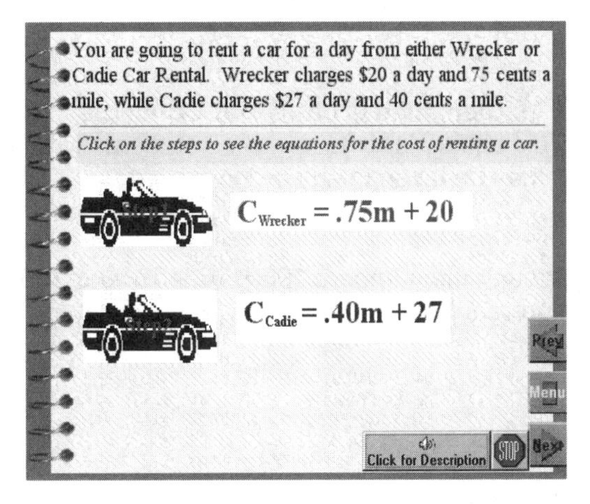

What Math Course Should I Take Next?
Advising Information for Mat 011 Students

Math courses available to students who pass MAT 011:

MAT 100 Intermediate Algebra

This course is designed as a prerequisite for students who are required to take MAT 125 (Discrete Math), MAT 131 (Statistics I), MAT 140 (Finite Math), and/or MAT 161 (Precalculus I). If you think you might major in Business, Computer Science, Math, or a Science, then this is the course you should take. This course generally does not transfer. When it does transfer it is as a free elective, not as a fulfillment of a math requirement. It is fast paced and challenging.

MAT 100B Intermediate Algebra with Review

This course covers the same material as MAT 100 but also includes a review of the material in MAT 011. It is suggested that students who get a C in MAT 011 and need to take MAT 100 should consider taking MAT 100B. This course meets 4 hours a week and students receive 3 credits. Students pay for 4 credits.

MAT 103 Math for Elementary Education

This is a course designed for Elementary Education majors. You should check with a counselor or an advisor about the transferability of the course.

MAT 106 Math Applications

This course is for Liberal Arts students who need one or two college level math courses. If you think you might major in Criminal Justice, Social Science, Humanities, Secondary Education (except math or science concentrations), or Communications, then this is the course you should take. The exception is a major in Psychology which may require MAT 131 (Statistics I). Check the requirements of the four year school.

MAT 108 Mathematics Culture and Concepts

This course is for Liberal Arts students who need a second college level math. MAT 106 and MAT 108 may be taken in any order.

Note: Although the numbers 103, 106, 108, and 115 are higher than 100, the courses do **<u>not</u>** need MAT 100 as a prerequisite.

General Advice:

1. It is very important to meet with a counselor or an advisor. You need to be aware of the latest transfer and graduation requirements.
2. If you have chosen a major, then you should follow the course listings for that major in the catalog. The Counseling and Advising Centers have catalogs for most of the area colleges.
3. If you know what college you are going to transfer to, then you should follow the catalog for your transfer school and find the equivalent courses offered by Montgomery County Community College. If the math course you need doesn't seem to be offered by MCCC, contact the four year college for advice.
4. If you are undecided as to what you want to do, then you may want to spend some time contemplating your career choices. The Counseling Center has many resources to help with your career options. The math course you take after MAT 011 may set the path for your career.

NOTE TO THE INSTRUCTOR: PHILOSOPHY OF THE AUTHORS

The practical application of mathematics is of paramount importance to our culture in the twenty-first century. Whether one is attempting to balance the weekly budget, to secure a well-paying job, or to advance to a higher level mathematics course, understanding the process is imperative. However, at the same time, improper use of technology has given some students the erroneous impression that calculators are the end result rather than the tools. These students fail to comprehend the human intellectual role in the process.

In an attempt to circumvent some of the negative thinking and frustrating experiences students bring to the classroom, the authors have attempted to present the beginning algebra material in this text in a non-threatening manner. We use applications not only to justify the material in the course but also to give concrete examples of the abstract concepts. At the same time, we understand the importance of imparting traditional mathematical skills.

In walking this fine line, we have intentionally chosen to present the rules of arithmetic informally, especially in the first section of the text. Our primary goal in this approach is to help the students feel successful from the beginning of the course. Additionally, we also purposely delay presenting the formal rules for solving equations until after students are introduced to them using applications.

If we can convince the learners that simple language and concrete study strategies are effective, perhaps they will be more willing to move ahead, regardless of past negative experiences.

We have included in the appendices the more formal definitions of addition and subtraction of signed numbers. The instructor can refer to these pages whenever it seems appropriate. Also, we have included pages of exercises to use when drill seems necessary.

Acknowledgements: Aileen Conway
Rich Kern
Irene Yarbrough
Marion Graziano
Megan Malizia
Leslie Helm
Alison Sawyer

AMATYC INPUT AWARD is presented to innovative curriculum that utilizes modern technology in courses before calculus. AMATYC, American Mathematical Society of Two Year Colleges, is the leading national organization for community college mathematics teachers.

CHAPTER 1

INTRODUCTION TO ALGEBRA

SECTION 1.1 SIGNED NUMBERS
PREVIEW

Objectives: In this section, you will add, subtract, multiply, and divide signed numbers. Also, in solving arithmetic expressions, you will use the order of operations including exponents.

Intuitive Approach to Addition and Subtraction:

Example 1. I have $40, and I owe you $75. What is my net worth?

To find the answer:

Having $40 is equivalent to + 40.
Owing $75 is equivalent to – 75.

My net worth will be indicated by 40 – 75.

or

$40 - 75 = -35$

My net worth is –$35.

Since I owe more than I have, the answer has to be a negative number.

Rule: Intuitive Rule for combining numbers with **unlike** signs:
Find the difference (subtraction) of the two numbers and use the sign of the larger number.

A way to use this rule is to cover the signs of the numbers. Find the difference between the numbers with the signs covered. Use the sign of the larger number.

Example 2. I am in debt for $50, and I owe you $60. What is my net worth?

To find the answer:

Being in debt for $50 is equivalent to –50.
Owing $60 is equivalent to – 60.

My net worth is indicated by –50 – 60.

or

$-50 - 60 = -110$
My net worth is –$110.

Since I am in debt and I owe you money, then my net worth has to be negative.

Rule: Intuitive Rule for combining numbers with like **signs**: Add the two numbers and use the common sign.

Study Tip: Make a note card with the rules for adding and subtracting like and unlike signed numbers. Review note cards at least twice a week as part of your homework routine.

Multiplication and Division:

Vocabulary: The **product** is the answer to a multiplication problem.
The **quotient** is the answer to a division problem.

Example 3. I will lose $9 a day for each of the next 6 days. How much money will I lose?

To find the answer:
Losing $9 is equivalent to –9.
Since I am losing $9 everyday for the next 6 days, I will have $-9 \cdot 6$ fewer dollars.

or

$-9 \bullet 6 = -54$
I will lose $54 in the next 6 days.

Since I am losing money, the answer has to be a negative number.

In the example above, –54 is the **product**.

Vocabulary: The **factors** are the numbers being multiplied.
In the example above, $-9 \bullet 6 = -54$, –9 and 6 are the **factors**.

Rule: The product or quotient of two numbers with **unlike signs** is always negative.

Example 4. I lost $8 a day for the previous 7 days. How much more money did I have 7 days ago?

Since I had more money 7 days ago, the answer has to be a positive number.

To find the answer:
Losing $8 is equivalent to –8.
Previous 7 days is equivalent to –7

Since I have lost $8 everyday for the past 7 days,
I will have $-8 \bullet -7$ fewer dollars.

or

$-8 \bullet -7 = 56$
I had 56 more dollars 7 days ago.

Rule: The product or quotient of two numbers with **like signs** is always positive.

Example 5. Divide $\dfrac{-24}{-8}$.

Since the numerator and denominator are both negative the quotient must be positive.

$$\frac{-24}{-8} = 3$$

Study Tip: Make note cards for all of the rules and vocabulary in the course.

Multiplication problems can be expressed in several ways: $-4 \bullet 9 = -36$

$(-4)(9) = -36$

$-4 * 9 = -36$

Division problems can be expressed in several ways: $-45 \div 9 = -5$

$\frac{-45}{9} = -5$

$-45/9 = -5$

Zero in a Division Problem

Division can be checked using multiplication. For example, $\frac{18}{6} = 3$ because $18 = 3 * 6$.
18 divided by 6 is the same as asking what number times 6 equals 18?

How does zero in the numerator affect a division problem?

For example, $\frac{0}{31}$, is the same as asking, what number times 31 equals 0?

So, $\frac{0}{31} = 0$ because $0 * 31 = 0$.

Zero divided by any number equals zero.

How does zero in the denominator affect a division problem?

For example, $\frac{17}{0}$, is the same as asking, what number times 0 equals 17?

A number doesn't exist that when multiplied by 0 is 17.

Thus, the answer to, $\frac{17}{0}$ is undefined.

Any number divided by zero is undefined.

How does zero in both the numerator and denominator affect a division problem?

For example, $\frac{0}{0}$, is the same as asking, what number times 0 equals 0?

Five times zero equals zero, so $\frac{0}{0} = 5$.

Also, 3 times zero equals zero, so $\frac{0}{0} = 3$.

In fact, every number times zero equals zero, so $\frac{0}{0}$ equals any every number.

Zero divided by zero can not be uniquely determined and is called indeterminate.

Study Tip: Division by zero (zero in the denominator) is **undefined.** Zero in both numerator and denominator is called **indeterminate**. Put these concepts on a note card.

Vocabulary: 3 and –3 are **opposites** because they both are the same distance from zero on the number line but in opposite directions. They are also called **additive inverses** because their sum is zero.

The opposite of –6 is 6. In mathematical notation, – (–6) = 6. The first negative sign means to use the opposite; the second negative sign means that 6 is negative or to the left of zero on the number line.

In the application below, the word "profit" is used even if the number is negative, which really indicates a loss.

Example 6. **An Application:** The graph below shows the profit and loss of SRH Inc. for the years 2001 through 2006.

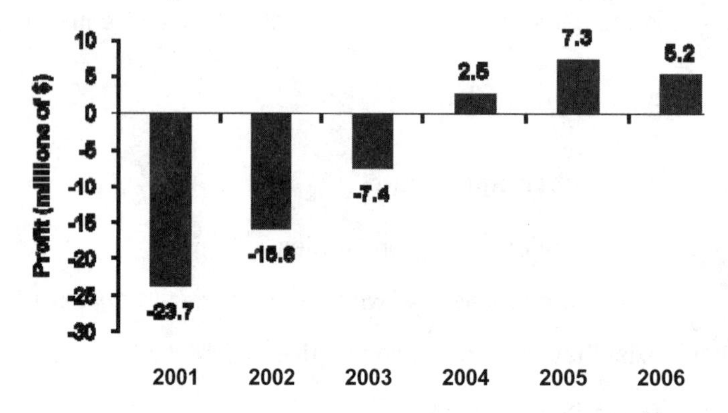

a. What was the difference between the profit in 2005 and the loss in 2002?

"Difference" means subtraction. So to answer the question, subtract the loss in 2002 from the profit in 2005:

(2005 profit) – (2002 loss).

7.3 – (–15.8)	From the chart, find the appropriate profit and loss.
= 7.3 + 15.8	Interpret – (–15.8) as finding the opposite of –15.8.
= 23.1	Add the two numbers.

The difference between the profit in 2005 and the loss in 2002 was 23.1 million dollars. The answer is positive because SRH's profits increased from year 2002 to 2005.

b. What was the difference between the profit in 2006 and profit in 2005? What is the significance of the negative sign in your answer?

(profit in 2006) – (profit in 2005)

5.2 – 7.3 = –2.1

The difference in profit was –2.1 million dollars.

The answer is negative because SRH's profits decreased from year 2005 to 2006.

c. What is the mean (average) profit for the six years?

To find the average, add the profits and losses; then divide by the number of years.

$$\frac{-23.7+(-15.8)+(-7.4)+2.5+7.3+5.2}{6}$$

= –31.9/6 Add the profits.
= –5.317 Divide.

Explanation: –31.9/6 does not actually equal –5.317, the answer is rounded to three decimal places.

The average profit for the six years was a loss of 5.317 million dollars or –5.317 million dollars in profit.

Using a calculator to add, subtract, multiply, or divide:
(The TI–30X II S calculator is recommended for the course. See appendix B or the CD to learn how to use the calculator.)

The keys for multiplication, addition, and division are the standard ones.
Note that the key for multiplication on the calculator is ×, but it appears as * on the calculator screen. For division, the division key is ÷, but appears as / on the screen.

Example 7. – 7.4 – 8.6 = –16

– 7.4 indicates that 7.4 is negative. To input a negative number into a calculator you must use the (–) key which is different from the subtraction key –.

Study Tip: Before using a calculator, you should take a couple of seconds to mentally estimate the answer. This is covered on page 6.

Vocabulary: **Exponents:** **b**^{n} means that the number **b** is used as a factor **n** times.

Example 8. $(-7)^2 = (-7)(-7)$
$= 49$

Order of Operations: When a numerical algebra problem has more than one operation, the order is as follows:

First: Inside **P**arentheses, ( ).

Second: **E**xponents

Third: **M**ultiplication or **D**ivision (left to right)

Fourth: **A**ddition or **S**ubtraction (left to right)

Study Tip: **P**lease **E**xcuse **M**y **D**ear **A**unt **S**ally is a mnemonic used to learn the order of operations. P (Parentheses), E (Exponents), M (Multiplication), D (Division), A (Addition), and S (Subtraction).

Example 9. $-6(8-13)$

$= -6(-5)$	Add the signed numbers inside the parentheses.
$= 30$	The product of numbers with like signs is positive.

Example 10. $-6-(-3)^2$

$= -6-(+9)$	Compute the quantity $(-3)^2$
$= -6-9$	Compute the opposite of +9.
$= -15$	Subtract using the rules of signed numbers.

Estimation: It is important to estimate the result before using a calculator. This will help you determine if your answer is reasonable. Estimation should be quick and performed mentally. The key to estimating is rounding.

Example 11. Estimate –43.896 + 5.213.

Round –43.896 to –44 and 5.213 to 5.

Mentally compute –44 + 5 = –39.

An estimate of –43.896 + 5.213 is –39.

The actual answer is –38.683.

Example 12. Estimate (–26.5)(–1.8)

Round –26.5 to –27 and –1.8 to –2.

Mentally compute (–27)(–2) = 54.

An estimate of $-26.5 \bullet -1.8$ is 54.

The actual answer is 47.7.

Summary: Signed numbers are a key concept in Beginning Algebra. Initially, they can be confusing, but once the rules are learned and practiced, these numbers function in very predictable ways. Along with signed numbers, the order of operations must be mastered early in the semester. Answers will vary dramatically if the correct order of operations is not followed.

1. Intuitive rules for **adding** and **subtracting** signed numbers:

a. Unlike Signs: Find the difference (subtraction) of the two numbers and use the sign of the larger number.

Example 13. $-9 + 12 = 3$

Example 14. $8 - 13 = -5$

b. Like Signs: Add the two numbers and use the common sign.

Example 15: $-4 - 7 = -11$

Example 16. $12 + 9 = 21$

2. Rules for **multiplying** and **dividing** two signed numbers:

a. Unlike signs: The result is always negative.

Example 17. $(-5)(8) = -40$

Example 18. $\frac{48}{-6} = -8$

b. Like signs: The result is always positive.

Example 19. $\frac{-21}{-3} = 7$

Example 20. $(+4)(+7) = 28$

3. Order of Operations:

First: Inside parentheses, ( )
Second: Exponents
Third: Multiplication and Division (left to right)
Fourth: Addition and Subtraction (left to right)

Example 21. $(-4)^2(7-12)$

$= (-4)^2(-5)$

$= 16(-5)$

$= -80$

Example 22. $\frac{-8}{2} + (-5)(3)$

$= -4 - 15$

$= -19$

CLASS WORK

I. Adding and subtracting signed numbers:

1. I have $60, and I owe you $90. What is my net worth?

2. I am in debt for $50, and you give me $10. What is my net worth?

3. I am in debt for $30, and you give me $40. What is my net worth?

4. I am in debt for $20, and I owe you $50. What is my net worth?

5. Write the rules for adding and subtracting signed numbers.

6. Perform the operation.

a. $-7 + 5 =$ b. $6 - 10 =$ c. $2 - 11 =$ d. $-8 - 15 =$

e. $\frac{-5}{9} - \frac{7}{12} =$ f. $\frac{1}{4} - \frac{5}{6} =$

II. Addition and subtraction using a calculator:

1. Locate the subtraction key on your calculator.

2. Locate the negative key on your calculator.

3. Perform the operation.

a. $-8.6 + 11.4 =$ b. $-16.85 - 28.42 =$

III. What is the opposite of a number or its additive inverse?

IV. The graph below shows the deficit or surplus (in billions of dollars) of the U. S. Government's budget for the years 1999 through 2004.

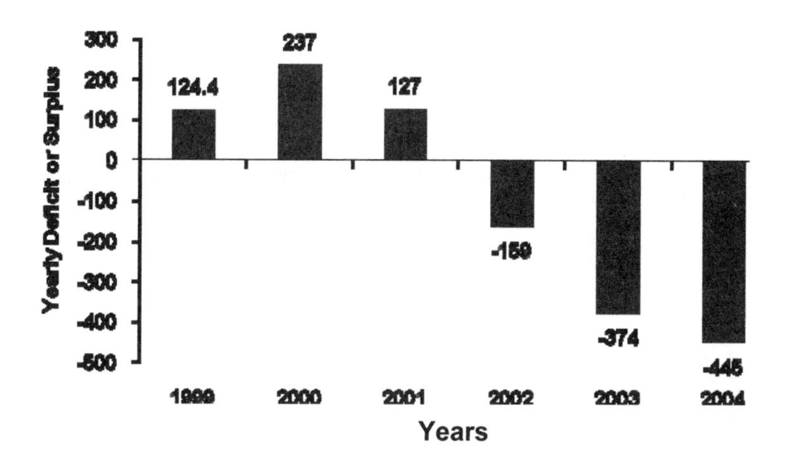

Source: Budget of the United States Government

1. What was the difference between the deficit in 2003 and the surplus in 1999?

2. What was the difference between the deficit in 2003 and the deficit in 2002?

3. What was the difference between the surplus in 2001 and in 2000? What is the significance of the negative sign in your answer?

4. What was the sum of the deficits or surpluses for 2000, 2001, and 2002?

5. What is the mean (average) for the six years?

6. Write a question that would generate 237 + (–445) as an answer.

7. Write a question that would generate –445 – (–374) as an answer.

V. Multiplication and division:

1. I will lose $5 a day for the next three days. How much money will I lose?

2. I lost $6 a day for the previous four days. How much more money did I have four days ago?

3. Write the rules for multiplying and dividing signed numbers.

4. Perform the operation.

a. $(-6)(3) =$ b. $(-7)(-2) =$ c. $\frac{-48}{-6} =$

d. $\frac{18}{-3} =$ e. $\frac{-4}{15} \bullet \frac{5}{12} =$ f. $\frac{-2}{15} \div \frac{-6}{5} =$

g. $\frac{0}{10} =$ h. $\frac{8}{0} =$ i. $\frac{0}{0} =$

5. Estimate and then use a calculator to perform the operation. Show both answers.

a. $(-6.42)(-7.81) =$

b. $\dfrac{-8.42}{3.15} =$

c. $\dfrac{-10.81}{0} =$

6. Exponents:

a. $3^2 =$

b. $8^2 =$

c. $(-5)^2 =$

d. $(-2)^2 =$

VI. 1. List the order of operations.

2. Perform the operations.

a. $(-8)(2) - 6 =$

b. $7(8 - 10) =$

c. $(-8)(3) - \frac{-14}{2} =$

d. $(-7) - (-5)^2 =$

e. $\frac{6(-3)+(5)(-2)}{3-10} =$

f. $\frac{2(-3)^2+7}{25-5^2} =$

GROUP EXERCISE

1. Introduce yourself to other members of the group. Group success means individual success. Use only one sheet of paper for the entire group. This encourages all to participate.
2. Exchange cell phone numbers.
3. Use your group for homework issues.

The graph below shows the profit and loss of Black Paper, Inc. for the years 2002 through 2006.

Go Back: Review the bar graphs on pages 4 and 9.

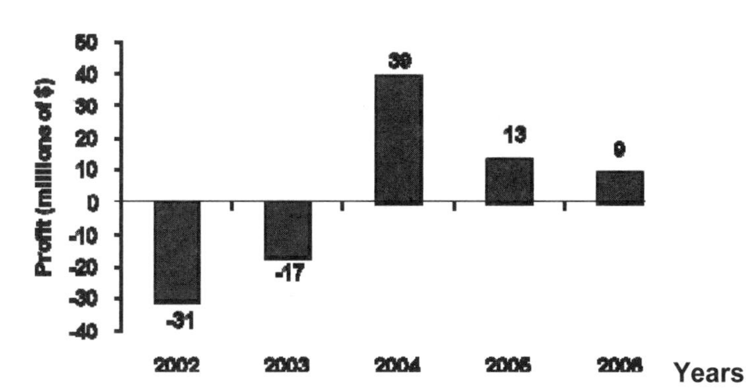

Write an arithmetic expression for each question and then answer the question.

1. What was the difference between the profit in 2004 and the loss in 2003?

2. What was the difference between the profit in 2006 and the profit in 2005?

3. What was the difference between profit in 2005 and the profit in 2004? What is the significance of the negative sign in the answer?

4. What is the sum of the profits and losses for 2003, 2004, and 2005?

5. What is the mean (average) for the five years?

6. Write a question that would generate –17 + 39 as an answer.

7. Write a question that would generate 9 – (–17) as an answer.

HOMEWORK EXERCISES

Skill Building Exercises

1. The homework sections of the textbook review the skills needed to pass MAT 011. In other words, success on the exams is directly proportional to the time spent on homework exercises. Please follow the suggestions below and do **all** of the problems.

   a. Collect materials: three-ring binder, lined paper, several sharpened pencils, eraser, calculator, timer, and highlighter.

   b. Label each homework sheet with the date, chapter, section, and textbook page numbers.

   c. Write neatly; leave plenty of white space; use as much paper as you need. Allow room for questions and/or comments.

   d. Set the timer for 30 minutes and begin. Check your answers in the back of the text. If you are correct, move on. If not, spend time (but no more than 10 minutes) analyzing and re-doing your work. Neat, legible homework makes this step easier. If you still are confused, highlight the number of the problem and move on.
   Hint: The Mat 011 text uses the **Go Back** *icon to indicate where to find a similar problem.*

   e. Students in Mat 011 having difficulties with the Practice Exercises, should attempt the Reading and Writing Exercises first. Often reviewing the material in a different manner will result in better comprehension. Experiment—see what method is better for your unique learning style.

   f. When the timer rings, stop everything and reward yourself for **five minutes**. Stretch, drink some water, or check your messages. Re-set the timer and continue. Plan to spend one to two hours on each homework section.

2. It is important for college students to budget their time in order to be successful in college. See page iv and complete a weekly planner for your first week of school.

3. Find the negative (opposite) key on your calculator; find the subtraction key.

Practice Exercises

For questions 4 through 8, write an arithmetic expression for each sentence. Then find the person's net worth. There are two steps to each problem:

1. Translate the sentence into an arithmetic expression.
2. Simplify the arithmetic expression.

4. I have \$80 in my checking account, and I owe RECO \$100. What is my net worth?

5. I am in debt for \$60, and I receive a check for \$90. What is my net worth?

6. I am in debt for \$210, and I owe M.C.C.C. \$80. What is my net worth?

7. I have \$60 in my checking account, and I owe \$50 to ZZT. What is my net worth?

8. I have \$97 in my checking account, and I owe ACME \$155. What is my net worth?

9. Perform the operation.

a. $7 - 5 =$	b. $-6 - 7 =$	c. $-15 + 6 =$
d. $-21 + 36 =$	e. $4 - 11 =$	f. $-8 + 15 =$
g. $-8 - 21 =$	h. $10 - 15 =$	i. $-11 - 21 =$
j. $-17 - (-28) =$	k. $-8 - 10 + 4 =$	l. $6 - 7 - 8 =$
m. $-3 + 6 - 11 =$	n. $7 - 11 + 4 - 15 =$	o. $(-5) - (-3) - (-5)$

10. a. What is the opposite or additive inverse of –12?

    b. What is the opposite or additive inverse of 17?

11. Which key do you press to compute the opposite of a number on your calculator?

12. Determine if the answer will be positive or negative <u>before</u> you do the calculation. Use your calculator to perform the operation.

Study Tip: Refer to Appendix B and the CD that accompanies the textbook to review how to use the TI–30X IIS calculator.

a. $4.3 - 8.7 =$	b. $-6.5 + 7.21 =$
c. $-6.83 + 7.42 =$	d. $\frac{1}{4} - \frac{5}{6} =$
e. $-18.3 - (-36.5) =$	f. $-\frac{7}{8} - (-\frac{2}{3}) =$

13. The high temperatures for a six day period in Boise , Idaho were 10ºF, 8ºF, 15ºF, 25ºF, –10ºF, and –2ºF. Calculate the average daily temperature for the six–day period.

14. Find the mean of the following temperatures: –6°C, 11°C, –56°C, –22°C, 68°C, and –4°C.

15. The following are elevations at selected points around the world. Use a negative number to represent an elevation below sea level.

Location	**Elevation**
Mt. Everest, Nepal	29,028 ft above sea level
Mariana Trench, Pacific Ocean	36,198 ft below sea level
The Dead Sea between Israel & Jordan	1,340 ft below sea level
Death Valley, CA	282 ft below sea level
Mt. Kilimanjaro, Africa	19,340 ft above sea level

Find the mean of the elevations.

16. The bar graph below shows the annual profit and loss, in millions of dollars, for the National Silver Company.

Go Back: Review Group Work on page 13 or problem IV on page 9.

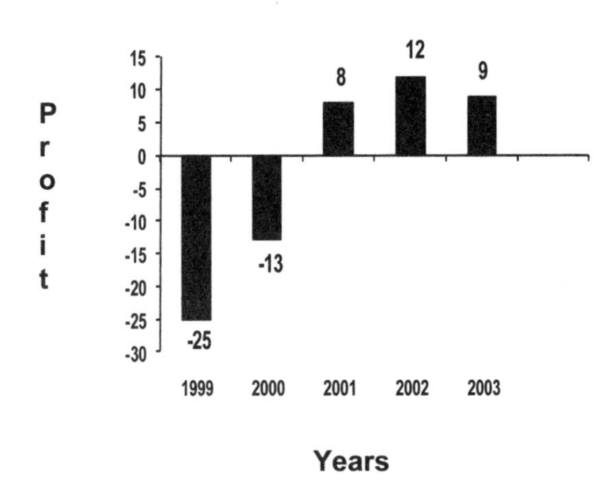

a. Determine the total profit or loss for the five years.

b. What is the difference between the profit in 2003 and 1999?

c. What is the difference between the profit in 2003 and 2002?

d. Why is the answer to question b positive but in question c negative?

e. Write a question that would generate 12 – (–13) as an answer.

f. What is the mean (average) profit for the five years?

17. Perform the operations.

a. $(-6)(7)$	b. $(-5)(-6)$	c. $3(-5)$
d. $-21(-3)$	e. $\frac{18}{-3}$	f. $\frac{-35}{7}$
g. $\frac{0}{11}$	h. $\frac{11}{0}$	i. $\frac{0}{0}$
j. $\frac{-25}{-5}$	k. $\frac{-4}{9} \div \frac{5}{12} =$	l. $4(-3)(-5)$
m. $(-8)(-4)(-3)$	n. $9(-3)(-4)(0)(5)$	o. $\frac{-6}{35} \div \frac{3}{-7} =$

18. Use your calculator to perform the operation. Determine if the answer will be positive or negative before you do the arithmetic.

a. $(-3.56)(-7.41)$ b. $-7.83(6.3)$

c. $\dfrac{-13.88}{4.7}$ d. $\dfrac{-6.21}{-3.51}$

19. Perform the operations.

a. $2(3-8)$ b. $-7(2)-\dfrac{-20}{5}$ c. $\dfrac{-12+14}{2}$

d. $\dfrac{36}{-12}-4(-8)$ e. $(-3)^2+8(-5)$ f. $-6-(-2)^2$

g. $\dfrac{8(-2)-5(4)}{(-3)^2}$ h. $\dfrac{(-5)^2+3^2}{2(-17)}$ i. $\dfrac{3(-5)-2(-8)}{2}$

Study Tip: Division by zero (zero in the denominator) is **undefined.** Zero in both numerator and denominator is called **indeterminate**,. Put this on a note card.
See problems 17 h and 17 i.

20. **Estimate** the following arithmetic problems. Estimates should be done quickly.

a. $-56.543+21.41$ b. $4.23 \bullet -5.78$

c. $65.89 \div -21.3$ d. $-127.9-34.34$

Study Tip: Reading and Writing Mathematics Exercises may appeal to students whose learning styles require a different approach than is being offered in the classroom. If you are having difficulties with the Practice Exercises, attempt the Reading and Writing Exercises first. Often reviewing the material in a different manner will result in better comprehension. Experiment – see what works for your unique learning style.

Reading and Writing Mathematics

21. What is the rule for adding numbers with the same sign?

22. What is the rule for adding numbers with different signs?

23. Explain how you would find the mean (the average) of a set of five numbers.

24. What is the rule for multiplying or dividing two numbers with the same sign?

25. What is the rule for multiplying or dividing two numbers with different signs?

26. Dividing by what number gives you an undefined answer?

27. Having a zero in both the numerator and denominator results in what important mathematical fact?

28. List the order of operations.

Study Tip: Make a note card listing the order of operations.

29. In each problem, find the **mistake** and write a sentence describing it. Also, write a suggestion so that any student who makes this type of error will have a way to remember not to make the mistake again.

a. $14 - 5(6 - 9) = 9(6 - 9)$
$= 9(-3)$
$= -27$

b. $4^2 - 7^2 = 16 + 49$
$= 65$

Study Tip: The answers to the homework questions appear on page 431. Always check to see if you are doing the problems correctly. If you got a problem wrong, try to figure out what you did incorrectly. Be prepared to ask your teacher, either in class or during office hours, to help you with the problems you can't do.

Study Tip: Detailed solutions to problems 5, 7, 9 a, c, e, g, I, k, m, o, 12 a, c, e, 13, 15, 16, 17 a, c, e, g, I, k, m, o, 18 a, c, 19 a, c, e, g, I, 20, a, c, 29 can be found on the MAT 011 Electronic Resource page. See page vii.

SECTION 1.2 INTRODUCTION TO VARIABLES
PREVIEW

Objectives: By performing similar arithmetic steps, you will discover the need for variables.

Example 1: You need to rent a moving van. Class Movers charges a basic rate of \$24.95 plus 32 cents per mile.

a. Calculate the cost of renting a van if you drive the following miles:

MILES	CALCULATION		COST
10	$0.32(10)+24.95$	**Explanation:** Since you drove 10 miles and it costs 32 cents a mile, then the cost is .32 times 10 plus 24.95, the basic rate.	\$28.15
20	$0.32(20)+24.95$		\$31.35
30	$0.32(30)+24.95$	**Explanation:** The only numbers that change in the calculation column are 10, 20, and 30. These numbers represent different mileage, so we let the variable m represent the number of miles driven.	\$34.55
m	$0.32(m)+24.95$		c

Vocabulary: A **variable** in algebra is a letter that represents a quantity that can change. In the example above, m represents the number of miles, and c represents the cost. Both miles and cost can vary or change. A **variable term** contains a letter and a number multiplying it; 0.32m is a variable term. A **constant** is a number that never changes value; 24.95 is a constant.

b. What is the equation that relates cost and number of miles driven?

The last row in the table above contains the answer. $c = 0.32m + 24.95$

c. Another rental company, Zippo Movers, charges a flat rate of \$42.95. How many miles would you have to drive for Zippo and Class to charge the same?

The cost equation for Zippo is: $c = 42.95$

To calculate when the two companies' charges are the same, set their cost equations equal to each other.

Cost of Zippo = Cost of Class

$$42.95 = 0.32m + 24.95$$

Because we have only just begun to study algebra, we will guess at the solution.

Substitute a guess for the number of miles into the equation for Class Movers,

$$c = 0.32m + 24.95.$$

GUESS NUMBER OF MILES	CALCULATION OF COST	COST	TOO HIGH/ TOO LOW
50	$0.32(50) + 24.95$	\$40.95	Too Low
60	$0.32(60) + 24.95$	\$44.15	Too high
55	$0.32(55) + 24.95$	\$42.55	Close

If you drive 55 miles, then the two companies will charge about the same. Guessing is very tedious and not precise. Later in the chapter, we will use algebra to solve the problem. Algebra is direct and is more precise than guessing.

Example 2: It is estimated that a 2007 Toyota Sienna Minivan loses \$1,800 a year in value. The minivan originally cost \$42,000.

a. Calculate the value of the minivan for the following years.

YEAR	YEARS SINCE 2007	CALCULATION	VALUE
2008	1	42,000 – 1,800	40,200
2010	3	42,000 – 1,800(3)	36,600
2015	8	42,000 – 1,800(8)	27,600
	t	42,000 – 1,800(t)	v

Explanation: Use the number of years since 2007 because the van loses 1,200 for every year after 2007.

b. What is the equation that relates the value of the van and the number of years since 2007?

The last row in the table above contains the answer. $v = 42{,}000 - 1{,}800t$

c. When will the van be worth \$20,400?

To answer the question, you must find a value for y that will make $v = 20{,}400$ or

$$20{,}400 = 42{,}000 - 1800t.$$

Since we don't know how to solve the problem using algebra yet, we will guess at the solution. Substitute a guess for t, the number of years since 2007, into the equation

$$V = 42{,}000 - 1{,}800t.$$

Repeatedly doing this will generate the following table.

GUESS NUMBER OF YEARS	CALCULATION OF VALUE	VALUE	TOO HIGH/ TOO LOW
10	42,000 – 1,800(10)	$24,000	Too high
13	42,000 – 1,800(13)	$18,600	Too low
12	42,000 – 1,800(12)	$20,400	Correct

The minivan will be worth $20,400 twelve years after 2007.
In year 2019, the minivan will be worth $20,400.

Summary:

Learning to generate a table is another key step in beginning algebra. Be sure your table contains the correct number of columns for the information you need. Use a ruler to draw the tables to ensure the information does not get confusing.

For every problem in this section you should be able to:

1. Generate a table.

Explanation: The calculation column is the most important. It indicates how you get your equation.

2. When you have determined the equation, you should understand what each term of the equation represents.

   For example:

$$c = 0.32m + 24.95$$

- c is the cost of renting a moving van.
- 0.32 is the amount Class Movers charges per mile.
  m is the number of miles you drive the van.
- 24.95 is the basic rate or fixed cost.

Study Tip: Use descriptive letters for variables in application problems. In Example 1, c was used for **c**ost and m for number of **m**iles driven.

CLASS WORK

1. The manager of a 33 Flavors Ice Cream Shop pays $800 per month for fixed expenses such as rent, lights, and insurance. She sells ice cream cones for $1.85 each. The cost of the ice cream and cone is $1.40.

   A. Without considering the fixed expenses of $800 per month, how much income is made per cone?

   B. Calculate the monthly profits when the following number of ice cream cones are sold. Make sure you include fixed costs in the equation for profit.

CONES	CALCULATION	PROFIT
10,000		
15,000		
20,000		
C		

   C. What is the equation that relates profit and the number of cones sold?

   D. Estimate the number of ice cream cones that must be sold if the manager wants to make $7,750 a month.

GUESS NUMBER OF CONES	CALCULATION OF PROFIT	PROFIT	TOO HIGH/ TOO LOW

   E. Suppose the expenses increase to $875 a month, and the charge is now $2.10 a cone ($1.40 still goes for ice cream and cone,). What will be the new equation for the monthly profits?

2. A rental car company, Wrecker, charges \$21.95 plus 41¢ a mile.

A. Calculate the cost of renting a car for one day if you drive the following number of miles:

MILES	CALCULATION	COST
10		
20		
30		
M		

B. What is the equation that relates cost and number of miles driven?

C. Another rental company, Limo, charges a flat rate of \$39.95 a day with unlimited miles. How many miles would you have to drive to make Limo cost the same as Wrecker?

GUESS NUMBER OF MILES	CALCULATION OF COST	COST	TOO HIGH/ TOO LOW

D. A third company, Ertz, charges \$18.95 a day and 50¢ a mile. What is the formula that calculates the cost of renting a car from Ertz for a day?

3. A truck rental company, They Haul, charges $24.95 plus $0.25 per mile after the first 20 miles.

A. Complete the table below and find an equation for the cost of renting a truck.

Miles	**Calculation**	**Cost**
10		
20		
30		
50		
m		

B. What is the equation that relates miles and cost?

C. Use the table to estimate how many miles you can drive if it costs $29.45.

4. The problem below requires you to review a fellow student's work. Read the problem carefully. Then make suggestions to your classmate. Try to evaluate the problem from the instructor's point of view.

There is nothing wrong with the numbers in the problem below; however it isn't ready to be submitted. List 5 improvements the student should make in order to get a good grade on the assignment.

Steven's making plans for a summer job. He wants to enter the lawn–mowing business. He can buy a power mower for $200, and he plans to charge $7.50 an hour for his work.

a. Calculate Steven's income for the summer if he has worked the following number of hours.

Hours	Calculation	Income
20	7.50*20=150	150–200 -50
50	~~7.50*50=475~~ 7.50*50=375	175
90	7.50*90=675	675 475
h	7.50*h	7.50h–200

b. What is the equation that relates income and hours worked?

7.50h–200

c. Estimate the number of hours Steven would have to work if he wants to earn $235 for the summer.

GUESS NUMBER OF HOURS	CALCULATION OF INCOME	INCOME	TOO HIGH/ TOO LOW
80	7.50*80 600	400	H
60	455	~~[illegible]~~ 255	H
58	435	235	

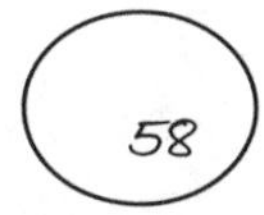

d. What would the income equation be if he buys a lawn mower for $300 and charges $9 an hour?

9h – 300

GROUP EXERCISE

Study Tip: Group Suggestion: Use only one sheet of paper for the entire group. This encourages all to participate. Group success means individual success.

Today we will look at the cost of renting a car from three different rental companies. Elvis will rent us a car for $35 plus $0.25 a mile. Quartz rents the same model for $25 plus $0.50 a mile. AUTO will rent it to us for a flat daily rate of $55 with no mileage charge.

Go Back: Review the problem on page 24.

1. For each company, find a formula for the cost of renting a car for a day. Complete the table below. (Pick numbers for the variable miles.) (Hint: see part 3.)

Elvis			**Quartz**			**AUTO**
Miles	**Calculation**	**Cost**	**Miles**	**Calculation**	**Cost**	**Cost**
m			m			

2. What are the equations that relate cost and number of miles driven for each company?

3. From which company would you rent if you planned to drive the car 20 miles? 60 miles? 100 miles?

HOMEWORK EXERCISES

Study Tip: You should have a separate loose leaf notebook for your math homework. This will help you to organize your exercises and give you an opportunity to redo some of the more difficult problems. There isn't enough room in the textbook to adequately do and redo the problems. Have all note cards handy for easy reference. Work for short periods of time, but do some math every day. Consider doing your homework with a classmate. Two heads are better than one! Review problem 1 on page 15.

Skill Building Exercises

Study Tip: The first three problems should help you get comfortable replacing the variables with numbers in the formulas.

1. Complete the table for each rectangle.

WIDTH, W IN.	**LENGTH, L IN.**	**AREA $A = L \cdot W$ SQ. IN.**	**PERIMETER $P = 2(L+W)$ IN.**
5 in.	6 in.	$A = 6 \cdot 5 = 30$ sq. in.	$P = 2(6+5) = 22$ in.
7 in.	8 in.		
9 in.	12 in.		
8 in.		80 sq. in.	
11 in.			60 in.

2. The formula $C=\frac{5}{9}(F-32)$ converts temperature in Fahrenheit to Celsius.

   a. If it is 32° F, find the temperature in Celsius.
   b. If it is –5° F, find the temperature in Celsius.
   c. If it is 98.6° F, find the temperature in Celsius.

Practice Exercises

3. Megan's making plans for a summer job. She wants to enter the lawn mowing business. She can buy a power mower for $160, and she hopes to charge $8 an hour for her work.

   a. Calculate Megan's income for the summer if she works the following number of hours.

Hours	**Calculation**	**Income**
40	8(40) – 160	$160
60		
80		
h		

   b. What is the equation that relates income and the number of hours worked?

   c. Estimate the number of hours Megan would have to work if she wants to earn $280 for the summer.

   d. What would the income equation be if she buys a lawn mower for $200 and charges $9 an hour?

4. A cell phone company, Ringer, charges \$7.46 per month plus \$0.13 a call.
   a. Calculate your phone bill if you make the following number of calls per month:

Go Back: This problem is similar to Problem 2 from "Class Work" on page 24.

CALLS	CALCULATION	PHONE BILL
10		\$8.76
15		
20		
c		

   b. What is the equation that relates the phone bill and the number of calls made?

   c. A second phone company, Busy, charges \$6.17 per month plus \$0.17 per call. What is the equation for your phone bill if your phone company is Busy?

   d. Fill in the table to estimate when Ringer charges less than Busy.

CALLS	RINGER	BUSY

   e. For what number of calls is the cost the same for both companies?

5. A \$56,000 office copy machine depreciates (loses value) \$2,700 a year.
   a. Calculate the value of the copy machine as it ages.

Go Back: This problem is similar to Example 2 from "Preview" on page 21.

AGE	CALCULATION	VALUE
2		\$50,600
5		
10		
A		

   b. What is the equation that relates the value of the copy machine and its age?

   c. Estimate how old the copy machine will be when it is worth \$15,000.

   d. What would the equation be if the copy machine were \$86,000 and depreciates \$3,400 a year?

6. A 10 cm stick is broken into two pieces. One piece is placed at a right angle to form an upside down "T" shape. By attaching wires from the ends of the base to the end of the upright piece, a framework for a sail will be formed.

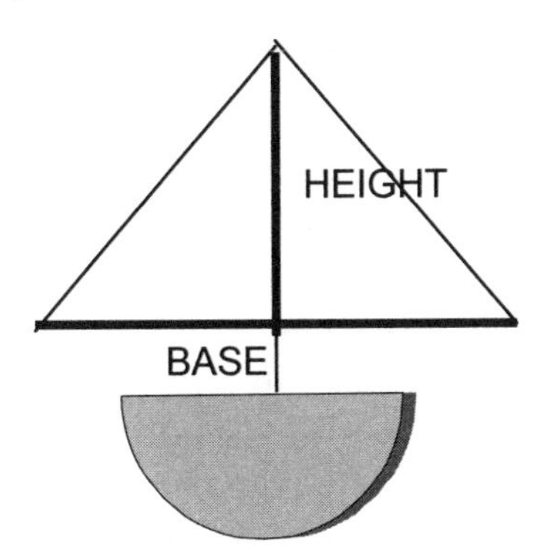

a. The 10 cm stick that is broken into two pieces is described by the diagram below. The slash mark represents where the stick is broken.

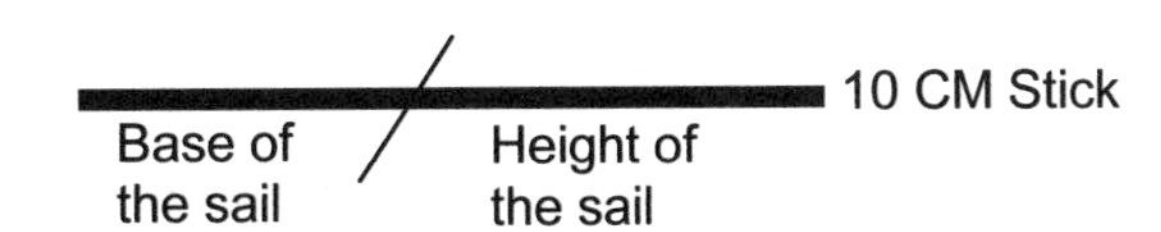

The base of the sail plus the height of the sail equals 10. If the base is 4 cm then the height of the sail must be 10 – 4 or 6 cm. If the base of the sail is 8 cm, what is the height?

b. Calculate the area of the sail for the given length of the base.

Recall that the area of a triangle is $A = \frac{1}{2} b \bullet h$.

Base b	**Height** h	**Area** $A = \frac{1}{2} b \bullet h$
4 cm	10 – 4 = 6 cm	$\left(\frac{1}{2}\right) \cdot (4)(6) = 12$ sq. cm.
5 cm		
8 cm		
b		

c. What is the equation that relates area and the base of the sail?

d. Why can't the base be 15 cm long?

e. Use the table to determine what base gives the maximum area.

7. A cell phone company charges 25 cents a call and 8 cents a minute after the first 10 minutes.

Go Back: This problem is similar to Problem 3 from "Class Work" on page 25.

a. Complete the table below.

Min.	Calculation	Cost
2		
5		
12		
30		
m		

b. What is the equation that relates cost and minutes?

Reading and Writing Mathematics

8. A friend from class asks you to review his work on the following problem. He has to submit this problem tomorrow. What did he do wrong? Correct his **mistake** and finish the problem.

A server at the gourmet restaurant, the Shark Trap, earns \$120 per week in salary and averages \$42.50 in tips per table.

a. Calculate the server's wages when he has served the following number of tables per week.

TABLES	CALCULATION	WAGES
10	$42.50(10) - 120$	305
15	$42.50(15) - 120$	517
20	$42.50(20) - 120$	730
t	$42.50t - 120$	w

b. What is the equation that relates wages and number of tables served?

$$42.50t - 120 = w$$

c. If he waited on 36 tables, how much money would he make?

$42.50t - 120 = 36$ *After trying a bunch of numbers for t, I got between 3 and 4.*

d. If he averaged \$37.00 per table and earned \$105 in salary, how would the equation change?

$$37t - 105 = w$$

Exercises 9 and 10 require you to review a fellow student's work. Read each section carefully. Then make suggestions to your classmate. Try to evaluate the problem from the instructor's point of view. There is nothing wrong with the numbers in the problems; however they are not ready to be submitted. List 5 improvements that should make in order to get a good grade on the assignment.

9. A friend from class asks you to review his work on the following problem. He has to submit this problem tomorrow.

Steven's making plans for a summer job. He wants to enter the lawn mowing business. He can buy a power mower for $250, and he plans to charge $9.50 an hour for his work.

a. Calculate Steven's income for the summer if he has worked the following number of hours.

Hours	Calculation	Income
20	9.50*20=190	190-250 -60
50	~~9.50*50=475~~ 9.50*50=475	225
90	9.50*90=855	855 605
h	9.50*h	9.50h-250

b. What is the equation that relates income and hours worked?

9.50h-250

c. Estimate the number of hours Steven would have to work if he wants to earn $490 for the summer.

GUESS NUMBER OF HOURS	CALCULATION OF INCOME	INCOME	TOO HIGH/ TOO LOW
80	9.50*80 760	510	H
70	665	~~[illegible]~~ 415	low
78	741	491	

78

d. What would the income equation be if he buys a lawn mower for $300 and charges $9 an hour?

9h - 300

10. Write a problem where the following table would help the student determine the equation. You should used descriptive variables as headings for the first and third columns.

	Calculation	
10	7.65(10) – 225	–148.50
25	7.65(25) – 225	–33.75
40	7.65(40) – 225	81.00

Study Tip: Reading and Writing Mathematics Exercises may appeal to students whose learning styles require a different approach than is being offered in the classroom. If you are having difficulties with the Practice Exercises, attempt the Reading and Writing Exercises first. Often reviewing the material in a different manner will result in better comprehension. Experiment – see what works for your unique learning style.

Study Tip: The answers to the homework questions are given on page 431. Always check to see if you are doing the problems correctly. If you get a problem wrong, try to figure out what you did incorrectly. Most instructors begin the class asking for questions concerning the assigned homework. Be prepared to ask your teacher to help you do the problems you can't figure out.

Study Tip: Detailed solutions to problems 1,3, 5, 7, and 9 can be found on the MAT 011 Electronic Resource page. See page vii.

SECTION 1.3 SIMPLIFLYING ALGEBRAIC EXPRESSIONS PREVIEW

Objectives: This section begins the process of solving equations. You will understand how to **combine like terms** and to use the **distributive property**.

Vocabulary: **Terms:** terms are parts of an algebraic expression separated by addition or subtraction signs.

Example 1. For 3 + 5 = 8, 3 and 5 are **terms.**

Example 2. For 3x – 5y, 3x and -5y are **terms**.

Coefficient: the number multiplying the variable.

Example 3. For the expression 7x – 2y + z,

7 is the **coefficient** of x;
–2 is the **coefficient** of y, and
1 is understood to be the **coefficient** of z.

Like Terms: terms which have the same variable and exponent; terms which are both numerical.

Example 4. For the expression 4x + 7y – 3x + 4z, 4x and –3x are **like terms.**

Rule: To **combine like terms**, add their coefficients. 4x + (–3x) = x or 1x.

Example 5. Combine like terms.

3x – 5 – 6x + 7 =	Identify the like terms, 3x and –6x, –5 and 7.
–3x + 2	Add the coefficients of the like terms.

Vocabulary: **Distributive Property:** Definition $a(b + c) = a \bullet b + a \bullet c$

Example 6. These two arithmetic problems demonstrate the distributive property.

a. $2(5+7) =$
$2 \bullet 12 =$
24

b. $2 \bullet 5 + 2 \bullet 7 =$
$10 + 14 =$
24

> **Explanation:** Always work inside parentheses first. Only use the distributive property when you cannot simplify what is inside the parentheses. Examples are given on the next page.

Study Tip:
1. You may want to review the order of operations on page 5.
2. Write these important definitions and rules on note cards and use them to do your homework.

Example 7. Use the distributive property.

$3(6x-5)=$	Can't combine terms inside the parentheses because they are unlike terms.
$3(6x)-3(5)=$	Using the distributive property, multiply 6x and –5 by 3.
$18x-15$	Multiply. Cannot add these unlike terms.

Example 8. Use the distributive property.

$-5(4x+2)=$	Can't combine terms inside the parentheses because they are unlike terms.
$(-5)\bullet 4x+(-5)\bullet 2=$	Using the distributive property, multiply 4x and 2 by –5.
$-20x-10$	Multiply.

Simplifying Algebraic Expressions:

Example 10. Simplify the expression.

$4-(2x-3)=$	In the same way that –x means –1*x, –(2x – 3) means –1(2x – 3)
$4-2x+3=$	Using the distributive property; multiply 2x and –3 by –1.
$-2x+7$	Combine Like terms.

Example 11. Simplify the expression.

$11x-14-3(4x-2)=$	Using the distributive property, multiply 4x and –2 by –3.
$11x-14-12x+6=$	Combine like terms, 11x and –12x, and –14 and 6.
$-1x-8=$	–1 x means the same as –x.
$-x-8=$	

Summary: Simplifying Algebraic Expressions

We are now ready to do the real work of algebra. Key definitions include:

1. The **distributive property**.

   $a(b+c) = a\bullet b+a\bullet c$

   The factor "a" multiplies both "b" and "c" inside the parentheses.

2. **Terms** are separated by addition or subtraction signs.

3. **Like terms** have the same variable and exponent.

4. **Coefficient** is the number multiplying the variable.

5. **Factors** are items being multiplied.

An important last question:

Vocabulary: What is an algebraic expression? An algebraic expression consists of terms, some of which contain variables.

CLASS WORK

What are like terms?

How do we add or subtract like terms?

Combine like terms:

1. $x + x + x + x$

2. $3x + 7 + 2x + 5$

3. $6x - 8 - 11x + 2$

4. $-\frac{1}{2}x - \frac{3}{4}x + \frac{7}{5}$

Use the distributive property:

1. $2(3x + 5)$

2. $-(x - 8)$

3. $-6(2x + 4)$

Simplify:

1. $4x + 2(3x + 8)$

2. $6x - (5x + 7)$

3. $9 - 3(4x + 6)$

NOTE TAKING IN A MATHEMATICS CLASS

Before Class (This should take 10 to 15 minutes).

1. Prepare one or two questions from the homework to ask your instructor.

2. Survey the section that will be covered that day in class.

3. Create note cards with definitions (vocabulary) and rules for each section. In the MAT 011 book, notice the icons, **Vocabulary:** and **Rules:** which identify the important terminology and procedures.

In Class

1. Record the date at the top of each new page.

2. Don't stop taking notes even if you get confused or believe you already know the material.

3. Copy all steps shown, regardless of your experience level.

4. Leave white space, especially in places where you're having a hard time understanding. You can fill these in later while you're studying. This is particularly helpful if you are not the neatest person. If there isn't enough space in your MAT 011 book, insert lined paper into the section.

5. Use abbreviations to save writing time.

6. Listen carefully for potential test questions and highlight.

After Class (This should take 10 to 15 minutes).

1. Review your notes as soon as possible, ideally within 15 minutes of the end of class.

2. Highlight key words and examples. Don't over highlight.

3. If there is something you don't understand, put a question mark by it. Write down a question you could ask that will clear up your confusion.

Take the time; make the effort!

Review the student's notes below and comment on how they can be improved.
The problem is from page 25.

3. A truck rental company, They Haul, charges $24.95 plus $0.25 per mile after the first 20 miles.

A. Complete the table below and find an equation for the cost of renting a truck.

Need parentheses because the company only charges 25 cents after the first 20 miles.

Miles	Calculation	Cost
10	Don't need any calculations because miles is before 20.	24.95
20		24.95
30	.25X10 + 24.95 .25(30 − 20)+24.95	
50	.25X30 + 24.95 .25(50 − 20)+24.95	32.45
m		C

B. What is the equation that relates miles and cost?

$$.25(m - 20) + 24.95$$

C. Use the table to estimate how many miles you can drive if it costs $29.45. 30

GROUP EXERCISE

Go Back: 1. Review pages 37 and 38.
2. Remember good group principles.

Simplify

1. $\frac{1}{5}x - \frac{2}{3} + \frac{2}{15}x - 4$

2. $3(2x - 5) - 7x$

3. $4(6 - x) - 3(4x + 5)$

4. Describe what is **wrong** with the following problems.

a. $6x - 7 + 4x + 8 =$
$10x + 1 =$
$11x$

b. $4(3x + 5) - 9x =$
$12x + 5 - 9x =$
$3x + 5$

c. $5(3x - 8) - 4x =$
$15x - 40 - 4x =$
$19x - 40$

d. $4x + 2x =$
$8x$

e. $6 - 2(4x + 5) =$
$4(4x + 5) =$
$16x + 20$

Study Tip: In addition to your instructor and the Learning Assistance Lab, the MAT 011 web site is another excellent source of information available outside of class, particularly if you are a visual learner.

HOMEWORK EXERCISES

Study Tip: Do the following exercises. If you need help go to the Learning Assistance Lab (L. A. L.), in College Hall at the Blue Bell campus or Room 159 at the Pottstown campus. The L. A. L. is a free service provided by the College that includes individual tutoring, group tutoring sessions, and study skills tips to all Montgomery County Community College students. See page vi for L. A. L. hours at the Blue Bell and Pottstown campuses.

Skill Building Exercises

1. Which of the following are like terms?

   a. 7, 14y, 8x, or –21x b. 3x, –8, –7y, or 5

2. In each term below, what is the coefficient?

   a. –7x b. –x

Practice Exercises

3. Simplify.

   a. $9x - 4x$ b. $6x + 11x - 13$ c. $\frac{1}{2}x - \frac{3}{5} + \frac{2}{3}x$

   d. $3(2x + 5)$ e. $6 - 4(3x - 8)$ f. $4(2x - 5) + 3(7 - 2x)$

   g. $4x + 5(3x + 1)$ h. $9x - 18x + 2(4x - 8)$ i. $4 - 2(3x + 4) - (x - 8)$

Reading and Writing Mathematics

4. What are like terms?
5. What are factors?
6. How are like terms combined?
7. State the distributive property.
8. In each problem, find the **mistake** and write a sentence describing it. Also, write a suggestion so that any student who makes this type of error will have a way to remember not to make the mistake again.

   a. $6x + 5x = \mathit{30x}$

   b. $5x - 3 + 4x - 8 =$
   $9x - 11 = -2x$

   c. $6(4x - 5) - 7x =$
   $24x - 5 - 7x =$
   $17x - 5$

   d. $2(5x - 8) - 3(2x - 4) =$
   $10x - 16 - 6x - 12 =$
   $4x - 28$

   e. $4x - (x - 7) =$
   $4x - x - 7 =$
   $3x - 7$

   f. $3(4x - 8) - (3x - 5) =$
   $12x - 24 - 3x + 5 =$
   $15x - 19$

Study Tip The answers to the homework questions are given on page 431. Always check to see if you are doing the problems correctly. If you got a problem wrong, try to figure out what you did incorrectly. Be prepared to ask your teacher to help you.

SECTION 1.4 SOLVING EQUATIONS
PREVIEW

Objectives: In "Introduction to Variables", we solved equations by guessing. In this section, you will learn how to solve equations using algebra. Algebra is easier and more precise than guessing.

Note: The example is from "Introduction to Variables", page 20.

Example 1. You need to rent a moving van. Class Movers charges a basic rate of $24.95 plus 32 cents per mile.

a. Calculate the cost of renting a van if you drive the following miles.

MILES	CALCULATION	COST
10	$0.32 \bullet 10 + 24.95$	28.15
20	$0.32 \bullet 20 + 24.95$	31.35
30	$0.32 \bullet 30 + 24.95$	34.55
m	$0.32 \bullet m + 24.95$	c

Explanation: Since you drove 10 miles and it costs 32 cents a mile, then the cost is .32 times 10 plus 24.95, the basic rate.

Explanation: The only numbers that change in the calculation column are 10, 20, and 30. These numbers represent different miles, so we let m represent the number of miles driven.

The cost equation is $c = 0.32m + 24.95$.

b. Use the equation to calculate how many miles you drove if the cost is $42.87.

Logical Solution. The cost $42.87 contains the basic rate $24.95. Subtracting $24.95 from $42.87 yields $17.92. This is how much of the cost is attributed to the number of miles driven. Since it costs 32 cents per mile, dividing 17.92 by 0.32 determines the number of miles driven or 56 miles. This same logic is algebra.

Algebraic Solution: Find m when c = 42.87.

$42.87 = 0.32m + 24.95$	Substitute 42.87 for c.
$42.87 - 24.95 = 0.32m$	Subtract 24.95 from 42.87 because the cost, 42.87, contains the basic rate, 24.95.
$17.92 = 0.32m$	Combine like terms, 42.87 and 24.95.
$\frac{17.92}{0.32} = m$	The miles driven cost 17.92. Since it costs 32 cents per mile, divide 17.92 by 0.32.
$56 = m$	Answer.

You can drive 56 miles for $42.87.

c. Check your answer.
Substitute m = 56 into the equation $c = 0.32m + 24.95$; the cost should be $42.87.

$$c = 0.32 * 56 + 24.95$$
$$c = 17.92 + 24.95$$
$$c = 42.87$$

Study Tip: You should answer the problem with a sentence, like example 1 above, (You can drive 56 miles for $42.87.) that refers to both variables in the problem.

Rule: How to solve an equation:

1. Simplify each side of the equation by using the **distributive property** and **combining like terms**.

2. The second objective is to write the equation in the form:

   Variable term = constant

   This is done by using the addition or subtraction properties of equations.

> **Explanation:** a **variable term** contains a letter that can represent different values. A **constant** is a number that never changes value.

3. Divide both sides by the coefficient (the number multiplying the variable) of the variable.

Example 2. Solve.

$42.87 = 0.32 \bullet m + 24.95$	Subtract 24.95 from **both sides** of the equation.
$42.87 - 24.95 = 0.32 \bullet m + 24.95 - 24.95$	Combine like terms, 42.87 and – 24.95, 24.95 and – 24.95. This is our first objective in solving the problem.
$17.92 = 0.32m$	Divide **both sides** by the coefficient of m, 0.32
$\frac{17.92}{0.32} = \frac{0.32m}{0.32}$	Perform the division.
$56 = m$	Answer.

Example 3. Solve.

$7x - 4 = 5(2x + 9) + 3x$	Use the **distributive property**; multiply 2x and 9 by 5.
$7x - 4 = 10x + 45 + 3x$	**Combine like terms**; add 10x and 3x
$7x - 4 = 13x + 45$	Need a variable term equal to a constant term. Since there is a constant term on both sides of the equation, **add 4** to both sides of the equation.
$7x - 4 + 4 = 13x + 45 + 4$	**Combine like terms**, –4 and 4, 45 and 4
$7x = 13x + 49$	Need a variable term equal to a constant term. Since there is a variable term on both sides of the equation, **subtract 13x** from both sides of the equation.
$7x - 13x = 13x - 13x + 49$	**Combine like terms**, 7x and –13x, 13x and –13x.
$-6x = 49$	Now there is a variable term equal to a constant term, so divide both sides by –6, the **coefficient** of x.
$\frac{-6x}{-6} = \frac{49}{-6}$	Divide.
$x = -8.167$	Answer is rounded to 3 decimal places.

Example 4. Solve.

$4-2(6x-7)=-12x+10$

Use the **distributive property**; multiply 6x and −7 by −2.

$4-12x+14=-12x+10$

Combine like terms, 4 and 14.

$-12x+18=-12x+10$

Need a variable term equal to a constant term. Since there is a variable term on both sides of the equation, **add 12x** to both sides of the equation.

$-12x+12x+18=-12x+12x+10$

Combine like terms.

$18=10$
No solution.

18 can never equal 10, so the conclusion is, the problem has no solution.

> **Explanation:** Look at $-12x+18=-12x+10$ Notice that −12x is on both sides of the equation, but one side has 18 and the other 10. Do you see why you can't find a solution?

Example 5. Solve.

$21x-10+10x=5(6x-2)+x$

Use the **distributive property**.

$21x-10+10x=30x-10+x$

Combine like terms.

$31x-10=31x-10$

Need variable term equal to a constant term. Since there is a variable term on both sides of the equation, **subtract 31x** from both sides.

$31x-31x-10=31x-31x-10$

Combine like terms.

$-10=-10$

All numbers are solutions.

−10 is always equal to −10, so the conclusion Is that every number is a solution.

> **Explanation:** Look at $-31x-10=-31x-10$ Notice that the same algebraic expressions are on both sides of the equal sign. Do you see why any number will make the equation true?

Vocabulary: a. A **conditional equation** has a finite number of solutions. In this section, a conditional equation will have one solution. Examples 1, 2, and 3 are conditional equations.

b. When an equation doesn't have a solution, it is called a **contradiction**. Example 4 is a contradiction because when all of the variables are eliminated there is a false arithmetic statement.

c. When all numbers are solutions to an equation, then it is called an **identity**. Example 5 is an identity because when all of the variables are eliminated there is a true arithmetic statement.

Example 6. Solve. $6x-5=2x+11$.

$$6x-5+5=2x+11+5$$
$$6x=2x+16$$
$$6x-2x=2x-2x+16$$
$$4x=16$$
$$\frac{4x}{4}=\frac{16}{4}$$
$$x=4$$

Explanation: Solving equations rests on the **principle of equality.** The principle of equality states: in order to preserve the equality, whatever you do to one side of the equation you must do to the other. In this example, 5 was added to both sides; 2x was subtracted from both sides, and both sides were divided by 4.

Summary: Algebra and arithmetic are different. Arithmetic involves operations with numbers. Algebra has variables that can represent many different numbers. If you think back to the section, Introduction to Variables, in the last row of the tables we created, we used variables to represent all of the arithmetic in the previous rows. Algebra is the generalization of repeated arithmetic operations. The equations from Introduction to Variables contained two variables. If you know a value for one of the variables, then you can use the procedures in this section to find the value of the other. Solving equations is a basic function of algebra.

How to solve equations:

1. Simplify both sides of the equation by using the distributive property, $a(b + c) = ab + ac$, and combining like terms.

2. The first goal is to write the equation in the form:

   Variable term = constant

   This is done by using the addition and subtraction principles.

3. Divide both sides of the equation by the coefficient, the number multiplying the variable.

4. The solution to an equation for this type has three possible outcomes:
   a. One solution, a conditional equation.
   b. No solution, a contradiction.
   c. All numbers are solutions, or the problem has an infinite number of solutions, an identity.

Study Tip: You should write the steps on a note card along with an example.

CLASS WORK

1. A rental car company, Wrecker, uses the formula $C = 0.41m + 21.95$ to calculate the cost, C, of renting a car driven m miles. If your vacation budget allows you to spend $100 for car rental, how far can you drive?

2. Consider the equation $5x + 6 = 3x - 2$

   Is $x = 4$ a solution?

   Is $x = -4$ a solution?

3. Solve the basic equation.

   a. $x + 8 = -3$ b. $4x = -12$ c. $4x = 8x$

4. Solve the equation and describe each step.

a. $8x - 2 = 11x + 7$ STEP

b. $2(4x + 5) - 3x = 24 - 2x$ STEP

5. Solve each equation.

a. $3x + 5 = 4 - 5x$

b. $3x - 8 = 4(5 - 3x) + 9$

c. $3(2x + 8) = 6x - 7$

d. $3(2x + 8) = 8x + 24 - 2x$

GROUP EXERCISES

Study Tips: Group suggestion: Use only one sheet of paper for the <u>entire group</u>.
This encourages all to participate.

Go Back: For help, see page 49 or your notes from the "Class Work" section.

1. Describe each step.

	Step
$5(4x - 8) - 13x = 2x + 10$	
$20x - 40 - 13x = 2x + 10$	________________
$7x - 40 = 2x + 10$	________________
$7x - 2x - 40 = 2x - 2x + 10$	________________
$5x - 40 = 10$	________________
$5x - 40 + 40 = 10 + 40$	________________
$5x = 50$	________________
$\frac{5x}{5} = \frac{50}{5}$	________________
$x = 10$	________________

2. Find where the first mistake occurs.

$$3(4x - 5) + 4 = 3x + 47$$
$$12x - 15 + 4 = 3x + 47$$
$$12x - 11 = 3x + 47$$
$$12x - 11 + 11 = 3x + 47 - 11$$
$$12x = 3x + 36$$
$$12x - 3x = 3x - 3x + 36$$
$$9x = 36$$
$$\frac{9x}{9} = \frac{36}{9}$$
$$x = 4$$

3. Solve each equation.

a. $6x - 5 = 8 - 4(2x + 7)$

b. $5(3 + 2x) = 10x - 11$

HOMEWORK EXERCISES

Study Tip: Use your loose leaf homework notebook; review your note cards; work with a friend.

Basic Skills Exercises

1. Simplify the following algebraic expression. $4 - 3(2x - 8)$

2. Simplify the following algebraic expression. $-3x + 2(7x - 8)$

Practice Exercises

3. A cell phone company, Ringer, charges $7.46 per month plus 13 cents a minute. A second company, Busy, charges $6.17 per month plus 17 cents per minute. How many minutes does it take for the two companies to charge the same for a month?

Go Back: Review the problem 4 on page 30.

4. Solve each equation.

Go Back: Review page 49 or your "Class Work" notes to help with the problems below.

a. $4x = -24$ b. $2x - 7 = 15$ c. $-2x + 5 = 7x - 31$

d. $6x - 8 = 3x + 7$ e. $2x + 5(4x - 7) = 18x - 42$ f. $3(2x - 5) = 6 + 6x$

g. $2 - (x+4) = 2x - 5$ h. $4 + 3x = 2(5x + 2) - 7x$ i. $4 - 3(2x + 6) = -(x - 5)$

Reading and Writing Mathematics

5. Describe each step.

a. $4(2x + 5) - 11x = 3x - 4$	Step
$8x + 20 - 11x = 3x - 4$	____________
$-3x + 20 = 3x - 4$	____________
$-3x - 3x + 20 = 3x - 3x - 4$	____________
$-6x + 20 = -4$	____________
$-6x + 20 - 20 = -4 - 20$	____________
$-6x = -24$	____________
$\frac{-6x}{-6} = \frac{-24}{-6}$	____________
$x = 4$	____________

Study Tip: Detailed solutions to problems 1, 3, 4 a, c e, g, I, 5, 6, and 11 can be found on the MAT 011 Electronic Resource page. See page vii.

b. $7x + 2 = 2(5x - 3) - 3x$	Step
$7x + 2 = 10x - 6 - 3x$	________________
$7x + 2 = 7x - 6$	________________
$7x - 7x + 2 = 7x - 7x - 6$	________________
$2 = -6$	________________
no solution	________________

6. In each problem, find the **mistake** and write a sentence describing the error. Also, write a suggestion so that any student who makes this type of mistake will have a way to remember not to make the error again.

a. $4 - (x + 6) = 4x + 7$

$$4 - x - 6 = 4x + 7$$
$$-x - 2 = 4x + 7$$
$$-x - 4x - 2 = 4x - 4x + 7$$
$$-5x - 2 = 7$$
$$-5x - 2 + 2 = 7 - 2$$
$$-5x = 5$$
$$\frac{-5x}{-5} = \frac{5}{-5}$$
$$x = -1$$

b. $5x - 6 + 9x = 15 - 3x$

$$5x - 5x - 6 + 9x - 5x = 15 - 3x$$
$$-6 + 4x = 15 - 3x$$
$$-6 + 4x - 4x = 15 - 3x - 4x$$
$$-6 = 15 - 7x$$
$$-6 - 15 = 15 - 15 - 7x$$
$$-21 = -7x$$
$$\frac{-21}{-7} = \frac{-7x}{-7}$$
$$3 = x$$

7. Describe the procedure to solve an equation.

8. When does an equation not have a solution?

9. When does an equation have every number as a solution?

10. Many students confuse simplifying algebraic expressions and solving algebraic equations. Review the section "Simplifying Algebraic Expressions" and write a paragraph comparing simplifying and solving. Include an example of each.

11. A classmate asks you to look over her work. The mathematics is correct. Make five suggestions that would improve the presentation of the problem. Review the problem the way a teacher might look at it.

Solve $4x - 3(2x + 5) = 4x + 9$

$4x - 6x + {}^{-}15 =$

$-2x - 15$

$-4x \qquad -4x$

$-6x \qquad 0x$

$\qquad 15 \qquad 15$

$-6x = \qquad 24$

$-6 \qquad -6$

(circled) -4

SECTION 1.5 APPLICATIONS OF LINEAR EQUATIONS PREVIEW

Objective: This section is a review of the course to date. You will create tables to find equations and then solve them using algebra.

Study Tip: If you have trouble with this section, review Section 1.2 "Introduction to Variables" and Section 1.4, "Solving Equations".

Example 1. A student buys a new car in 2006 for $36,000, and the car depreciates $3,100 per year.

a. Write an equation that relates the value of the car to the car's age.

YEAR	YEARS SINCE 2006	CALCULATION	VALUE
2008	2	36,000 – 3,100 • 2	$29,800
2010	4	36,000 – 3,100 • 4	$23,600
2015	9	36,000 – 3,100 • 9	$8,100
	t	36,000 – 3,100 • t	v

Explanation: Use the number of years since 2006 because the car loses $3,100 for every year after 2006.

The equation is v = 36,000 – 3,100t. Where t is the number of years since 2006.

b. When will the car be worth $20,000?

Find y when v = 20,000.

20,000 = 36,000 – 3,100t	Substituted 20,000 for v.
–16,000 = – 3,100t	Subtracted 36,000 from both sides.
5.161 = t	Divided both sides by –3,100.

The car will be worth approximately $20,000 in 5 years, namely 2011 (2006 + 5).

c. When will the car be worthless?

A car is worthless when its value is zero.
Find y when v = 0.

0 = 36,000 – 3,100t	Substituted 0 for v.
3,100t = 36,000	Added 3,100t to both sides.
t = 11.61	Divided both sides by 3,100.

The car will be worthless in about 12 years, namely 2018 (2006 + 12).

Study Tip: In the last problem, we wrote down fewer steps. You should take a couple of minutes to work out the problem in detail. You must know how each step was done. Use your homework notebook. Allow plenty of space so you don't get confused.

Example 2. Class Truck rental company charges a basic rate of \$34.99 plus \$0.20 a mile after the first 15 miles.

a. Write an equation for the cost of renting from Class.

Miles	Calculation	Cost
25	$0.20(25-15)+34.99$	\$36.99
40	$0.20(40-15)+34.99$	\$39.99
55	$0.20(55-15)+34.99$	\$42.99
m	$0.20(m-15)+34.99$	C

Explanation: They charge 20 cents after 15 miles, so if you drive for 25 miles you are only charged 20 cents for 10 miles, 25 – 15. Since you subtracted 25 – 15 before you multiplied by 0.20, you need parentheses.

The cost equation is $c = 0.20(m - 15) + 34.99$.

b. Simplify the equation.

$C = 0.20(m-15)+34.99$

$C = 0.20m - 3 + 34.99$ Used the distributive property; multiplied m and –15 by 0.20, 0.20m and 0.20(–15) = –3

$C = 0.20m + 31.99$ Combined like terms, –3 and 34.99.

c. How many miles can you go if the cost is \$85?

Find m when C = 85.

$85 = 0.20m + 31.99$ Substituted 85 for C.

$53.01 = 0.20m$ Subtracted 31.99 from both sides.

$265.05 = m$ Divided both sides by 0.20.

Rounding to the nearest mile, you can drive approximately 265 miles for \$85.

Summary: This section reviews most of the material presented thus far in the course and, therefore, is <u>extremely</u> important. You should be able to:

1. Read the problem and create a table in order to find the equation.

2. Solve algebraic equations to obtain the desired solution. We have advanced to a level of difficulty where "guessing" is a time consuming method for determining algebraic solutions; use algebra.

Study Tips:

1. If any of the above steps is not clear to you, ask questions in the next class session, see your instructor during office hours, go to the tutoring center, or use online tutors

2. Do not proceed until you have mastered this section.

CLASS WORK

A. Two women want to enter the lawn mowing business for the summer. They plan to buy a lawn mower for $180, and they plan to charge $8 an hour.

1. If they work for 20 hours, how much money will they make?

HOURS	CALCULATION	PROFIT
20		
h		

2. What is the equation that relates profit and hours worked?

3. How many hours will they have to work in order to break even?

4. How many hours will they have to work in order to make $780 for the summer?

B. You are offered two very similar jobs selling math textbooks. One pays 8% commission plus $10,000 a year, and the other pays 12% commission.

1. If you sell $200,000 for the year, which job would pay you more?

COMPANY A		
Sales	**Calculation**	**Wages**
200,000		
S		

COMPANY B		
Sales	**Calculation**	**Wages**
200,000		
S		

2. What are the equations that relate wages and sales for Companies A and B?

3. How much would you have to sell for the two companies to pay you the same amount of money for the year?

C. The Horizon Wired cell phone company's small business plan for a month:

Shared Anytime Minutes	Talk & Text	Per-Minute Rate After Allowance
1400	$119.99	40 cents

1. Complete the table:

MINUTES	CALCULATION	COST
1000 min.		
2000 min		
2500 min.		
m min.		C

2. What is the equation that relates minutes and cost? Simplify the equation.

3. How many minutes did your company use if the monthly bill was $309.59.?

4. How many minutes did your company use if the monthly bill was $827.19.?

5. What is the monthly bill if the company used 100 minutes?

GROUP EXERCISES

A. A company pays $10,000 a year plus 10% commission on sales over $50,000.

Go Back: Review the problem on page 60.

1. Complete the table below.

SALES	CALCULATION	WAGES
80,000		
100,000		
S		

2. What is the equation that relates wages and sales? Simplify the equation.

3. If you want to earn $30,000 a year, how much do you have to sell?

B. Rental Car Company, Silver Star, charges $0.21 a mile plus $31 a day.

1. Complete the table below.

MILES	CALCULATION	COST
20		
m		

2. What is the equation that relates cost and miles?

3. If you spent $44.02 renting a car for the day, how many miles did you drive?

3. A second company, Limo, charges $0.11 a mile and $42 a day. How many miles do you have to drive for both companies to charge you the same amount of money?

Study Tip: You should be able to find the equation for Limo by understanding the components of the equation for Silver Star.

HOMEWORK EXERCISES

Skill Building Exercises

1. This is a very important section, so it is vital that you do the homework properly. Review the suggestions below and check off the ones that you are already doing. You should follow all of the suggestions.

☐ Collect materials: three-ring binder, lined paper, several sharpened pencils, eraser, calculator, timer, and highlighter.

☐ Label each homework sheet with the date, chapter, section, and textbook page numbers.

☐ Write neatly; leave plenty of white space; use as much paper as you need. Allow room for questions and/or comments.

☐ Set the timer for 30 minutes and begin. Check your answers in the back of the text. If you are correct, move on. If not, spend time (but no more than 10 minutes) analyzing and re-doing your work. Neat, legible homework makes this step easier. If you still are confused, highlight the number of the problem and move on.
Hint: The Mat 011 text uses the **Go Back** *icon to indicate where to find a similar problem.*

☐ Students in Mat 011 having difficulties with the Practice Exercises, attempt the Reading and Writing Exercises first. Often reviewing the material in a different manner will result in better comprehension. Experiment—see what works for your unique learning style.

☐ When the timer rings, stop everything and reward yourself for **five minutes**. Stretch, drink some water, or check your messages. Re-set the timer and continue. Plan to spend one to two hours on each homework section.

2. Solve the following equations.

   a. $4x - 45 = 17 + 2.45x$

   b. $7(0.25x - 6.12) + 2.25x = 4.12x - 23.56$

Practice Exercises

3. You plan to rent a car for the day; you are told it costs $25.00 for the day and $0.16 a mile.

Go Back: Review the problems on page 56 or 62.

a. Complete the table below.

MILES	CALCULATION	COST
20		
m		

b. What is the equation that relates cost and miles?

c. If you drive 31 miles, how much will it cost?

d. If you want to spend $31 on renting a car, how far can you drive?

e. If you want to spend $65 on renting a car, how far can you drive?

4. A company buys a $450,000 piece of equipment in 2005. It depreciates $33,000 a year. For tax purposes the company needs to know the following:

a. Complete the table below.

YEARS	CALCULATION	VALUE
10		
t		

b. What is the equation that relates years and value?

c. What is the value of the equipment in the year 2008?

d. In what year will the equipment be worth $300,000?

e. In what year will the equipment be worth $100,000?

5. A cell phone company Ringer charges 8 cents per minute and 50 cents per call while Company Busy charges 10 cents per minute and 25 cents per call.

a. Complete the table below.

RINGER			BUSY		
MIN.	**CALCULATION**	**COST**	**MIN.**	**CALCULATION**	**COST**
10			10		
m			m		

b. What are the equations that relate cost and minutes on the phone for the two companies?

c. How long would you have to talk for the cost of the phone call to be the same for both Ringer and Busy?

6. You are offered two very similar jobs selling encyclopedias. One job pays 7.5% commission and $5,000 a year while the second company pays 5% commission and $9,000 a year.

Go Back: Review the problem on page 59.

a. If you sold $100,000 for the year, which job would pay more?

Company A			Company B		
Sales	**Calculation**	**Wages**	**Sales**	**Calculation**	**Wages**
100,000			100,000		
s			s		

b. What are the equations that relate wages and sales for the two companies?

c. How much would you have to sell for the two companies to pay you the same amount of money for the year?

7. A job pays 15% commission on sales over $1,000 a week.

Go Back: This problem is like the example in the "Preview" Section on page 60 or question A on page 61.

a. Complete the table below.

SALES	CALCULATION	WAGES
1,500		$75
2,000		
s		

b. What is the equation that relates wages and sales? Simplify the equation.

c. If you sell $10,000 in a week, how much money will you earn?

d. If you earned $270 in a week, how much did you sell?

e. If you earned $3,372 in a week, how much did you sell?

8. The Horizon Wired cell phone company's small business plan for a month:

Shared Anytime Minutes	Talk & Text	Per-Minute Rate After Allowance
2000	$129.99	35 cents

Go Back: Review the problem on page 64.

a. Complete the table:

MINUTES	CALCULATION	COST
3000 min.		
3500 min		
4500 min.		
m min.		C

b. What is the equation that relates minutes and cost? Simplify the equation.

c. How many minutes did your company use if the monthly bill was $555.24.?

d. How many minutes did your company use if the monthly bill was $1,117.30.?

e. What is the monthly bill if the company used 100 minutes?

9. Cell phone Company Hook charges 22 cents a call and 10 cents a minute after the first 5 minutes.

a. Complete the table below.

MINUTES	CALCULATION	COST
2		
5		
7		
12		
m		

b. What is the equation that relates cost and minutes? Simplify the equation.

c. If a phone call costs $2.02, how long were you on the phone?

d. If a phone call costs $3.82, how long were you on the phone?

10. Nader Rental car company charges 27 cents per mile plus $25.95 while Trump Rental car agency charges 33 cents per mile plus $31.95. How many miles do you have to drive for both companies to charge the same. Why does no solution apply in this situation? Compare the cost per mile and start up costs for each company.

Study Tip: Construct a table which contains all the information you need.

Reading and Writing Mathematics

11. This section is a review of the course to date. Read Example 1 on page 55 or the example on page 56 and list 4 topics that were covered in previous sections.

12. Create an application problem of your own that you may see on an exam.

13. Create another an application problem of your own. Make sure this problem requires the use of parentheses.

Study Tip: Detailed solutions to problems 3, 5, 7, and 9 can be found on the MAT 011 Electronic Resource page. See page vii.

SECTION 1.6 LITERAL EQUATIONS
PREVIEW

Objectives: In this section, you will learn how to solve equations that have two variables. The algebra is the same as in the previous sections. The difference is that the solution will be an equation not a number.

Vocabulary: A **literal equation** is an equation that involves more than one variable.

Example 1. A cell phone company charges a basic rate of \$1.25 plus \$0.15 per minute after the first 10 minutes.

a. Complete the table to find the cost of making phone calls that last longer than ten minutes.

Minutes	Calculation	Cost
20	$0.15(20-10)+1.25$	\$2.75
30	$0.15(30-10)+1.25$	\$4.25
m	$0.15(m-10)+1.25$	c

Explanation: Parentheses are needed because the charge is not 15 cents per minute until after 10 minutes.

b. What is the equation that relates cost and minutes? Simplify the equation.

$c = 0.15(m-10)+1.25$

$c = 0.15m - 1.50 + 1.25$ Distributive property: multiplied m and –10 by 0.15

$c = 0.15m - 0.25$ Combined like terms, –1.50 + 1.25

c. If the call costs \$2.90, how long were you on the phone?

Find m when c = 2.90.

$2.90 = 0.15m - 0.25$ Substituted 2.90 for c.

$3.15 = 0.15m$ Added 0.25 to both sides.

$21 = m$ Divided both sides by 0.15

d. Solve for m in the equation from Part b.

(This is the only new information in this section.)

Why would you want to do this? Imagine a situation where you know the cost of ten different calls. Instead of solving for C ten separate times, you can solve for C once and then use arithmetic to find the ten different values of m.

$c = 0.15m - 0.25$

$c + 0.25 = 0.15m$ Added 0.25 to both sides.

> **Explanation:** The algebraic steps are the same as in Part c. The difference is that the solution is not a number.

$\frac{c + 0.25}{0.15} = m$ Divided both sides by 0.15

$m = \frac{c + 0.25}{0.15}$

> **Explanation:** The usual format for literal equations is to write the variable solved for on the left side of the equation.

Summary: 1. A **literal equation** is an equation that involves more than one variable.

2. To **solve** a literal equation, the algebraic steps are the same as the problems from Sections 1.4 and 1.5. The only difference is the solution is not a number but an algebraic formula.

Example 2. Solve for y.

Traditional Equation		**Literal Equation**
Solve for **y**.		Solve for y.
$6 + 5\mathbf{y} = 24$		$6x + 5\mathbf{y} = 24$
$5\mathbf{y} = 18$	Subtract 6 from both sides.	$5\mathbf{y} = 24 - 6x$
$\mathbf{y} = \frac{18}{5}$	Divide both sides by 3.	$\mathbf{y} = \frac{24 - 6x}{5}$

CLASS WORK

1. An appliance repair store charges $50 for the first hour and $18 an hour for each additional hour.

   a. Complete the table to find the cost of repairing an appliance.

HOURS	CALCULATION	COST
3		
8		
h		

   b. What is the equation that relates cost and hours? Simplify the equation.

   c. If the repair costs $230, how long did it take?

   d. Solve for h in the equation from Part b.

2. Scientists use the length of the femur, the bone from the hip to the knee, to approximate the height of a person. The equation below is used to approximate the height of a man knowing the length of his femur:

$$h = 69.1 + 2.24f,$$

where f is the length of the femur and h is the height of the person. The lengths are measured in centimeters. Solve the equation for f.

3. $F = P(1 + rt)$ is used to compute the future value of an investment that earns simple interest.

F is the future value of the investment.
P is the principal or the amount invested.
r is the annual interest rate.
t is the number of years the money is invested.

a. Find t if $1,000 is invested at an annual interest rate of 6%, and the future value is $1,420.

b. Solve the formula for t.

d. Solve for r.

Study Tip: New students must learn to budget their time in order to be successful in college. It is especially important when are preparing for a test. See page iv and complete a weekly planner for the week of your first MAT 011 test. Make sure you include three one hour blocks to study for your upcoming MAT 011 exam.

GROUP EXERCISE

The table below shows the number of registered shareholders (in thousands) of PPG Company at the end of each year between 2001 and 2005. The data in this figure can be modeled by the equation:

$$s = 788 - 28t,$$

where s is the number of registered shareholders (in thousands) of stock at the end of year *t*, and *t* is the number of years since 2000. The equation is derived from the data using the linear regression command on the graphing calculator. If you take Intermediate Algebra, you will learn how to find linear regression lines.

Years	Variable t	Number of Shareholders (in thousands)
2001	1	755
2002	2	732
2003	3	710
2004	4	675
2005	5	642

1. When will there be 600,000 PPG Company shareholders?
   (Hint: Because the units for shareholders is in thousands, s = 600)

2. Solve for the variable t in the equation s = 788 – 28t.

Go Back: Review Part d. on page 68 or 1d. on page 70.

3. When will there be 544,000 PPG Company shareholders?
   (Hint: Because the units for shareholders is in thousands, s = 544)

HOMEWORK EXERCISES

Study Tip: Remember your guidelines for meaningful homework time.

Skill Building Exercise

1. Consider the equation $v = -1.2t + 72$

   a. Find v when $t = 22$. b. Find t when $v = 61$.

Practice Exercises

2. From a modest beginning, Q–Mart Stores have become one of the largest retailing chains in America. The table below shows the number of stores at the end of selected years in the period 2001 – 2005. The data in this table can be modeled by the equation:

$$s = 236t + 28,$$

where s represents the number of stores at the end of year t, and t is the number of years since 2000. The equation is derived from the data using the linear regression command on a graphing calculator. If you take Intermediate Algebra, you will learn how to find regression lines.

Go Back: Review the group work problem on page 73 for a similar problem..

Years	Variable t	Number of Q-Mart Stores
2001	1	315
2002	2	408
2003	3	786
2004	4	954
2005	5	1225

   a. According to the equation, when will Q–Mart have 1,500 stores?

   b. Solve for t in the equation $s = 236t + 28$.

   c. According to the equation, when will Q–Mart have 2,600 stores?

3. The wind chill produced by a 45 mph wind can be approximated by the equation

$$W = 1.6T - 54.6,$$

where W is the wind chill and T is the temperature. Solve the above equation for T.

4. $F = P(1 + rt)$ is used to compute the future value of an investment that earns simple interest.

F is the future value of the investment.
P is the principal or the amount invested.
r is the annual interest rate.
t is the number of years the money is invested.

Go Back: Review the problem on page 71 for a similar problem.

a. Find r if $1,500 is invested for 6 years, and the future value is $1,950.

b. Solve the formula for r.

5. Solve for the indicated variable.

a. $P = 2L + 2W$, solve for L.

b. $D = rt$, solve for r.

c. $3x - 4y = 12$, solve for y.

d. $6x + 4y = 9$, solve for y.

6. Final velocity V, the speed of the object when it hits the ground, can be found using the formula:

$$V = v^2 + 2as.$$

Where v is the initial velocity measured in meters per second; a is the acceleration measured in meters per second squared, and s is the distance the object falls measured in meters. Solve the formula for s.

7. The velocity of a falling object is indicated by the formula $v = v_0 + at$, where v_0 is the initial velocity measured in meters per second; a is the acceleration measured in meters per second squared, and t is time measured in seconds. Solve for t.

8. The cost C of a product that sells for P dollars with a tax of r percent is given by the equation:

$$C = P + rP.$$

Solve for the variable r.

Reading and Writing Mathematics

9. Describe each step.

a.

$2L + 3W = 542$, solve for W.	Step
$3W = 542 - 2L$	____________________
$W = \dfrac{542 - 2L}{3}$	____________________

b.

$\frac{4}{5}y - 3x = 24$, solve for y

Step

$\frac{4}{5}y = 24 + 3x$ ______________________

$\frac{5}{4}\left(\frac{4}{5}y\right) = \frac{5}{4}(24 + 3x)$ ______________________

$y = 30 + \frac{15}{4}x$ ______________________

10. In the problem below, find the **mistake** and write a sentence describing the error. Also, write a suggestion so that any student who makes this type of mistake will have a way to remember not to make the error again.

$3h + 2(4w - 6) = 14$, solve for h.

$3h + 8w - 12 = 14$

$3h - 4w = 14$

$3h = 14 + 4w$

$h = \frac{14 + 4w}{3}$

11. A classmate asks you to look over his work. The mathematics is correct. Make four suggestions that would improve the presentation of the problem. Review the problem the way an teacher might look at it.

Solve $5x + 4y = 15$, solve for y.

$-4y$

$5x = 15 - 4y$

-15

$5x - 15 = -4y$

$\frac{5x - 15}{-4}$

Study Tip: Detailed solutions to problems 1, 3, 5 a, b, c, d 7, 10 and 11 can be found on the MAT 011 Electronic Resource page. See page vii.

SECTION 1.7 PERCENTAGES
PREVIEW

Overview: This section will explain how to apply algebra to percentage problems.

In algebra problems, percentages are usually written as decimals.

Example 1. Ethan got 80% of the questions correct on a test, and there were 55 questions. How many did he get right?

The number of questions correct is given by:

80% of 55

$0.80 \bullet 55 = 44$

Explanation: % means "per one hundred". So 80% means 80/100 = 0.80.

Ethan got 44 questions correct.

Example 2. A math teacher, Dr. Pi, computes a student's grade for the course as follows:

20% for homework
50% for the average of 5 tests
30% for the final exam

a. Compute Darrel's grade for the course if he has a 91 on the homework, 84 for his test average, and a 98 on the final exam.

$G = 0.20 \bullet 91 + 0.50 \bullet 84 + 0.30 \bullet 98$	Wrote percents as decimals.
$G = 18.2 + 42 + 29.4$	Multiplied
$G = 89.6$	Added

Darrel's grade for the course is an 89.6, or a B+.

b. Suppose Selena has an 89 homework average and a 97 test average. What does Selena have to get on the final exam to get a 90 for the course?

The difference between Part a and Part b is that in Part b we don't know Selena's grade on the final exam.

So instead of multiplying 30% times a number, multiply 30% times E. E is the variable that represents what Selena has to get on the final exam to get a 90 for the course.

$90 = 0.20 \bullet 89 + 0.50 \bullet 97 + 0.30 \bullet E$	Set up the equation.
$90 = 66.3 + 0.30E$	Simplified
$23.7 = 0.30E$	Subtracted 66.3 from both sides.
$79 = E$	Divided both sides by 0.30.

Because Selena studied all semester, she only has to get a 79 on the final to get a 90 for the course.

Example 3. Sink Hardware store is having a 15% off sale. The sale price of a toilet is \$97; find the retail price of the toilet.

a. Complete the table to find an equation relating the sale price to the retail price (the price before the sale).

Vocabulary: **Retail price** is the sale price to the consumer or the price before the sale.
Discount is how much the consumer saves, usually a percentage of the retail price.
Sale Price is equal to the retail price minus the discount.

Retail Price	**Discount**	**Sale Price** Retail – Discount = Sale Price
\$110	$0.15 \bullet 110 = 16.50$	$110 - 0.15 \bullet 110 = 93.50$
\$140	$0.15 \bullet 140 = 21.00$	$140 - 0.15 \bullet 140 = 119$
R	$0.15 \bullet R$	$R - 0.15 \bullet R = S$

b. Simplify the equation.

$$R - 0.15 \bullet R = S$$
$$0.85 \bullet R = S$$

Explanation: The coefficient of R is one, so the arithmetic for combining like terms is 1 – 0.15 = .85. In other words, the sale price is 85% of the retail price.

c. Solve the equation when the sale price is \$97.

$0.85 \bullet R = 97$ Substituted 97 in for S.
$R = 114.12$ Divided both sides by 0.85.

The retail price for the toilet was \$114.12.

Note: the answer was rounded to the nearest cent.

The following diagram is meant as a visualization of problem 3.

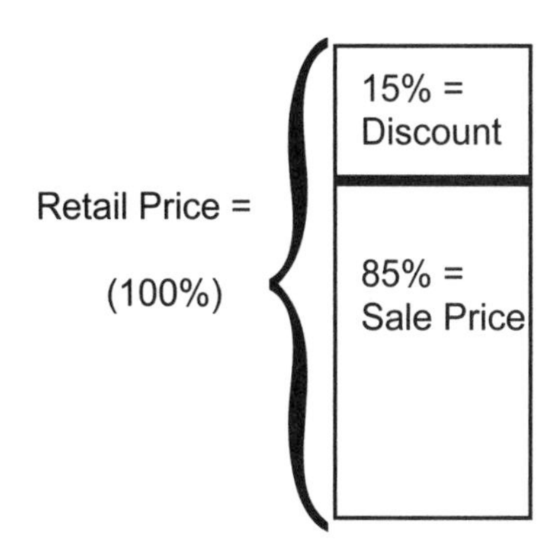

The large rectangle represents the retail price. The retail price has two components, the sales price and the discount. So

Retail Price = Sale Price + Discount

If Discount is subtracted from both sides of the equation, a formula for Sale Price is found.

Sale Price = Retail Price - Discount

Summary: Percentages play an integral role in our everyday lives, including computing discounts, calculating mortgages, savings, investments, and estimating final grades.

When working with percentages, remember to write them as decimals, to create tables to derive equations, and to follow the proper procedures to solve equations.

Study Tip: Remember to use descriptive letters to describe the variables.

CLASS WORK

1. Review of basic percentage problems.

   a. Write the percentage as a decimal.

      1. 5% 2. 0.45% 3. 500%

   b. A stock is worth $2,800 and drops 20% in one day. What is its new value?

   c. A stock is worth $2,240 and grows 20% in one day. What is its new value?

   d. A stock was worth $2,800 and dropped 20% to $2,240 in one day. What percent does the stock have to grow the next day to get back to $2,800?

2. A math teacher, Dr. Kay, computes a student's grade for the course as follows:

10% for homework
65% for the average of 4 tests
25% for the final exam

a. Compute Bill's grade for the course if he has a 78 on the homework, 81 for his test average, and a 79 on the final exam.

b. Suppose Sue has an 82 homework average and a 63 test average. What does Sue have to get on the final exam to get a 70 for the course?

3. Phillip's Hardware Store is having a 20% off sale.

a. Complete the table.

Retail Price	**Discount**	**Sale Price** Retail Price – Discount = Sales Price
60		
50		
R		

b. A step ladder has a sale price of $44. What was the retail price before the sale? Set up the appropriate equation and solve it.

4. a. Walden Department Store computes retail prices (the price Walden charges its customers for an item) by marking up the wholesale price (the price Walden pays for the item) by 40%. Complete the table. **Recall that wholesale price plus markup equals retail price.**

WHOLESALE PRICE ($)	**MARKUP ($)**	**RETAIL PRICE ($)** WHOLESALE + MARKUP = RETAIL PRICE
$10		
$20		
$40		
w		

b. What is the equation that relates retail price to wholesale price and markup?

c. Suppose an item costs $82 at the Walden Department Store. How much did Walden pay for the item?

5. SRH Inc. gave everyone a 4% raise. The wages are per hour.

a. Complete the table below.

Current Hourly Wage	**Calculation**	**New Hourly Wage**
$12.50		
$14.75		
C		N

b. What is Joyce's current hourly wage if her new hourly wage will be $21.55.

c. Find an equation for the percent increase.

GROUP EXERCISE

Study Tip: Group suggestion: Use only one sheet of paper for the entire group. This encourages all to participate.

1. A grocer purchases a can of fruit juice for 68 cents. Find the selling price if the markup is 30%.

2. A grocer marks up his produce by 25% of the wholesale price.

   a. Complete the table.

WHOLESALE PRICE	**MARKUP**	**RETAIL PRICE** WHOLESALE + MARKUP = RETAIL
.85		
1.00		
s		

   b. If the grocer sells a bunch of bananas for $1.15, how much did the grocer pay for the bananas?

3. Professor Passall computes his grades as follows:

   15% for homework
   55% for the average of 3 tests
   30% for the final exam

   a. Compute Howie's grade if he has a 71 homework average, an 83 test average, and a 68 final exam.

   b. Nancy wants to get an 80 for the course. She has an 82 homework average and a 74 test average. What does Nancy have to get on the final exam to get an 80 for the course?

HOMEWORK EXERCISES

Study Tip: Remember to use your homework notebook.

Skill Building Exercises

1. Write each percent as a decimal.

   a. 42% b. 3% c. 0.25% d. 98.7%

2. a. A stock is worth $47,230 and drops 12% in one day. What is its new value?

   b. A stock is worth $12,500 and grows 8% in one day. What is its new value?

   c. A stock was worth $35,675 and dropped 33% in one day. What percent does the stock have to grow the next day to get back to $35,675?

Practice Exercises

3. Dairy Prince has given each employee a 12% raise.

   a. Complete this table.

Employee	Susan	Joe	Mary	Pat
Current earnings per hour	$3.35	$3.50		
New earnings per hour			$4.48	$4.20

> **Explanation:** To find Mary's current earnings per hour, answer Part b first.

   b. What is the equation that relates new earnings to current?

4. Your employer increases your hourly wages by $1.35 per hour. Find the percent increase in your salary if your old salary was $9.00 an hour.

> **Explanation:** For problem 5 use the formula $P = \frac{\text{New} - \text{Old}}{\text{Old}} * 100$.

5. An item originally listed as $14.50 is on sale for $11.60, find the sale price percentage.

6. a. Harry's Hardware Store is having a 32% off sale. Complete the table.

Retail Price ($)	**Discount ($)**	**Sale Price ($)** Retail Price – Discount = Sale Price
25	0.32(25) = 8	25 – 0.32(25) = 17
35		
45		
C		

Go Back: This problem is like example 3 from "Preview" on page 79.

b. What is the retail price if the sale price is $37.40?

7. A math teacher, Dr. Pi, computes a student's grade for the course as follows:

10% for homework
65% for the average of the 5 tests
25% for the final exam

Compute the following students' grades for the course.

Go Back: Review pages 78 and 81.

a. George: 78 homework, 88 for the 5 tests, 71 for the final

b. Darrel: 87 for homework, his 5 test scores of 89, 71, 95, 97, 88, and a 90 for the final.

c. Rachel wants an 80 for the course. She has an 81 homework average and a 75 test average. What does Rachel have to get on the final exam to get an 80 for the course?

8. An English teacher, Dr. Austin, computes a student's grade for the course as follows:

15% for a research paper
15% for short essays
50% for the average of 4 tests
20% for the final

a. Harold wants a 75 for the course. He has an 82 for the research paper, 61 for the short essays, and a 71 average for the 4 tests. What does Harold need to get on the final exam to get a 75 for the course?

b. Thomas wants a 90 for the course. He has a 78 for the research paper, 80 for the short essays, and a 69 average for the 4 tests. What does Thomas need to get on the final exam to get a 90 for the course? What do you conclude about Thomas' chances of getting a 90?

Study Tip: If you are having difficulties with the Practice Exercises, attempt the Reading and Writing Exercises first. Often reviewing the material in a different manner will result in better comprehension. Experiment – see what works for your unique learning style.

Reading and Writing Mathematics

9 a. To compute the retail price, a store owner uses the formula R = 1.20W. What was the markup? Explain what the coefficient (the number multiplying the variable) means.

b. To compute the sale price, a store owner uses the formula S = 0.85R. What was the percent off for the sale?

c. Why is the coefficient in Part a greater than 1?

d. Why is the coefficient in Part b less than 1?

10. In the problem below, find the **mistake** and write a sentence describing the error. Also, write a suggestion so that any student who makes this type of mistake will have a way to remember not to make it again.

Darrel's Hockey Shed is having a 20% off sale.

a. Complete the table.

Retail Price ($)	**Discount ($)**	**Sale Price ($)** Retail Price – Discount = Sale Price
25	*0.20(25) = 5*	*20*
35	*0.20(35) = 7*	*28*
45	*0.20(45) = 9*	*36*
c	*0.20c*	*0.20c*

b. Find the retail price if the sale price is $28.

0.20c = 28

c = $5.60 The current price is $5.60.

Study Tip: Detailed solutions to problems 1, 3, 5, 6, 7, and 9 can be found on the MAT 011 Electronic Resource page. See page vii.

CHAPTER 1 REVIEW

This unit introduces algebra by examining similar models. You should be able to read a problem and create a table to find an equation that relates two variables. If you are given information about one of the variables, you should be able to use algebra to find the other variable.

Section 1.1 Signed Numbers:

Informal Rules: (See Appendix A for formal presentation)

Adding or subtracting like signs: Add the two numbers and use the common sign.

Example 1. a. $-3-5=-8$ b. $+3+5=+8$

Adding or subtracting unlike signs: Subtract the two numbers and use the sign of the larger. (More precisely, the sign of the number whose absolute value is largest.)

Example 2. a. $-5+2=-3$ b. $+5-2=+3$

Multiplying or dividing like signs: The product or quotient of two numbers with like signs is always positive.

Example 3. a. $\frac{-35}{-7}=5$ b. $(-3)(-7)=21$

Multiplying or dividing unlike signs: The product or quotient of two numbers with unlike signs is always negative.

Example 4. a. $-6\bullet 9=-54$ b. $\frac{-36}{9}=-4$

Order of operations: **P**lease **E**xcuse **M**y **D**ear **A**unt **S**ally

1. Inside **P**arentheses, ( ).
2. **E**xponents.
3. **M**ultiplication and **D**ivision (left to right)
4. **A**ddition and **S**ubtraction (left to right)

Example 5. $-4(7-10)=$
$-4(-3)=12$

Example 6. $7-5^2=$
$7-25=-18$

Study Tip: All of these informal rules should be written on note cards.

Section 1.2 Introduction to Variables:

Generate a table to find an equation that relates two variables.

Example 6. A car company charges $14.95 plus 35 cents per mile.

Miles	Calculation	Cost
15	$0.35\bullet 15+14.95$	$20.20
25	$0.35\bullet 25+14.95$	$23.70
m	$0.35m+14.95$	C

Section 1.3 Simplifying Algebraic Equations:

Distributive property: $a(b + c) = a \bullet b + a \bullet c$

Combine like terms:

Example 7. Simplify. $8x - 2(3x - 5)$

$$8x - 6x + 10 =$$
$$2x + 10$$

Sections 1.4 Solving Equations:

Solving Equations

1. Simplify both sides of the equation.
2. Write the equation as a variable term equal to a constant.
3. Divide both sides by the coefficient or multiply by the reciprocal.
4. Three possible outcomes to solving an equation.
   a. One solution (a conditional equation)
   b. No solution (a contradiction)
   c. Every number is a solution (an identity)

Example 8. Solve $3x - 5(4x + 12) = 23 - 9x$

$$3x - 20x - 60 = 23 - 9x$$
$$-17x - 60 = 23 - 9x$$
$$-17x + 17x - 60 = 23 - 9x + 17x$$
$$-60 = 23 + 8x$$
$$-60 - 23 = 23 - 23 + 8x$$
$$-83 = 8x$$
$$-10.375 = x$$

Section 1.5 Applications of Linear Equations:

This section summarizes the major skills taught in this chapter.

Example 9. A cell phone company charges $12.50 plus 15 cents per minute after the first six minutes.

a. Create a table to find the equation that relates cost and minutes.

Minutes	Calculation	Cost
10	$0.15(10-6)+12.50$	$13.10
20	$0.15(20-6)+12.50$	$14.60
m	$0.15(m-6)+12.50$	c

b. Simplify the equation.

$$0.15(m - 6) + 12.50 = C$$
$$0.15m - .90 + 12.50 = C$$
$$0.15m + 11.60 = C$$

c. If the call costs $23.50, how long were you on the phone?

$$0.15m + 11.60 = 23.50$$
$$0.15m = 11.90$$
$$m = 79.33$$

If the call costs $23.50, then you were on the phone for approximately 79 minutes.

Section 1.7 Literal Equations:

A literal equation involves solving an equation for one of two variables.

Example 10. Solve for y. $2x + 5y = 8$

$$5y = 8 - 2x$$
$$y = \frac{8 - 2x}{5}$$

Section 1.8 Percentages:

Write percentages as decimals.

Example 11. An English teacher computes his grades as follows:

30% short essays
15% research paper
55% final exam.

Sue has a 87 on the short essays and a 72 on the research paper. If she wants an 80 for the course, what grade does Sue have to get on the final?

$$0.30 \bullet 87 + 0.15 \bullet 72 + 0.55E = 80$$
$$36.90 + 0.55E = 80$$
$$0.55E = 43.10$$
$$E = 78.36$$

Sue has to get a 78.36 in the final exam to get an 80 for the course.

Study Tips:

1. Make sure you have done all of the homework exercises.
2. Practice the review test that is given on the next page by placing yourself under realistic exam conditions.
3. Find a quiet place and use a timer to simulate the test period.
4. Write your answers in your homework notebook. You may then re–take the exam for extra practice or first make copies of the exam.
5. Check your answers. The answers to the review test are on page 438.
6. There is an additional exam available on the Beginning Algebra web page, **www.mc3.edu/aa/career/MATHSCI/mathprog/mat011/mat011.htm**
7. **DO NOT** wait until the night before the exam to study.

CHAPTER 1 REVIEW TEST

1. Water Witch Well Drillers charge their customers $350.00 to come to the well site and $20.00 per foot to drill a well.
   a. Complete the table.

DEPTH OF THE WELL (Feet)	CALCULATION	COST ($)
50		
70		
90		
d		

   b. What is the equation that relates cost and depth of the well?

   c. If a person is charged $4,150 for a well, how deep is the well?

2. The company Take–Taxi charges the passenger $1.35 immediately upon entering the cab. After the first 3 miles, an additional $1.80 per mile is charged.
   a. Complete the table.

MILES	CALCULATION	COST ($)
10		
15		
20		
m		

   b. What is the equation that relates cost and miles?

   c. If the taxi fare is $27.50, how far was your ride?

Study Tip: If you don't remember how to do a problem, look through the chapter for a similar problem.

3. Professor Newton computes his grades as follows:

Test Average: 60%
Homework: 15%
Final Exam: 25%

a. Otto has a test average of 82, a homework average of 99, and a final exam score of 71. What is Otto's grade for the course?

b. Tito has a test average of 71 and a homework average of 76. What does Tito have to get on the final to get a 70 for the course?

4. The equation:

$$G = 0.022B + 0.359$$

relates the price per gallon, G, of gasoline with the price per barrel, B, of crude oil.

a. Find the price per gallon if the price per barrel of crude oil is $87.50.

b. Find the price per barrel of crude oil if the price per gallon of gasoline is $3.27.

5. Clancy's Burgers has given a 12% raise to all of its employees. Complete the table.

a.

CURRENT SALARY	CALCULATION	NEW SALARY
$1.00 per hr.		
$3.00 per hr.		
C per hr.		N

b. What is the equation that relates current salary to new salary?

c. If your new salary will be $5.25 per hour, what is your current salary?

6. Stats' Department Store is having a 20% off sale.

   a. Complete the table.

RETAIL PRICE	CALCULATION	SALE PRICE
10.00		
20.00		
R		S

   b. What is the equation that relates the original price to the sale price?

   c. If the sale price is $81.00, what was the original price?

7. The net profits and losses for Rose Stores for the years 2000 through 2003 are shown in the graph below.

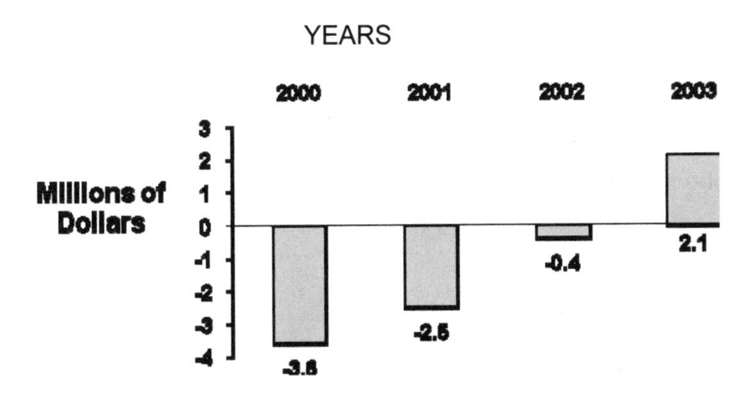

   a. What is the difference between the profit or loss in 2002 and that in 2000?

   b. What is the difference between the profit or loss in 2003 and that in 2001?

8. Simplify. $-2(x-3)+2(4-x)$

9. Solve.

a. $7x - 8 = -29$

b. $8x - 3(4x - 5) = -2x - 11$

10. A business manager has determined that the cost per unit for a camera is $70 and that the fixed costs per month are $3,500. Find the number of cameras that are produced during a month in which the total cost is $21,000. Use the equation

$$T = U \bullet N + F,$$

where T is the total cost, U is the cost per unit, N is the number of units produced, and F is the fixed cost.

11. $P = 2W + 2L$, solve for W.

12. Describe each step.

	Step
$3x + 2(4x-1) = 4x - 3$	
$3x + 8x - 2 = 4x - 3$	________________
$11x - 2 = 4x - 3$	________________
$11x - 2 + 2 = 4x - 3 + 2$	________________
$11x = 4x - 1$	________________
$11x - 4x = 4x - 4x - 1$	________________
$7x = -1$	________________
$\frac{7x}{7} = \frac{-1}{7}$	________________
$x = -0.1429$	________________

13. Find the mistake.

$$4(2x-5) = 3x + 7$$

$$8x - 20 = 3x + 7$$

$$8x - 20 + 20 = 3x + 7 + 20$$

$$8x = 3x + 27$$

$$8x + 3x = 3x + 3x + 27$$

$$11x = 27$$

$$\frac{11x}{11} = \frac{27}{11}$$

$$x = 2.\overline{45}$$

Study Tip: Detailed solutions to all the problems can be found on the MAT 011 Electronic Resource page. See page vii.

CHAPTER 2

GRAPHING

SECTION 2.1 INEQUALITIES
PREVIEW

Objectives: In this section, you will solve inequality algebra problems and represent the answers on a number line. Also, you will identify quantities as being *greater than*, *less than,* or *equal to* each other.

The following example comes from Section 1.7 "Percentages", page 78.

Example 1. A math teacher, Dr. Pi, computes a student's grade for the course as follows:

20% for homework
50% for the average of 5 tests
30% for the final exam

Suppose Selena has an 89 homework average and a 97 test average. What does Selena have to get on the final exam to get a 90 for the course?

Let E be the variable that represents what Selena has to get on the final exam to get a 90 for the course.

$90 = 0.20 \bullet 89 + 0.50 \bullet 97 + 0.30 \bullet E$	Set up the equation.
$90 = 66.3 + 0.30E$	Simplified.
$23.7 = 0.30E$	Subtracted 66.3 from both sides.
$79 = E$	Divided both sides by 0.30.

Because Selena studied all semester, she only has to get a 79 on the final to get a 90 for the course.

A More Practical Version of the Problem

What Selena really wants for the course is an A^+. So she would be happy with a grade of 95 or higher. The more realistic question would be:

What does Selena have to get on the final exam to get a 95 or higher for the course?

Let E be the variable that represents what Selena has to get on the final exam to get a 95 or higher for the course.

Explanation: We use the symbol $\geq$ to mean greater than or equal to. So instead of setting Selena's grade = to 95, we set Selena's grade $\geq$ 95.

$0.20 \bullet 89 + 0.50 \bullet 97 + 0.30 \bullet E \geq 95$	Set up the equation.
$66.3 + 0.30E \geq 95$	Simplified.
$0.30E \geq 28.7$	Subtracted 66.3 from both sides.
$E \geq 95.67$	Divided both sides by 0.30.

Selena has to get a 95.67 or higher on the final to get a 95 or higher for the course.

The only difference between the two problems is using the signs = and $\geq$. Using $\geq$ makes the problem more realistic in terms of the grade Selena wants for the course.

Inequality Notation:

1. $>$ means **greater than**.

   For example, $x > 3$ represents all the numbers larger than 3, but not 3.

2. $<$ means **less than**.

   For example, $x < 5$ represents all the numbers smaller than 5, but not 5.

3. $\geq$ means **greater than or equal to**.

   For example, $x \geq 7$ represents all the numbers larger than 7, and includes 7.

4. $\leq$ means **less than or equal to**.

   For example, $x \leq 6$ represents all the numbers smaller than 6, and includes 6.

Graphing Inequalities on the number line:

Graphing an inequality often conveys its meaning more clearly than just writing the inequality.

Rules: Two rules for graphing inequalities:

1. For $\geq$ and $\leq$ we use a shaded circle, • ,to show that we are including the number.

2. For $>$ and $<$ we use a open circle, ∘, to show that we are not including the number.

Example 2. Graph $x \leq -4$.

This means that we want the numbers smaller than and including –4. We put a shaded circle at –4 since we have $\leq$ and we draw an arrow going to the left of –4.

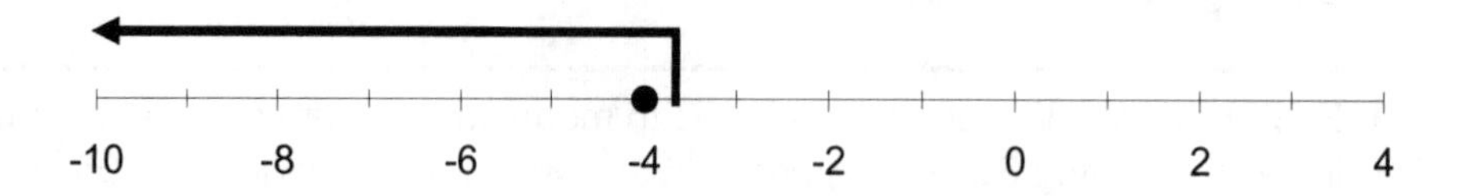

Example 3. Graph $-5 < x \leq 3$.

This means that we want numbers between –5 and 3, including 3 but not including –5. We will put a shaded circle at 3 and an open circle at –5 and draw a line between –5 and 3.

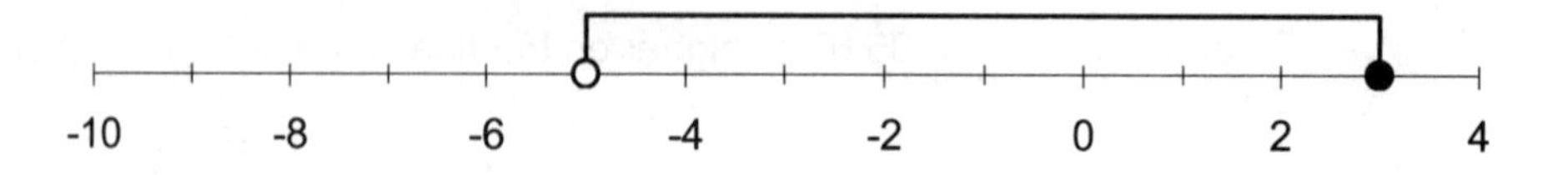

Solving Inequalities:

The only difference between solving equality equations and inequality equations is:

Rule: When you multiply or divide by a negative number, you must change the direction of the inequality.

> **Explanation:** Consider the two numbers 3 and 7. $3 < 7$ because 3 is to the left of 7 on the number line.
>
> -8 -6 -4 -2 0 2 4 6 8
>
> If we multiply both numbers by a negative 1, then we get -3 and -7. Graphing -3 and -7 on the number line:
>
> -8 -6 -4 -2 0 2 4 6 8
>
> You can see that -7 is to the left of -3, so $-3 > -7$. Multiplying by a negative reverses the order of the numbers.

Example 4. Solve and graph the solution on the number line.

$5 - 3x \leq -13$	
$-3x \leq -18$	Subtracted -5 from both sides.
$x \geq 6$	Divided both sides by -3. Since we divide both sides by a negative, we change the direction of the inequality.

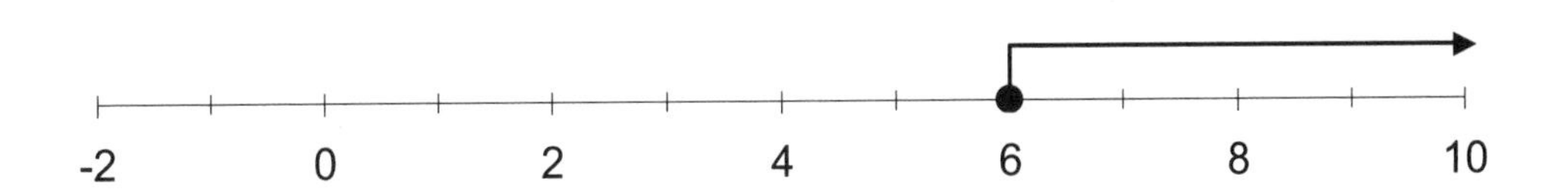

Study Tip: The rule explaining the difference between solving equality equations and inequality equations should be written down on a note card and memorized along with an example demonstrating the rule.

Example 5. Solve and graph the solution on the number line.

$-7 < 4x - 5 \leq 3$

This problem has three parts

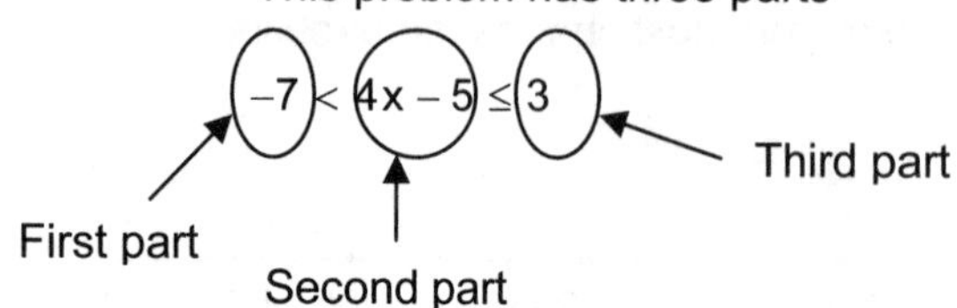

$$-7 < 4x - 5 \leq 3$$

$$-7 + 5 < 4x - 5 + 5 \leq 3 + 5$$ Added 5 to all three parts.

$$-2 < 4x \leq 8$$ Combined like terms.

$$\frac{-2}{4} < \frac{4x}{4} \leq \frac{8}{4}$$ Divided all three parts by 4.

$$-.5 < x \leq 2$$ Answer.

Explanation: This problem has two inequalities. The solution should contain x in the middle. Whatever operations we do on one part we must do to all three parts.

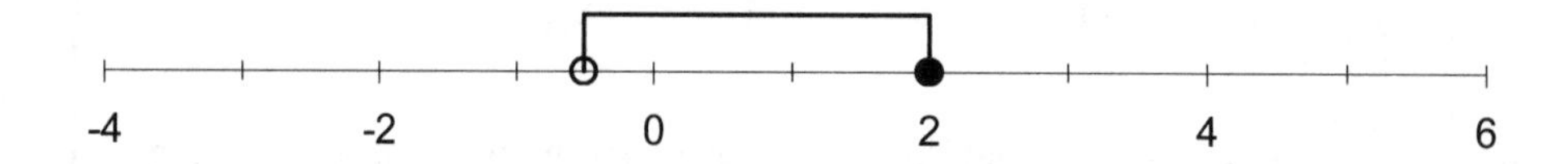

Summary: Adding inequalities to your algebra repertoire allows you to calculate when one quantity is more or less than another.

Major ideas:

1. When graphing inequalities on the number line, $\leq$, $\geq$ are represented by a small dot or shaded circle.

2. When graphing inequalities on the number line, $<$, $>$ are represented by a small opened circle.

3. When solving a problem with more than one inequality:

   a. Perform the same algebraic step to all three parts of the inequality.
   b. The answer should have x in the middle.

4. When solving inequalities, if you multiply or divide by a negative number, then you must change the direction of the inequality.

CLASS WORK

1. An English teacher, Bill Shakespeare, computes a student's grade for a course as follows:

    20% for a research paper
    40% for the average of 4 tests
    15% for short essays
    25% for the final exam

    A student, Rosetta Stone (author of *Because a Little Bug Went Ka-Choo*), wants to get a C for the course. This means that Rosetta's grade must be greater than or equal to 70, but less than 80. Rosetta has an 85 on the research paper, a 68 average for the tests, and a 62 average for the short essays. What does Rosetta have to get on the final exam to get a C?

2. a. Is $x = 3$ a solution to $x + 5 \geq 1$? b. Is $x = -4$ a solution to $x + 5 \geq 1$?

    c. Is $x = -2$ a solution to $x + 5 \geq 1$? d. Is $x = -8$ a solution to $x + 5 \geq 1$?

3. Use the number line to describe the solutions to the following inequality equation.

    a. $x \leq 5$

    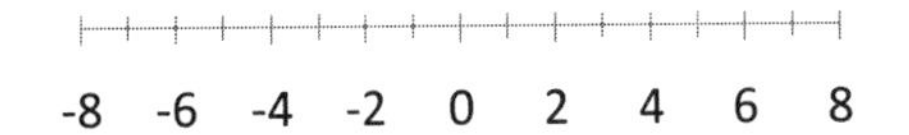

    b.  $x > -3$

    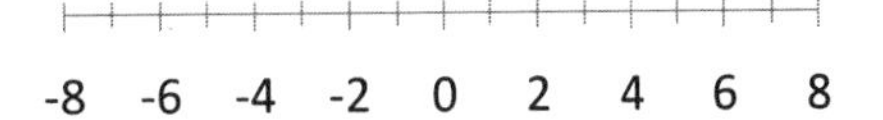

    c. $5 \geq x$

    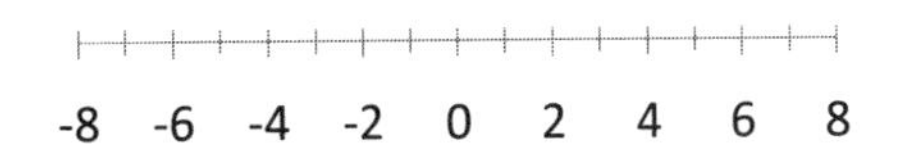

    d. 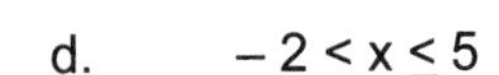 $-2 < x \leq 5$

    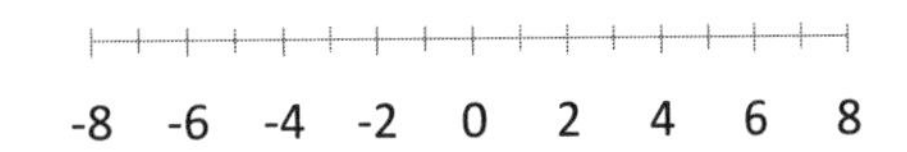

4. Solve the inequality and describe each step.

a. $4 - 3x \geq 22$ | STEP

b. $-6 \leq 15 + 7x < 50$ | STEP

5. Solve each inequality and graph the solution on the number line.

a. $3(2 - 8x) \leq 3x - 5$

b. $-8 < 7 - 3x < 31$

6. Solve $4x - 5y < 10$ for y.

GROUP EXERCISE

Study Tip: Group Suggestion: Use one piece of paper and have each group member determine a step and then pass the sheet to the next person. If someone gets stuck, the previous person should try to explain. If no one in the group can help, ask the professor for assistance.

1. Describe each step.

	Step
$4 - 8x > 19 - 3x$	
$-8x > 15 - 3x$	______________________
$-5x > 15$	______________________
$x < -3$	______________________

2. Find where the first mistake occurs.

$-6 \leq 4 + 5x \leq 15$

$-10 \leq 5x \leq 15$

$-2 \leq x \leq 3$

3. Solve and graph the solutions on the number line.

a. $8x - 5 \leq 4x + 23$

b. $-6 \leq 10 - 2x < 22$

Go Back: Review example 5 on page 98 or 5d on page 100.

-8 -6 -4 -2 0 2 4 6 8

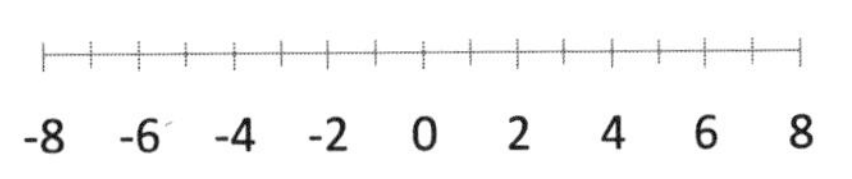

Problem 4 is on the next page.

4. A math teacher, Mrs. Lincoln computes a student's grade for the course as follows:

15% for homework
55% for the average of 4 tests
30% for the final exam

Sue wants to get a B for the course. This means that her grade must be greater than or equal to 80 but less than 90. Sue has a 68 on the homework and an 84 test average. What does Sue have to get on the final to get a B for the course?

HOMEWORK EXERCISES

Skill Building Exercises

1. Chapter 2 is more difficult than Chapter 1. If you scored less than 80 on the Chapter 1 test then you need to improve your homework skills if you want to pass MAT 011. It is vital that you do the homework properly. Review the suggestions below and check the ones that you are already doing. You should follow all of the suggestions.

☐ Collect materials: three-ring binder, lined paper, several sharpened pencils, eraser, calculator, timer, and highlighter.

☐ Label each homework sheet with the date, chapter, section, and textbook page numbers.

☐ Write neatly; leave plenty of white space; use as much paper as you need. Allow room for questions and/or comments.

☐ Set the timer for 30 minutes and begin. Check your answers in the back of the text. If you are correct, move on. If not, spend time (but no more than 10 minutes) analyzing and re-doing your work. Neat, legible homework makes this step easier. If you still are confused, highlight the number of the problem and move on.
Hint: The Mat 011 text uses the **Go Back** *icon to indicate where to find a similar problem.*

☐ Students in Mat 011 having difficulties with the Practice Exercises, should attempt the Reading and Writing Exercises first. Often reviewing the material in a different manner will result in better comprehension. Experiment—see what works for your unique learning style.

☐ When the timer rings, stop everything and reward yourself for **five minutes**. Stretch, drink some water, or check your messages. Re-set the timer and continue. Plan to spend one to two hours on each homework section.

2. Graph each inequality on the number line.

   a. $x \leq -2$ b. $x > 6$ c. $-3 < x \leq 1$

3. Solve each equation below.

   a. $3x - 7 = 21 + 5x$ b. $7x - 6(4 - 3x) = 170 - 12x$

4. a. Is $x = 5$ a solution to $3x - 4 > 8$?

   b. Is $x = 21$ a solution to $3x - 4 > 8$?

   c. Is $x = 1$ a solution to $3x - 4 > 8$?

Practice Exercises

5. An astronomy professor, Dr. Bachmann, computes a student's grade for the course as follows:

    15% for homework
    40% for the average of 4 tests
    20% for labs
    25% for the final exam

    Al Einstein wants to get a B for the course. This means that his grade must be greater than or equal to 80 but less than 90. Al has an 86 on the homework, a 72 test average, and an 88 for the labs. What does Al have to get on the final to get a B for the course?

6. Solve and graph the solutions on the number line.

Go Back: Review example 4 on page 97 or 4a on page 100 for help with parts a through

a. $-6x > 54$ b. $\frac{1}{5}x < 4$

c. $7 - x \leq 15$ d. $15 - 2x \geq 21$

e. $5x - 11 < 2x + 8$ f. $2(4x - 5) - 11 \leq 41$

Go Back: Review example 5 on page 98 or 4b on page 100.

g. $5 < x + 11 \leq 15$ h. $-6 \leq 5 - 2x \leq 11$

i. $0 \leq 4x - 8 < 18$ j. $-7 \leq 3x + 5 \leq 15$

k. $-6 < 8 - 2x < 24$

7. Solve the literal inequality problems for the given variable.

Go Back: Review example 6 on page 100.

a. $2x + 3y < 5$ for the variable y. b. $6x - 5y \geq 8$ for the variable y.

Reading and Writing Mathematics

8. Describe each step.

a. $6 - 3x \le 30 + x$ — Step

$-3x \le 24 + x$ ____________

$-4x \le 24$ ____________

$x \ge -6$ ____________

b. $-4 < 6 - 2x \le 14$ — Step

$-10 < -2x \le 8$ ____________

$5 > x \ge -4$ ____________

$-4 \le x < 5$ ____________

9. In each problem, find the **mistake** and write a sentence describing the error. Also, write a
suggestion so that any student who makes this type of error will have a way to remember not to make the mistake again.

a. $5 - 7x > 19$

$-7x > 14$

$x > -2$

b. $-15 \le 4x + 9 < 12$

$-24 \le 4x < 12$

$-6 \le x < 3$

10. a. What is the one difference between solving equality equations and inequality equations?

b. Describe the procedure to solve a single inequality equation.

c. Describe the procedure to solve a double inequality problem.

Study Tip: Detailed solutions to problems 3a, b, 5, 6 a, c, e, g, i, k, 7a, and 9 can be found on the MAT 011 Electronic Resource page. See page vii.

SECTION 2.2 APPLICATIONS OF INEQUALITIES PREVIEW

Objective: This section merges inequalities with the applications from the previous chapter.

Example 1. You are offered two sales positions after graduating from college. One, Math Inc., pays $10,000 plus 8% commission. The other, Hunter Company, pays $5,000 plus 12% commission. When does Math Inc. pay more than Hunter Company?

First determine the equations for each company. Create a table for each. Since both jobs are sales positions, we need a sales column, a calculation column, and a wage column. (You might be able to determine the equations by just reading the problem.)

Math Inc.			**Hunter Company**		
Sales	Calculation	Wage	Sales	Calculation	Wage
15,000	$0.08 \bullet 15,000 + 10,000$	11,200	15,000	$0.12 \bullet 15,000 + 5,000$	6,800
40,000	$0.08 \bullet 40,000 + 10,000$	13,200	40,000	$0.12 \bullet 40,000 + 5,000$	9,800
200,000	$0.08 \bullet 200,000 + 10,000$	26,000	200,000	$0.12 \bullet 200,000 + 5,000$	29,000
S	$0.08S + 10,000$	W	S	$0.12S + 5,000$	W

The equation for Math Inc: $W = 0.08S + 10,000$

The equation for Hunter Company: $W = 0.12S + 5,000$

Now that equations for both companies are determined answer the question: When does Math Inc. pay more than Hunter Company?

Wages from Math Inc. > Wages from Hunter Co.

$0.08S + 10,000 > 0.12S + 5,000$ Set up the inequality.

$0.08S > 0.12S - 5,000$ Subtracted 10,000 from both sides

$-0.04S > -5,000$ Subtracted 0.12S from both sides.

$S < 125,000$ Divided both sides by -0.04 and change the direction of the inequality.

Math Inc. pays more than Hunter Company for sales less than $125,000.

Example 2. A phone company charges a basic rate of 30 cents plus 8 cents after the first seven minutes.

a. Find the equation for the cost of making phone calls over seven minutes. Simplify the equation.

The company doesn't start charging a per minute rate until after the first seven minutes. You will have to subtract 7 from the number of minutes you were on the phone before multiplying by 0.08. This means you will have to use parentheses in the calculation column of the table.

Minutes	Calculation	Cost
10	$0.08(10-7)+0.30$	0.54
15	$0.08(15-7)+0.30$	0.94
m	$0.08(m-7)+0.30$	C

The equation for the cost is: $C = 0.08(m-7)+0.30$

Simplify the equation.

$C = 0.08(m-7)+0.30$

$C = 0.08m - 0.56 + 0.30$ Used the Distributive Property.

$C = 0.08m - 0.26$ Combined Like terms.

Note that this formula is only valid when $m > 7$.

b. How many minutes were you on the phone if the cost was more than $3.00.

$C > 3.00$ Cost is more than $3.00.

$0.08m - 0.26 > 3.00$ Substituted cost equation for c.

$0.08m > 3.26$ Added 0.26 to both sides.

$m > 40.75$ Divided both sides by 0.08.

If the cost is more than $3.00, then you were on the phone for more than 40.75 minutes.

c. How many minutes were you on the phone if the cost was between \$2.50 and \$3.25?

$2.50 < \text{Cost} < 3.25$	Cost is between \$2.50 and \$3.25.
$2.50 < 0.08m - 0.26 < 3.25$	Substituted cost equation for c.
$2.76 < 0.08m < 3.51$	Added 0.26 to all three parts.
$34.50 < m < 43.9$	Divided all three parts by 0.08.

If the cost is between \$2.50 and \$3.25 then you were on the phone between 34.5 and 43.9 minutes.

Summary: This section allows us to expand the applications from the previous unit to problems that deal with quantities greater than, less than, or equal to each other. The procedures include the following steps:

1. Creating tables that include all necessary information.
2. Setting up the inequality.
3. Using algebraic skills to solve the inequality.

CLASS WORK

1. The equation $S = 118t + 146$ represents the number of stores, S, ZZ-Mart has opened at the end of t years, where t is the number of years since 1982.

   a. When will ZZ-Mart have more than 1500 stores?

   b. When will ZZ-Mart have between 1000 and 1300 stores? (Make sure your interval truly expresses the time described.)

> **Explanation:** A model like the one above usually comes from a sample of data. Using the linear regression capability of a calculator or computer generates the equation, $S = 118t + 146$. This is often covered in Intermediate Algebra.

2. Two companies offer you very similar sales positions. Haunted House will pay you $10,000 a year plus 7% commission on the dollar amount of book sales. Reader Publishing Co. will pay you $8,000 a year plus 11% commission. For what dollar amount of book sales does Haunted House pay more than Reader Publishing Co.?

3. Pop Bell charges 20 cents per phone call and 11 cents for each minute over 3 minutes.

   a. Find an equation for the cost of making a phone call. Simplify the equation.

   b. How many minutes were you on the phone if the cost was more than \$2.50?

   c. How many minutes were you on the phone if the cost was between \$3.00 and \$4.50?

GROUP EXERCISE

Study Tips: Quietly go to the board and do the problem there. (You should ask the teacher first.)

1. Graphic Inc. offers you a sales position. They will pay you $18,000 a year plus 13% commission on sales over $100,000.

Go Back: Review the problems on pages 107 and 110.

a. Find an equation for your yearly salary. (You may need to make a table.) Simplify the equation.

b. How much do you have to sell if you want to earn more than $50,000 a year?

c. How much do you have to sell if you want to earn between $45,000 and $75,000 a year?

Study Tip: The following section begins graphing. For the next class, you should bring graph paper, colored pencils, and a ruler.

HOMEWORK EXERCISES

Skill Building Exercises

1. Solve each inequality and graph the solution on the number line.

   a. $7 - 4x \leq 35$ b. $-3 \leq 6 + 5x < 8$

2. A company buys a $350,000 piece of equipment in 2005. The equipment depreciates $25,000 a year. For tax purposes, the company needs to know a formula for finding the value of the equipment in future years.

   a. Complete the table below.

YEARS	CALCULATION	VALUE
5		
10		
t		

   b. What is the equation that relates years and value?

Practice Exercises

3. Use the equation from problem 2 to answer the following questions. For both questions you must set up an inequality equation.

   a. When will the equipment be worth less than $80,000?

   b. When will the equipment be worth between $170,000 and $260,000?

4. Two companies have offered you very similar jobs selling cars. Company A pays $30,000 a year, and Company B pays 8% commission plus $10,000 a year. When will Company A pay more than Company B? Set up an inequality and solve.

Go Back: Refer to problem 2 on page 109 for a similar problem to 4.

5. The accompanying table shows the population growth of the United States since 1980.

Years	Variable t	Population (in millions)
1980	0	226
1990	10	249
2000	20	281
2005	25	296

The equation $P = 2.81t + 224$ can be used to approximate the population of the U.S. In the equation, P represents the population in millions, and t is the number of years since 1980.

a. Use the equation to estimate the population in 2010.

b. Use the equation to determine when the population will be more than 325.5 million. (Set up an inequality and solve it.)

c. When will the population of the U.S. be between 300 million and 350 million? (Set up an inequality and solve it.)

6. Two girls want to enter the lawn mowing business for the summer. They plan to buy a power mower for $200, and they hope to charge $8.50 an hour.

a. Use the table below to help you find a formula for the girls' profit.

HOURS	CALCULATION	PROFIT ($)
30		
h		

b. What is the equation that relates profit and hours worked?

c. Determine how many hours the girls will have to work to make more than $200 for the summer.

d. Determine how many hours the girls will have to work to break even but not earn more than $500.

7. You are planning to rent a car. Wrecker charges 50 cents a mile and $28 for a day while Ertz charges 75 cents a mile and $20 for a day.

   a. Use the table below to help you set up a formula for finding the cost of renting a car for the day.

WRECKER			ERTZ		
MILES	**CALCULATION**	**COST ($)**	**MILES**	**CALCULATION**	**COST ($)**
20			20		
m			m		

   b. What are the equations that relate cost and miles for each of the two companies?

   c. When will Wrecker cost more than Ertz? Set up an inequality and solve it.

8. Two companies have offered you very similar jobs selling appliances. Company A pays 12% commission on sales over $50,000 a year plus $8,000, and Company B pays 5% commission plus $15,000 a year.

Go Back: Review similar problems on pages 107, 109 problem 2, and 111.

   a. Use the table below to find a formula for your wages.

COMPANY A			COMPANY B		
SALES	**CALCULATION**	**WAGES**	**SALES**	**CALCULATION**	**WAGES**
50,000			50,000		
100,000			100,000		
125,000			125,000		
s			s		

   b. What are the equations that relate wages and sales for the two companies? Simplify them.

   c. When does Company A pay more than Company B? Set up an inequality and solve it.

   d. For Company A, why is the formula not valid for sales $s = 20,000$?

9. You are trying to decide which long distance phone company to choose. Company WHAT?! charges 15 cents a call and 11 cents a minute after the first 4 minutes. Company Disconnect charges 10 cents a call and 14 cents after the first 5 minutes. Which company will you choose? Why? Find equations for both companies and state some limitations on the variable m by writing inequalities. (Hint: You may have to use a table to find the equation.)

Reading and Writing Mathematics

10. A classmate asks you to look over his work. The mathematics are correct. Make four suggestions that would improve the presentation of the problem. Review the problem the way an instructor might look at it.

    Cell phone company Busy charges customers 15¢ per call and 20¢ after 4 minutes. Company Ringer charges 80¢ per call and 15¢ after 6 minutes. Find equations for the cost of a phone call for both companies. Write a paragraph about which company you would choose. Make sure to include how long you like to talk on the phone and how that relates to the cost of the phone calls. You must set up an inequality and solve it in order to justify your answer.

BUSSY			RINGER		
MINUTES	**CALCULATION**	**COST**	**MINUTES**	**CALCULATION**	**COST**
3		0.15	**3**		0.80
7	0.20*7 - 4 + 0.15	0.75	**7**	0.15*7 - 6 + 0.80	0.95
12	0.20*12 - 4 + 0.15	1..75	**12**	0.15*12 - 6 + 0.80	1..70
n	0.20(n - 4) + 0.15	c	**n**	0.15*(n - 6) + 0.80	c

$$c = 0.15(n - 6) + 0.80$$
$$c = 0.20(n - 4) + 0.15$$

$$0.15(n - 6) + 0.80 < 0.20(n - 4) + 0.15$$
$$0.15n - 0.9 + 0.8 < 0 .20n - 0.8 + 0.15$$
$$0.15n - 0.1 < .2n - 0.65$$
$$0.15n + 0.55 < 0.2n$$
$$0.55 < 0.05n$$
$$11 < n$$

Since I don't like to talk on the phone for more than 11 minutes at a time, I would choose Ringer.

This student did an excellent job solving the problem. The suggestions that you should make are minor, but they **WILL** still improve his work.

Study Tip: 1. The following section begins graphing. For the next class, you should bring graph paper, colored pencils, and a ruler.

2. Detailed solutions to problems 1a, b, 3, 5, 7, and 9 can be found on the MAT 011 Electronic Resource page. See page vii.

SECTION 2.3 PLOTTING POINTS PREVIEW

Objective: This section describes the creation of graphs. A graph provides a visualization of the relationship between two quantities. A graph can be used to answer many questions.

Example 1. When NASA sends a rocket into space, engineers monitor the temperature of certain gases. The table below gives a sample of the data collected. Note that negative time represents time before takeoff.

Time (minutes)	–6	–4	–2	0	2	4	6	8
Temperature (Celsius)	–27	–13	–4	4	43	21	9	–2

a. Create a graph based on the data.

Before we graph our data, we must decide:

- What are the **independent** and **dependent** variables?

  Since the temperature depends on when the rocket is in the air, temperature is the dependent variable, and time is the independent variable. It is important to decide what the independent and dependent variables are because they determine how the graph is oriented. In equations involving x and y, x is the independent variable, and y is the dependent variable. For this class, the set of numbers that make up the values of the independent variable is called the **domain** and the set of numbers that make up the values of the dependent variable is called the **range**.

- How are **ordered pairs** or **coordinates** written?

  In a nonapplication problem, ordered pairs are the x and y coordinates written in parentheses and separated by a comma for example (x, y). Always write the ordered pair as (independent variable, dependent variable). In our example, (time, temperature). The points we will graph are:
  (–6, –27), (–4, –13), (–2, –4), (0, 4), (2, 43), (4, 21), (6, 9), and (8, –2).

- What variable represents the **horizontal axis**?

  The independent variable is always the horizontal axis. In our example, **time** is the horizontal axis. In equations involving x and y, x is the horizontal axis.

- What variable represents the **vertical axis**?

  The dependent variable is always the vertical axis. In our example, **temperature** is the vertical axis. In equations involving x and y, y is the vertical axis.

- What **scale** should we use along the horizontal axis?
  The scale is the distance between tick marks. To decide the scale, find the lowest and highest value for time and think about the easiest way to count between them. Since time ranges between –6 and 8, we will count by twos. So the scale will be by 2.

- What **scale** should we use along the vertical axis?

  To decide the scale, find the lowest and highest value for temperature and think about the easiest way to count between them. Since temperature ranges between –27 and 43, we will count by fives, starting at –30 and going to 45. The scale will be 5.

The graph of the data is given below.

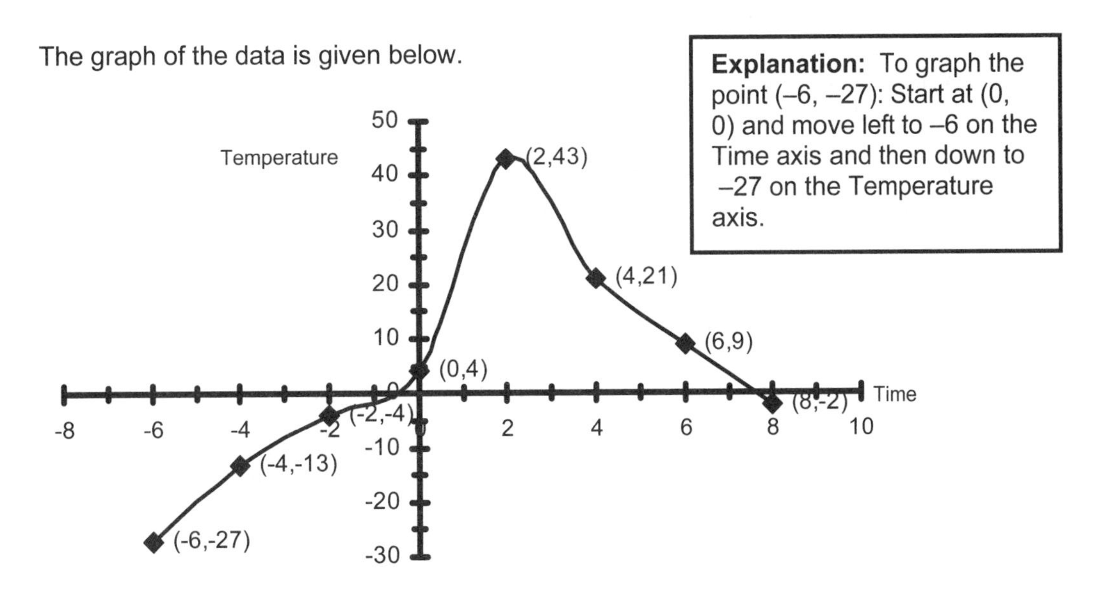

Explanation: To graph the point (–6, –27): Start at (0, 0) and move left to –6 on the Time axis and then down to –27 on the Temperature axis.

b. Answer the following questions based on your graph.

1. Estimate the temperature two minutes into the flight.

   Two minutes is two units to the right on the horizontal axis, Time. If you lightly draw a vertical line up from 2, the point where the vertical line intersects the graph is the answer. Put a dot at this point and read the temperature on the vertical axis. The temperature of the gas at two minutes is approximately 43 degrees Celsius.

2. What was the temperature at takeoff?

   When the rocket takes off, the time is zero. The point that represents the temperature of the gas is the point on the Temperature axis. This point is called the **Temperature intercept** because it is on the Temperature axis. Put a dot at this point and read the temperature on the vertical axis. The temperature at takeoff is 4 degrees Celsius.

3. When was the temperature zero?

   The temperature is zero when the graph crosses the Time axis.
   These points are called the **Time intercepts** because they are on the Time axis. Put a dot at these points and read the time on the horizontal axis. The temperature is 0 just before takeoff, approximately –0.5, and about 7.5 minutes.

4. When did the temperature increase the fastest?

   The temperature increased the fastest between 0 minutes and 2 minutes. This is where the graph is steepest.

Example 2. Identify the dependent and independent variables in the problem below.

Renting a van costs 10 cents per mile plus $20.00 a day.

The equation that relates miles and cost is c = 0.10m + 20.
The cost depends on the number of miles driven, so c is the dependent variable, and m is the independent variable. The ordered pairs are written as (m, c). The m (miles) axis is horizontal and the c (cost) axis is vertical.

Summary: This section covers the basic process of graphing. You must master these concepts to be successful in basic algebra.

Vocabulary:

1. **Independent Variable**.
   The independent variable was the first column in the tables made in previous sections. Miles, time, and sales are usually independent variables.
2. **Dependent Variable**.
   The dependent variable is the quantity that is contingent on the independent variable. The dependent variable was the third column in the tables made in previous sections. Cost and wages are usually dependent variables.
3. **Ordered Pair**.
   The ordered pair indicates the coordinates of a point on the graph. It always has the form:
   (Independent Variable, Dependent Variable) or (x, y).
4. **Scale**.
   The scale is the distance between the tick marks on the axis.
5. **Intercept**.
   The intercept is the place where the graph crosses an axis.

   The graph below highlights the 5 definitions:
   - The x axis is the horizontal axis, and x is the independent variable.
   - The scale of the x axis is 5.
   - The y axis is the vertical axis, and y is the dependent variable.
   - The scale of the y axis is 25.
   - The ordered pair is indicated by (x, y).
   - The x intercepts are approximately (-2.5, 0) and (27.5, 0).
   - The y intercept is approximately (0, 75).

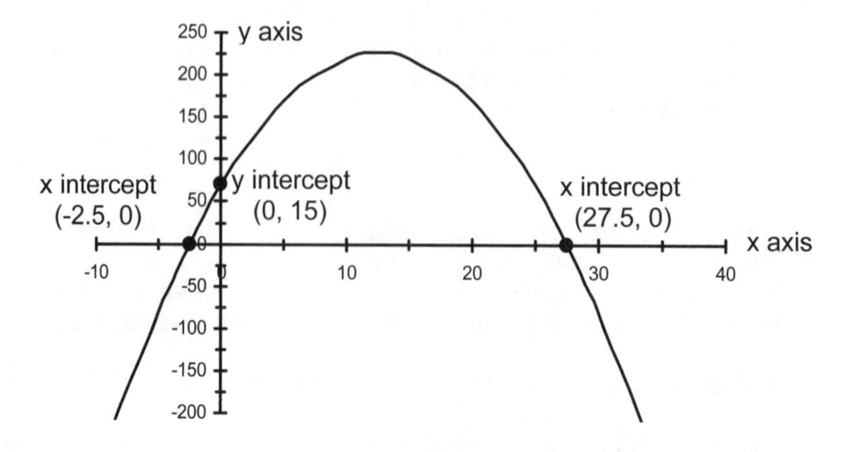

6. This type of graph uses the **Cartesian coordinate system**.

CLASS WORK

Sarah has a job that pays her 8% commission plus $10,000 per year. She has computed her possible wages in the table below.

Sales	$20,000	$30,000	$50,000	$70,000	$100,000	$120,000
Wages	$11,600	$12,400	$14,000	$15,600	$18,000	$19,600

Sarah's wages depend on her sales. Wages are called the dependent variable, and sales are called the independent variable.

The general rules:

1. The independent variable, S (Sales), goes on the horizontal axis. (In an equation involving the variables x and y, x is the independent variable.)

2. The dependent variable, W (Wages), goes on the vertical axis. (In an equation involving the variables x and y, y is the dependent variable.)

3. The ordered pair is written as (S,W) or (Independent, Dependent) or (x, y).

W

S

In each problem below, find the equation and then identify the independent and dependent variables, label the axes, and decide how an ordered pair needs to be written. These are problems from Unit 1.

1. Renting a car costs $25 plus $0.16 a mile.

2. A $100,000 piece of equipment depreciates at a rate of $8,000 a year.

3. The equation $s = 114t + 146$ represents the number of ZZ-Mart stores, S, at the end of the year t, where t is the number of years since 1982.

4. When NASA sends a rocket into space, engineers monitor the temperature of certain gases. The table below gives a sample of the type of data collected. Time is the independent variable, and temperature is the dependent variable. Notice that negative time is used to denote time before lift off.

Time Minutes	Temperature (C°)
-20	-20
-15	-20
-10	-10
-5	0
0	15
5	40
10	80
15	130
20	90
25	25
30	5
35	-15

a. Graph the data pairs, (time, temperature) and connect the dots.

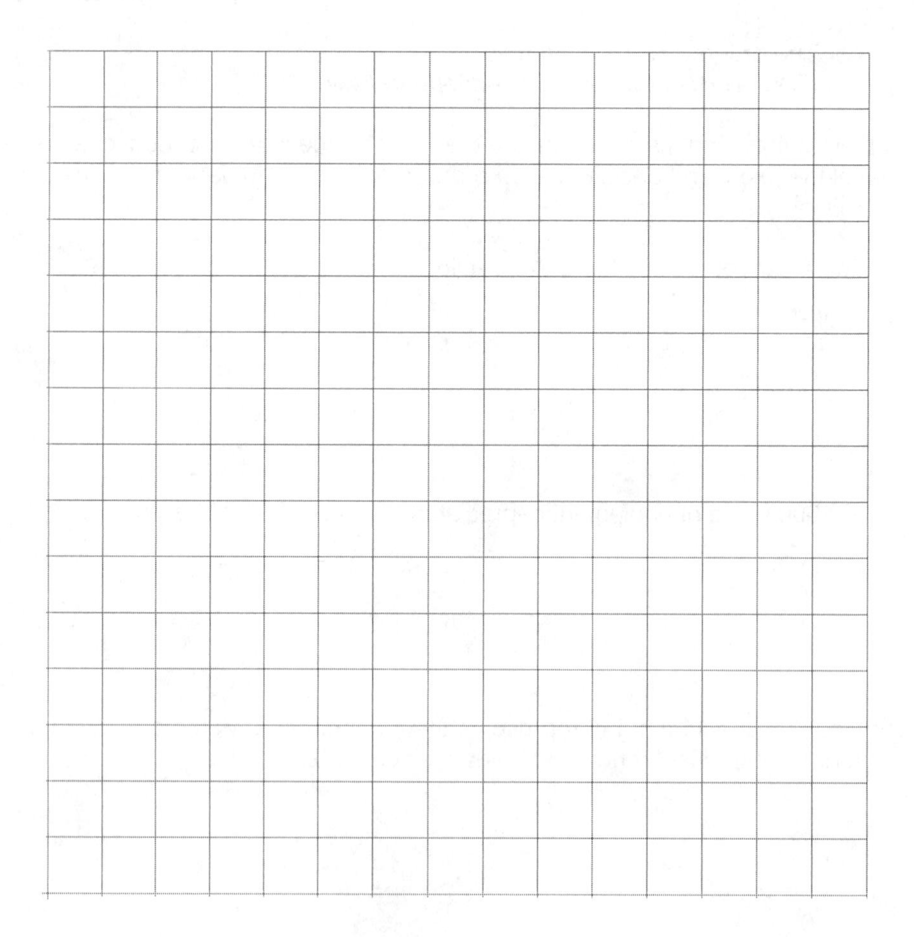

b. Answer each of the following questions about the temperature of the gas and give the coordinates you used to get the answer. Estimate where needed.

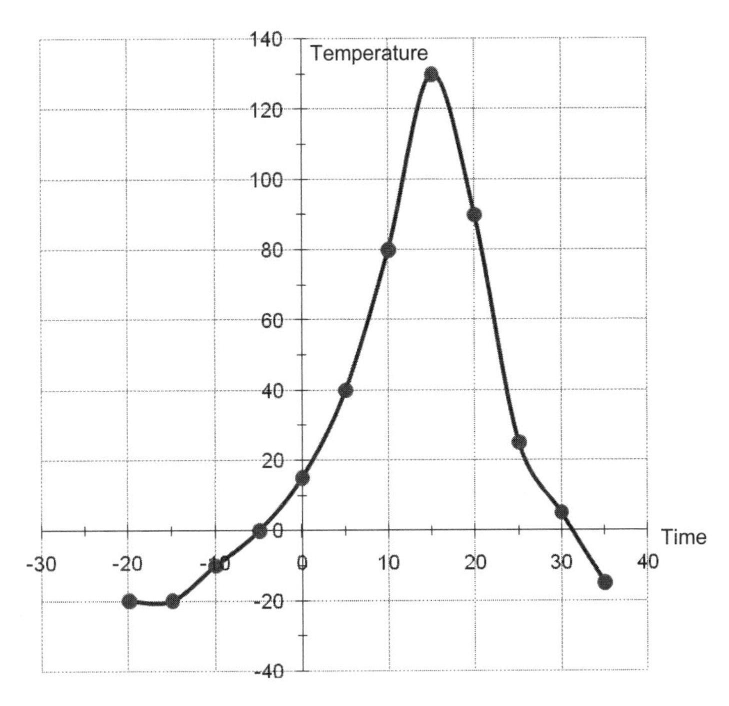

1) What was the temperature at take off?

2) What was the temperature 5 minutes into the flight?

3) What was the temperature 17 minutes into the flight?

4) At what times was the temperature 90°?

5) At what times was the temperature 0°?

6) What was the change in temperature for the first 15 min. of the flight?

7) What was the change in temperature of the flight between 15 min. and 35 min.?

8) What was the maximum temperature?

9) At what times was the temperature rising most quickly?

10) At what times was the temperature falling most quickly?

2. Animal populations tend to rise and fall in cycles. Suppose the following data shows how squirrel populations in a central Pennsylvania city varied from 1975 to 1984.

Year	75	76	77	78	79	80	81	82	83	84
Population	750	700	520	680	730	650	550	625	780	700

a. Graph the data on graph paper using the two different scales.

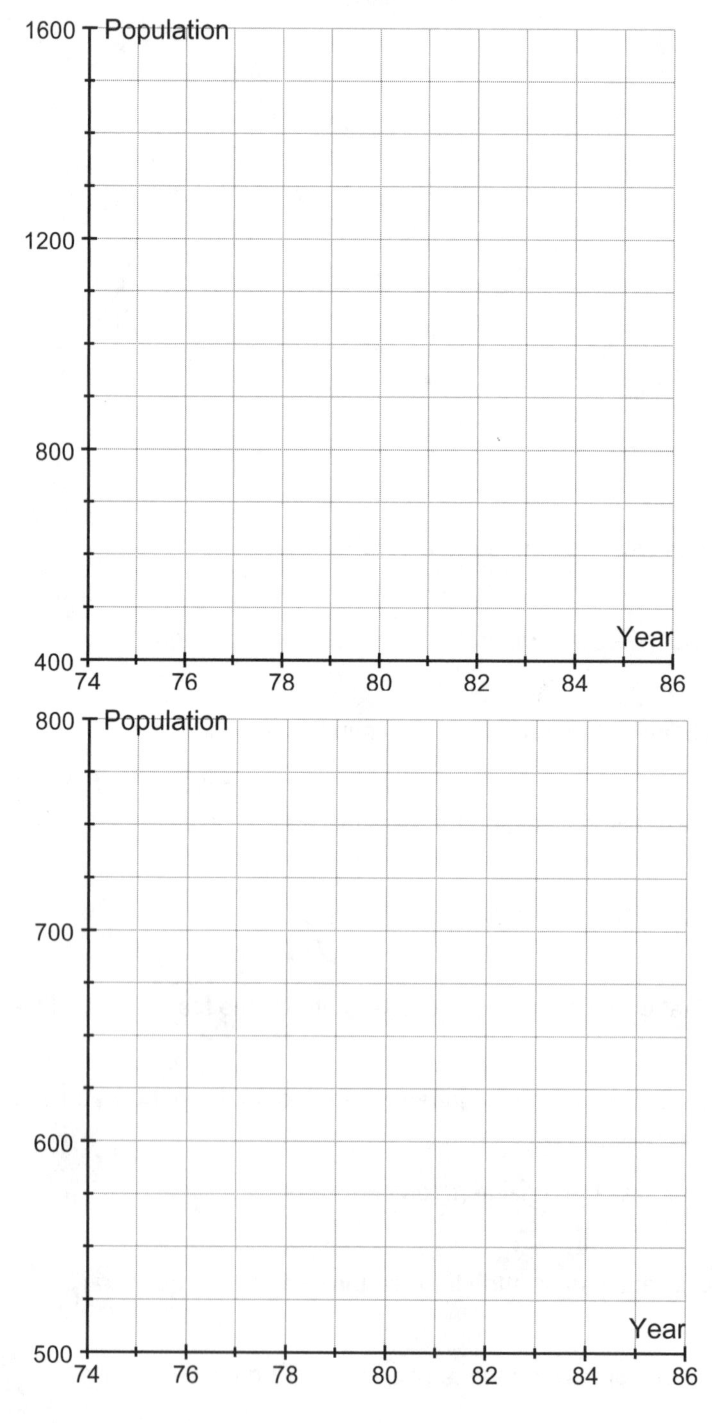

b. Which graph best describes the data? Why?

GROUP EXERCISE

**Go Back:** 1. Review the material on page 122.
2. Use a ruler, colored pencils, and graph paper.

1. You are given data relating two variables. Choose reasonable scales for axes on a graph and plot the given data. The price of crude oil is the independent variable and the price per gallon is the dependent variable. Write a sentence describing the pattern in the graph and what it says about the relationship between the two variables.

Prices for the year 2005		
Month	**Price per Barrel of Crude Oil**	**Price per Gallon of Gasoline**
Jan.	$46.84	$1.24
Feb.	$48.15	$1.22
Mar.	$54.19	$1.44
Apr.	$52.98	$1.48
May	$49.83	$1.37
Jun.	$56.35	$1.51
Jul.	$59.00	$1.59
Aug.	$64.99	$1.94
Sep.	$65.59	$2.13
Oct.	$62.26	$1.71
Nov.	$58.32	$1.47
Dec.	$59.41	$1.60

Source. Weekly Petroleum Status Report
Note: Price per gallon of gasoline does not include taxes.

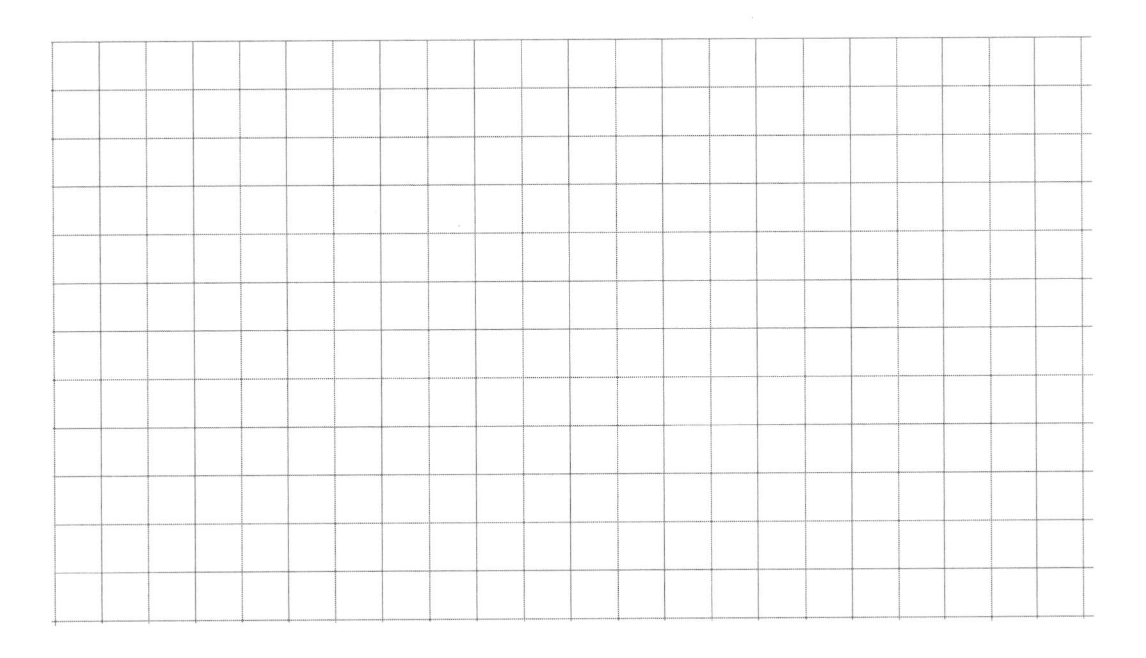

2. A 10 cm. stick is broken into two pieces. One piece is placed at a right angle to form an upside down "T" shape. By attaching wires from the ends of the base to the end of the upright piece, a frame work for a sail will be formed. This problem was first introduced on page 31.

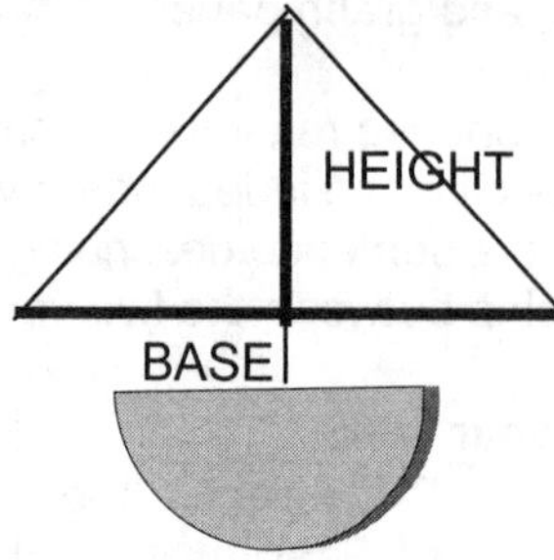

a. Calculate the area of the sail for the given length of the base.

Base, cm b	Height, cm h	Area, cm^2 $A=\frac{1}{2}b\cdot h$	Point (base, area)
0 cm			
2 cm			
4 cm	10 - 4 = 6 cm	$\frac{1}{2}(4)(6)=12\ cm^2$	(4, 12)
5 cm			
8 cm			
9 cm			
10 cm			
b			

b. What is the equation that relates area to the base?

c. Use the graph to estimate the maximum area.

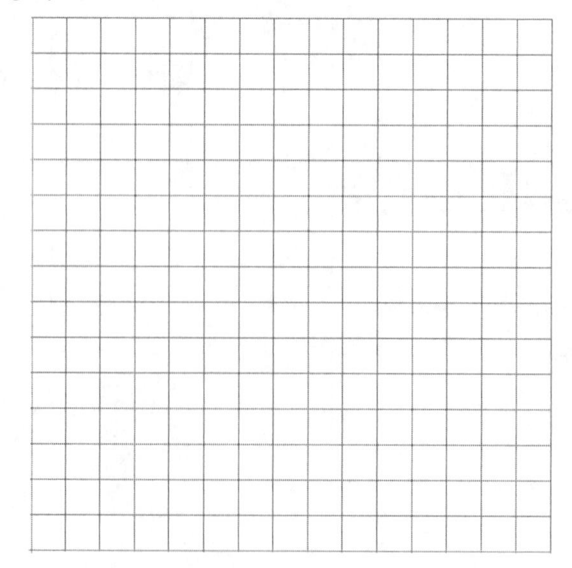

HOMEWORK EXERCISES

Study Tips:
1. Review the problem on page 122.
2. Have all necessary materials available: graph paper, ruler, and colored pencils.
3. Work for 20 minutes and then do something else. Complete your homework in short intervals.

Skill Building Exercises

1. For the ordered pair (3, 7) which number represents the independent variable?

2. For the ordered pair (3, 7) which number represents the dependent variable?

3. For the ordered pair (3, 7) which number represents the horizontal distance?

4. For the ordered pair (3, 7) which number represents the vertical distance?

Practice Exercises

In problems 5 and 6, you are given data relating two variables. Choose reasonable scales for axes on a graph and plot the given data. Then write a sentence describing the pattern in the graph and the relationship between the two variables.

5. The following table shows the school year and the total revenue spent for public elementary and secondary schools.

School Year	1930	1946	1954	1966	1974	1985	1990	2000
Revenues (millions of dollars)	2	3	8	25	58	137	208	400

Source: *Digest of Educational Statistics.*

6. The following table shows the number of insurance establishments in Montgomery County.

Year	1990	1991	1992	1993	1994
Number of Establishments	519	523	536	552	554

Source: *Pennsylvania County Industry Trends 1990-1994.*

7. At a pizza store, Sarah is in charge of scheduling workers. To help make these decisions, Sarah collected the following data on the number of people waiting for pizzas each hour, on the hour, for three days.

Time	**Day 1**	**Day 2**	**Day 3**	**Average**
11:00	11	9	8	
12:00	15	18	19	
1:00	18	21	20	
2:00	9	11	13	
3:00	5	4	6	
4:00	6	8	7	
5:00	12	11	15	
6:00	22	4	21	
7:00	15	17	9	
8:00	8	7	7	

a. Average the values for the different times and plot them on a graph.

b. Write a paragraph interpreting the data and the graph.

c. Suppose you were told that on the second day at 6:00 pm a water repair crew blocked the pizza shop's driveway. Would you change your interpretation of the graph? How?

8. Suppose that a baseball player hits a high pop-up above home plate. If the bat meets the ball 1.5 meters above the ground and sends it up at a velocity of 30 meters per second, then the height of the ball, in meters, *t* seconds later is indicated by the table.

Go Back: Review problem 4 on page 122.

t seconds	0	1	2	3	4	5	6
h meters	1.5	27	42	47	43	29	5

a. Use the table to make a graph. Choose your scales so that you can answer the questions that follow. Be sure to indicate time and height scales along the axes.

b. What point shows the starting height of the ball? Label this point B and indicate its coordinates.

c. What point shows the height of the ball at 2 seconds? Label this point *C* and indicate its coordinates.

d. What point(s) show(s) a height of 20 meters? Label it (or them) *D* and indicate the coordinates.

e. What point shows where the ball reaches its maximum height? Label this point *E* and indicate its coordinates.

f. What point shows when the ball hits the ground? Label this point *F* and indicate its coordinates.

g. What is the height of the ball when the time is 4.5 seconds?

h. At what times was the ball rising most quickly?

i. At what times was the ball falling most quickly?

Reading and Writing Mathematics

9. In the problem below, find the **mistake** and write a sentence describing the error. Also, write a suggestion so that any student who makes this type of mistake will have a way to remember not to make the error again.

   The cost of health care in the United States is given in the table below. Graph the data, and write a sentence describing the pattern of the graph.

Year	Cost (millions of $)
1960	26.7
1970	73.1
1980	245.8
1990	695.6
1995	987.0
1997	1093.9
1999	1210.7
2000	1310.0
2001	1425.5

I got the graph below for the data.

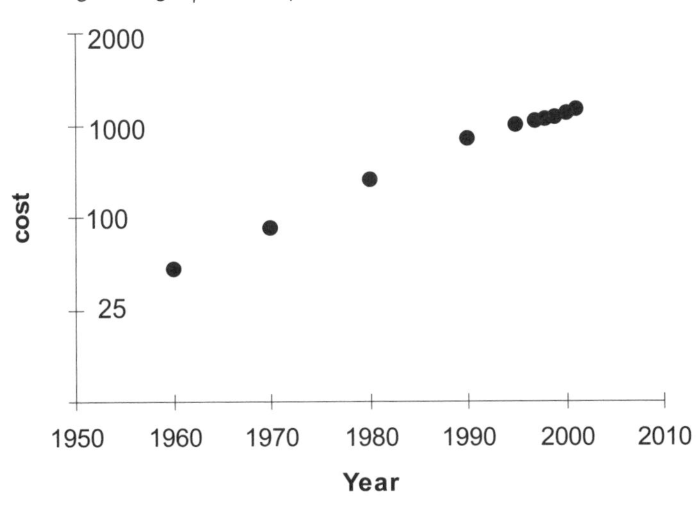

The graph looks like a line.

10. Over the next week, consciously look for data, either in another class, in a newspaper, or magazine article, and graph the data.

Study Tip: Detailed solutions to problems 5, 7, 8, and 9 can be found on the MAT 011 Electronic Resource page. See page vii.

SECTION 2.4 INTERPRETING GRAPHS
PREVIEW

Objective: This section covers the basic properties of graphs. You will learn about intercepts, vertices, and intersections. In order to answer questions correctly, pay attention to the scale of the graph.

Example The graph below shows the profit of two toy companies, Radio Control Inc. and Turbo Car Co.

Label the variables:

Let N represent the number of toys sold. The units for N are millions.
Let P represent the profit of the companies. The units for P are thousands.

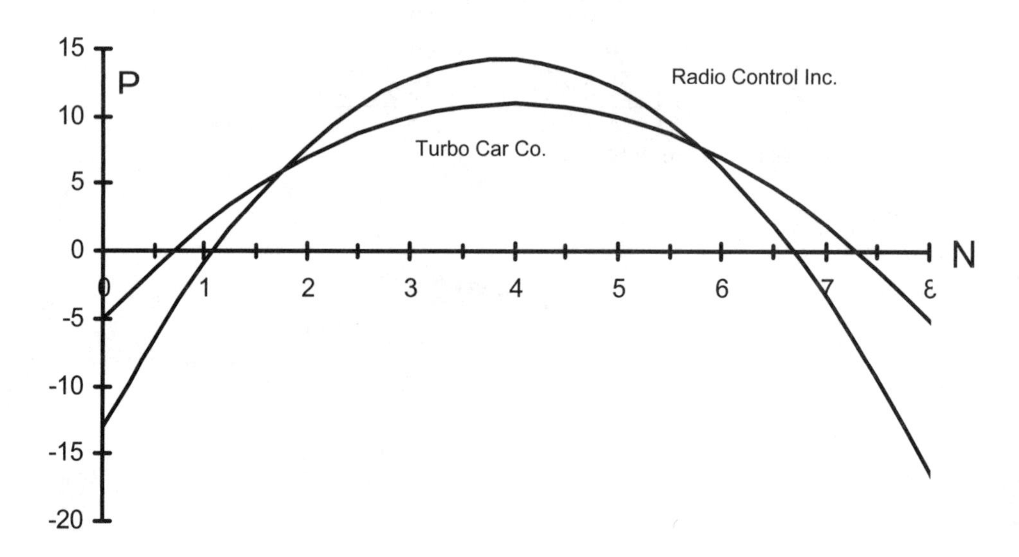

1. What is the independent variable?

   The independent variable is the horizontal axis, which in this example is the number of toy cars sold, N.

2. What is the dependent variable?

   The dependent variable is the vertical axis, which in this case is profit, P.

3. How many toy cars does Radio Control Inc. have to sell to break even?

   A company breaks even when the profit is zero. So the break even points are on the horizontal axis. The graph of Radio Control Inc. crosses the N axis at approximately (1.1, 0) and (6.6, 0). The break-even points are the N **intercepts**. Radio Control Inc. breaks even when sales are 1,100,000 and 6,600,000 toy cars.

4. For what number of cars sold is the profit the same for both companies?

   The two companies have the same profit where the two graphs **intersect** or cross. Put a dot where the two graphs intersect. The answer to the question is the independent variable, number of cars sold, N. The values for the independent variable are approximately 1.6, and 5.9. The two companies make the same profit when they sell 1,600,000 or 5,900,000 toy cars.

5. How much money does Turbo Car Co. lose if no cars are sold?

   If Turbo Car Co. doesn't sell any cars, then the independent variable, N, is zero. So the answer to the question is the **Profit intercept**. The profit coordinate of the Profit intercept is –5. Turbo Co. loses $5,000 if no toy cars are sold.

6. For what number of cars does Radio Control Inc have a maximum profit?

   The maximum profit is at the top of the graph. This point is called the **vertex** of the graph. The N (number of cars sold) coordinate is approximately 4. Radio Control Inc. will have a maximum profit if 4,000,000 cars are sold.

7. What is the maximum profit of Radio Control Inc.?

   The maximum profit occurs when Radio Control Inc. sells 4 million toy cars, N = 4. At that point, their profit will be $14,000.

Summary: Interpreting graphs is an extremely important skill. Visual representation of data is expected by both supervisors and customers. You should be comfortable with graphing concepts.

Vocabulary:

1. The **Cartesian coordinate system** is comprised of a horizontal axis and a vertical axis.
2. The **independent variable** was the first column in the tables made in previous sections. Miles, time and sales are examples of independent variables. The independent variable is represented by the horizontal axis.
3. The **dependent variable** is the quantity that is contingent on the independent variable. The dependent variable was the third column in the tables from previous sections. Cost and wages are examples of dependent variables. The dependent variable is represented by the vertical axis.
4. A point in the Cartesian coordinate system is called an **Ordered Pair**. An ordered pair always has the form *(independent variable, dependent variable)*.
5. The numbers in an ordered pair are called **coordinates.**
6. The **intercepts** are the points where the graph crosses an axis. One of the coordinates of an ordered pair representing an intercept is always zero.
7. The **intersection** is the point where two graphs cross.
8. The **vertex** is the peak or bottom of a curve.

Study Tip: Many students confuse **intercepts** and **intersection**. Draw a graph on a note card and label all the intercepts and intersections.

CLASS WORK

1. The graph below shows the temperature during a winter day in Chicago, Illinois.

TEMPERATURE
IN
CELSIUS

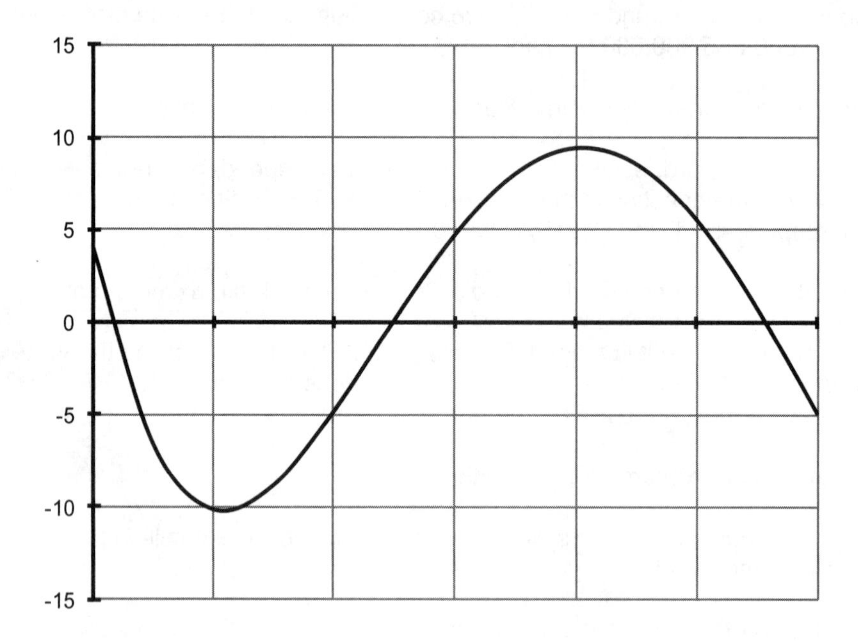

a. What was the temperature at noon?

b. When was the temperature 0°?

c. What was the high temperature for the day?

d. When was the high temperature?

e. What was the low temperature for the day?

f. When was the low temperature for the day?

g. When was the temperature rising?

h. When was the temperature decreasing?

2. The graphs below show the profit for the calculator companies, PA Instruments and Hewett Luggage.

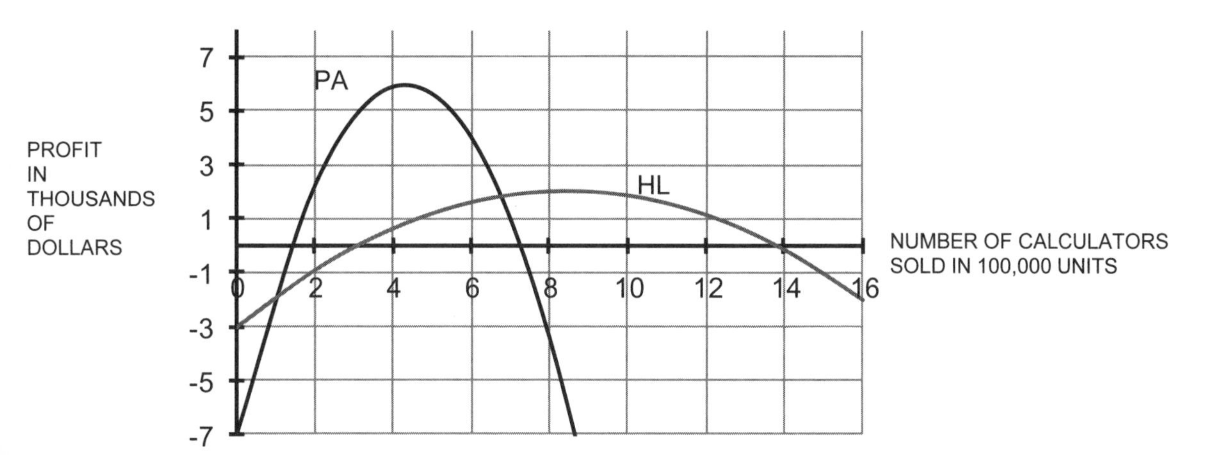

a. How many calculators does Hewett Luggage have to sell to break even?

b. How many calculators does PA Instruments have to sell to break even?

c. For what number of calculators sold is the profit the same for both companies?

d. How much profit does PA Instruments make (or lose) if they don't sell any calculators?

e. How much profit does Hewett Luggage make (or lose) if they don't sell any calculators?

GROUP EXERCISE

Go Back: 1. Review the problem on page 132.
2. Practice good group techniques.

1. The graph below shows the temperature during a winter day in Snowbound, Montana.

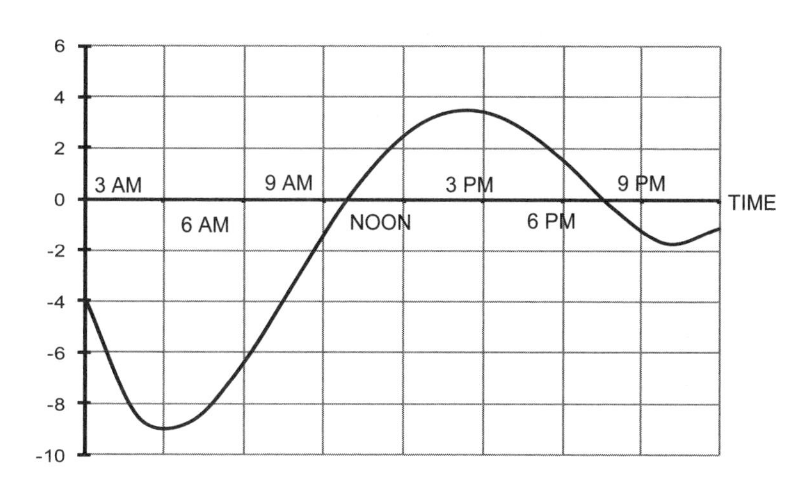

a. What was the temperature at 9 a.m.?

b. When was the temperature 0°?

c. What was the high temperature for the day?

d. When was the high temperature for the day?

e. What was the low temperature for the day?

f. When was the low temperature for the day?

g. When was the temperature rising?

h. When was the temperature falling?

2. The graph below shows the profit for two companies, AMATYC and PSMATYC.

Go Back: Review page 133.

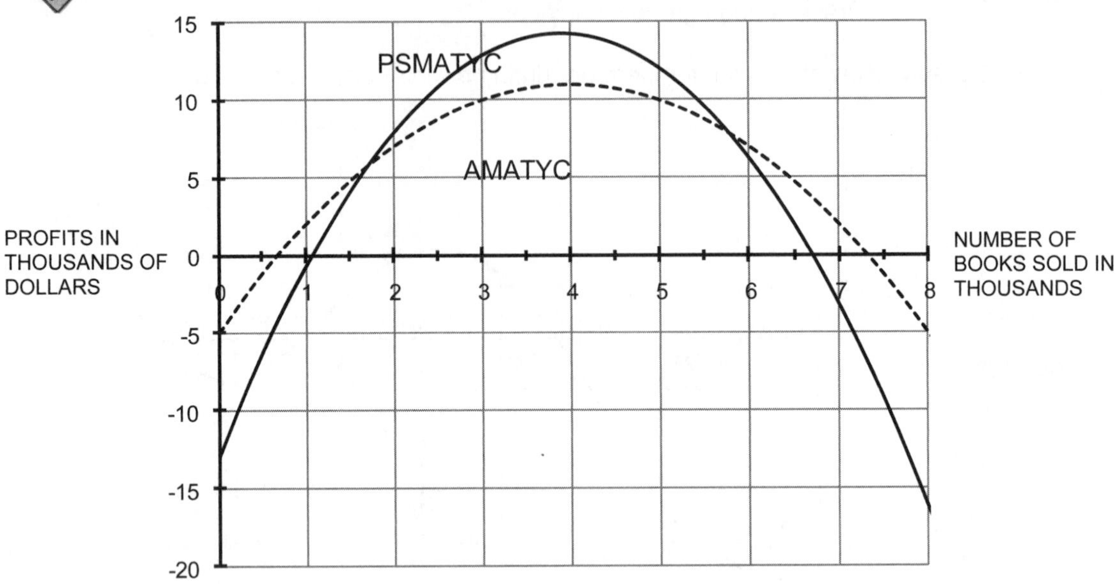

a. How many books does AMATYC have to sell to break even?

b. How many books does PSMATYC have to sell to break even?

c. For what number of books is the profit the same for both companies?

d. What is the maximum profit for AMATYC?

e. How many books does AMATYC have to sell to maximize profits?

f. How much profit does PSMATYC make (or lose) if they don't sell any books?

g. How much profit or loss does AMATYC experience if they don't sell any books?

h. When are AMATYC's profits decreasing?

HOMEWORK EXERCISES

Study Tips: 1. Have you tried doing homework with a friend?
2. Review page 132.

Skill Building Exercises

Exercises 1 to 4 use the graph at the right.

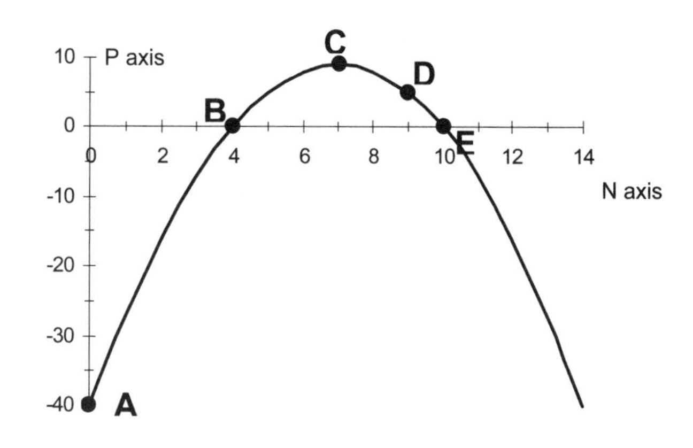

1. Find the ordered pairs of the points A, B, C, D, and E.

2. Which points are N intercepts?

3. Which point is the P intercept?

4. Which point is the vertex?

Practice Exercises

5. The graph below shows the temperatures during a winter day in Killington, Vermont.

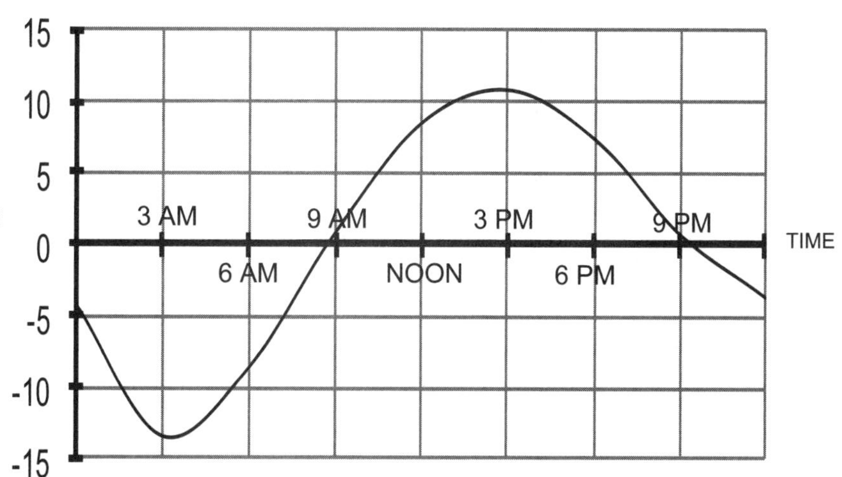

a. What were the high and low temperatures recorded during the day?

b. When were the high and low temperatures recorded?

c. During what time intervals was the temperature above 0° C?

d. During what time intervals was the temperature below 0° C?

e. When was the temperature 10° C?

f. What was the temperature at noon?

g. When was the temperature rising?

h. When was the temperature falling?

6. The graph below shows the monthly fish population of a lake beginning in January.

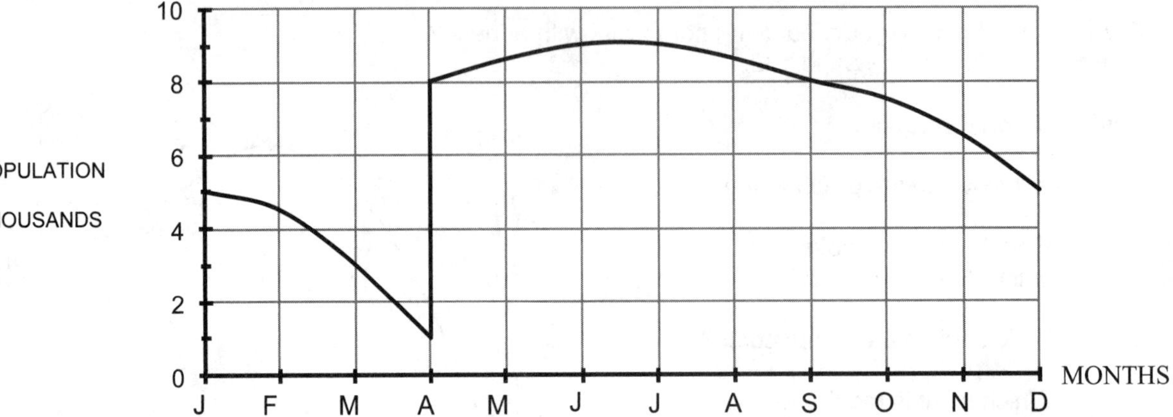

a. What is the fish population at the beginning of June?

b. When is the fish population the greatest?

c. What is the maximum number of fish in the lake?

d. When is the population of the fish increasing?

e. When is the population of the fish decreasing?

f. What do you think happened on April 1?

7. The graphs below show the cost of making a phone call for two different companies, WRONG # and BUZZ.

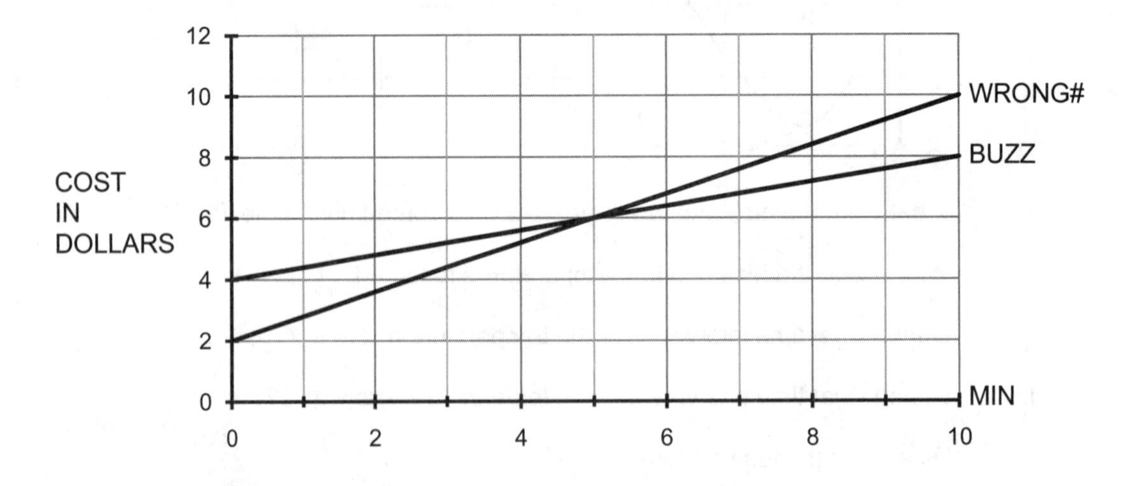

a. When do the two companies charge the same amount for a phone call?

b. Which company charges the most per minute?

c. Which company charges the most just to pick up the phone?

d. When is Buzz cheaper than Wrong #?

Reading and Writing Mathematics

8. Students often confuse the words "intercepts" and "intersects". Define each one in your own words and draw two lines on a graph. Indicate the intercept points as well as the intersection of the two lines.

9. Use one of the following to complete the blanks below:

Cartesian coordinate system	independent variable
dependent variable	ordered pair
coordinates	intercepts
intersection	vertex

a. The points graphed in the Cartesian coordinate system are called _______________.

b. The ____________________ of two lines is where they cross.

c. The first number in an ordered pair is the __________________ variable.

d. The top or bottom of a curve is called the _______________________.

e. The vertical axis represents the ______________________ variable.

f. If one of the coordinates of an ordered pair is zero, then this point must be an ___________________.

g. The numbers in an ordered pair are called ____________________.

h. The graphs created in this section are drawn in the ___________________________.

Study Tip: Detailed solutions to problems 2, 3, 5, and 7 can be found on the MAT 011 Electronic Resource page. See page vii.

SECTION 2.5 GRAPHING LINES BY PLOTTING POINTS PREVIEW

Objective: In this section, we will graph lines by finding three ordered pairs or points. Two points determine a line; the third point is used as a check that the other two are correct.

Example 1. You need to rent a moving van. Class Movers charges a basic rate of $24.95 plus $0.32 per mile.

(This example is from the Section 1.2 "Introduction to Variables," page 20 and Section 1.3 "Solving Equations", page 44.)

a. Calculate the cost of renting a van if you drive the following number of miles.

MILES	CALCULATION	COST
10	$0.32 \cdot 10 + 24.95$	28.15
20	$0.32 \cdot 20 + 24.95$	31.35
30	$0.32 \cdot 30 + 24.95$	34.55
m	$0.32 \cdot m + 24.95$	c

The cost equation is.
$c = 0.32 \cdot m + 24.95$

b. What are the independent and dependent variables?

The cost depends on the number of miles driven. So cost is the dependent variable, and miles are the independent variable.

c. What are the ordered pairs generated by the table?

This example has the form (miles, cost) because ordered pairs have the form (independent variable, dependent variable).

The ordered pairs are (10, 28.15), (20, 31.35), (30, 34.55).

d. Graph the equation $c = 0.32m + 24.95$.

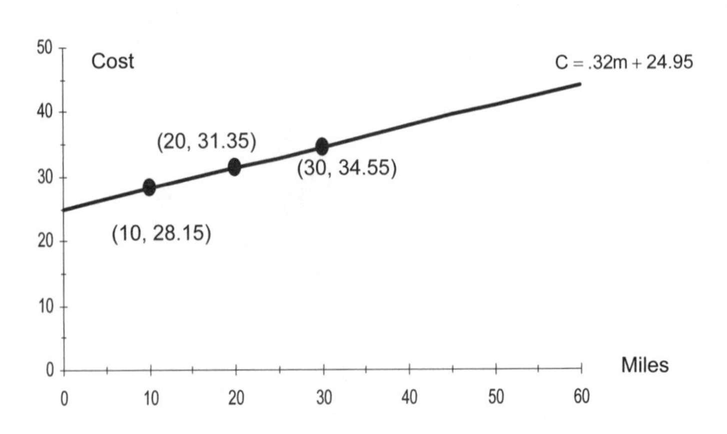

Example 2. Graph $2x + 5y = 26$

- x is the independent variable.
- y is the dependent variable.
- You must have two points or ordered pairs to graph a line, but we will find three. We use the third point to check our work. All three points **must** be on the line.

  Choose three values for x; then use algebra to find y.

  > **Explanation:** It doesn't matter what 3 values you pick for x, but don't choose numbers too close together and chose a negative number.

  1. Choose x = – 5.

$2(-5) + 5y = 26$	Substituted –5 for x.
$-10 + 5y = 26$	Multiplied
$5y = 36$	Added 10 to both sides.
$y = 7.2$	Divided both sides by 5.

     One point is (–5, 7.2).

  2. Choose x = 2.

$2(2) + 5y = 26$	Substituted 2 for x.
$4 + 5y = 26$	Multiplied
$5y = 22$	Subtracted 4 from both sides.
$y = 4.4$	Divided both sides by 5.

     The second point is (2, 4.4).

  3. Choose x = 15.

$2(15) + 5y = 26$	Substituted 15 for x.
$30 + 5y = 26$	Multiplied
$5y = -4$	Subtracted 30 from both sides.
$y = -0.8$	Divided both sides by 5.

     The third point is (15, –0.8).

- Graph the ordered pairs (–5, 7.2), (2, 4.4), and (15, –0.8).

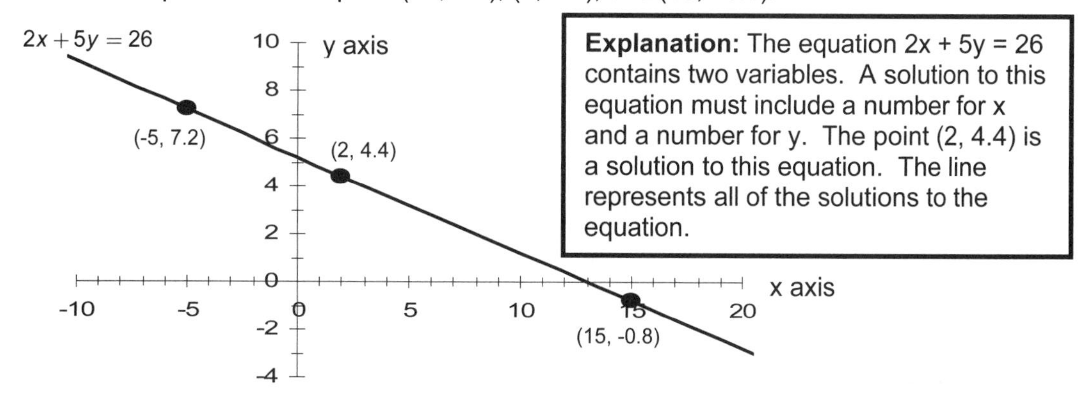

> **Explanation:** The equation 2x + 5y = 26 contains two variables. A solution to this equation must include a number for x and a number for y. The point (2, 4.4) is a solution to this equation. The line represents all of the solutions to the equation.

Example 3. Graph $y = \frac{4}{3}x - 8$.

- You need to choose three values for x. Since x is multiplied by the fraction $\frac{4}{3}$, picking multiples of three will make the arithmetic easier, even if you use a calculator. Once you pick a value for the independent variable x, substitute it into $y = \frac{4}{3}x - 8$ to find the dependent variable y.

Explanation: What happens if you pick a value for x that is **not** a multiple of 3? For example, choose x = 5, so

$y = \frac{4}{3}(5) - 8$.

$y = \frac{20}{3} - 8$

$y = \frac{20}{3} - \frac{24}{3}$

$y = \frac{-4}{3}$ or -1.3333

The arithmetic is harder.

1. Choose x = –6 and substitute it into $y = \frac{4}{3}x - 8$.

$y = \frac{4}{3}(-6) - 8$	Substituted x = -6 into the equation.
y = 4(–2) -8	Divided –6 by 3.
y = –8 – 8	Multiplied 4 and –2.
y = -16	Subtracted 8 from –8.

The ordered pair is (–6, –16)

2. Choose x = 3 and substitute it into $y = \frac{4}{3}x - 8$.

$y = \frac{4}{3}(3) - 8$	Substituted x = 3 into the equation.
y = 4(1) -8	Divided 3 by 3.
y = 4 – 8	Multiplied 4 and 1.
y = –4	Subtracted 8 from 4.

The ordered pair is (3, -4).

3. Choose x = 9 and substitute it into $y = \frac{4}{3}x - 8$.

$y = \frac{4}{3}(9) - 8$	Substituted x = 9 into the equation.
y = 4(3) – 8	Divided 9 by 3.
y = 12 – 8	Multiplied 4 and 3.
y = 4	Subtracted 8 from 12.

The ordered pair is (9, 4).

- Graph the three ordered pairs or points (–6, –16), (3, –4) and (9, 4).

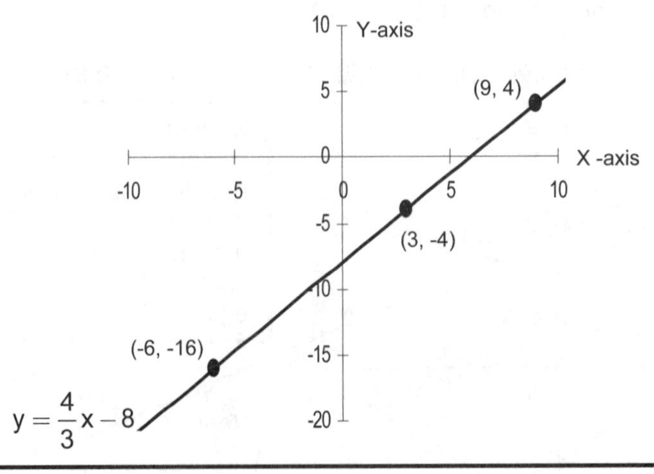

Explanation: The purpose of this example was to convince you that if you take a moment to carefully choose the values for x, then the arithmetic of the problem can be a lot easier.

Summary: Graphing is a very important topic in algebra. A graph provides a visualization of data or of an equation. For example, a graph allows you to see how the cost of renting a van is increasing as you drive more miles.

To graph a line:

1. Choose three different values to substitute for the independent variable. A minimum of two points is needed to graph a line. A third point is used to check the work.

2. For each of your chosen values of the independent variable, use algebra to find the corresponding value of the dependent variable.

3. Plot each point and connect them using a ruler. If the points are not forming a line, then you have made a mistake.

4. In a nonapplication problem, x is always the independent variable, and y is always the dependent variable.

5. In a nonapplication problem, there are no restrictions on the variables. Your graph should include both positive and negative values for x and y.

6. When graphing an application, you need to think about the restrictions on the variables. In Example 1 on page 140, it wouldn't make any sense to have negative values for miles.

Study Tip: Note card for graphing

1. Construct a table of values by choosing values for x then calculate the corresponding value for y.
2. Use graph paper, label axis, and set the scale.
3. Plot the points.
4. Connect the points.

Review the card as homework and use the card as a reference when you do the homework from this section.

CLASS WORK

1. An appliance repair shop charges an initial fee of $30 plus $15 per hour to fix an appliance.

   a. Complete the table to find the cost of repairing an appliance.

Hours	Calculation	Cost
3		
5		
10		
h		

   b. What is the equation that relates cost and hours?

   c. Use the results in Part a. to graph the equation in Part b. Choose an appropriate scale and only graph the portion that makes sense to the problem. Label the axes.

Hours	Cost	Point (h, c)
3		
5		
10		

2. Determine if the following ordered pairs represent a solution to the equation $y = 3x - 4$.

Is (3, -1) a solution?

Is (5, 11) a solution?

Is (-2, -10) a solution?

Is (3, 2) a solution?

3. Graph the line using the Cartesian Coordinate system. The line represents all of the solutions to the equation.

a. $y = 3x - 4$

x	**y**	**Point (x, y)**

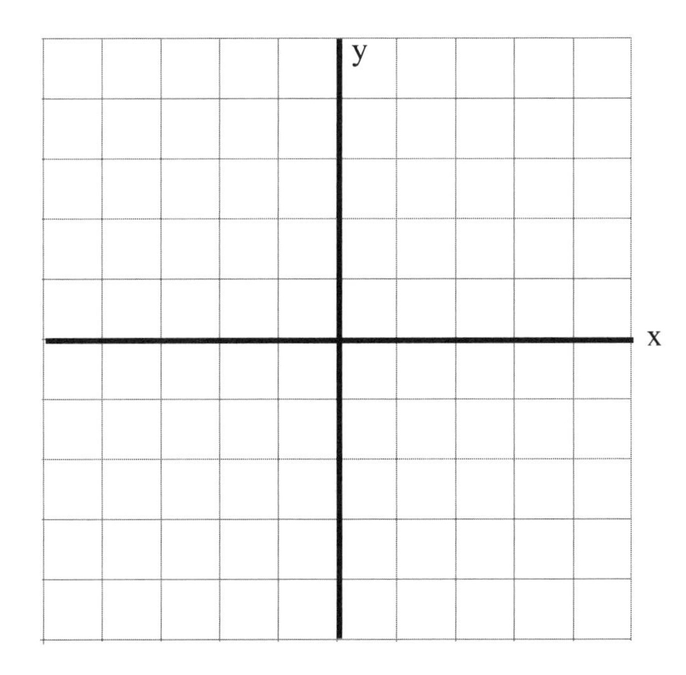

b. $6x - 4y = 18$

x	y	Point (x, y)

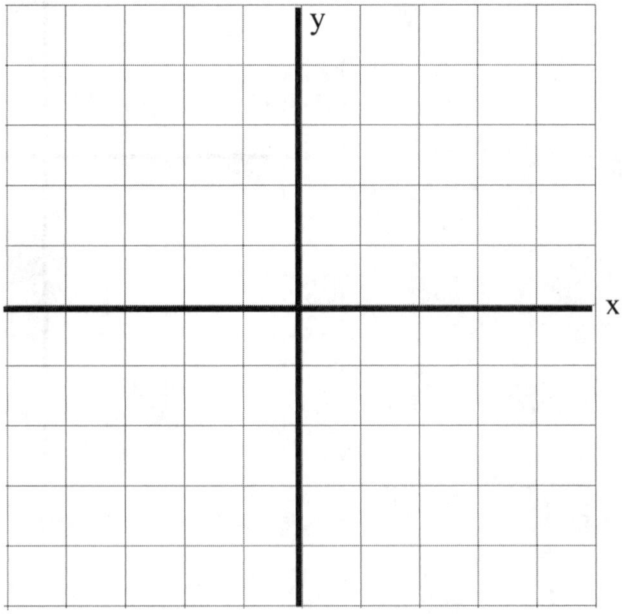

y

x

4. Graph the line by plotting points.

a. $y = \frac{-1}{2}x + 5$

x	y	Point (x, y)

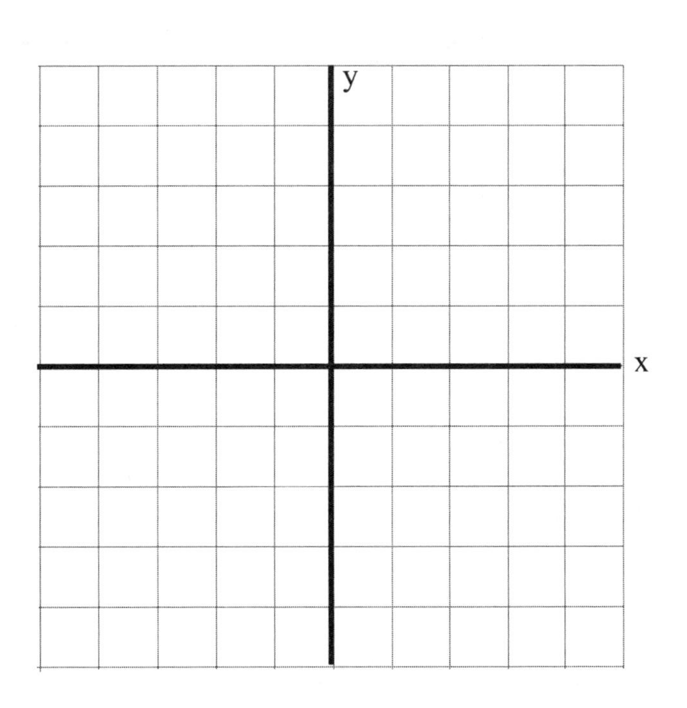

b. $6x + 5y = 35$

x	y	Point (x, y)

y

x

GROUP EXERCISE

Study Tip: 1. Use graph paper rather than the graphs provided in the text.

2. Choose one person to draw the graph.
3. Other group members should work on the table of values to guide the grapher.
4. All are responsible for knowing the complete process.

1. A sales position pays 12% commission plus $200 per week.

a. Complete the table below.

Sales	Calculation	Wages
500		
1000		
2000		
s		

b. What is the equation that relates wages and sales?

c. Use the results in Part a. to graph the equation in Part b. Choose an appropriate scale and only graph the portion that makes sense to the problem. Label the axes.

Sales	Wages	Point (s, w)
500		
1,000		
2,000		

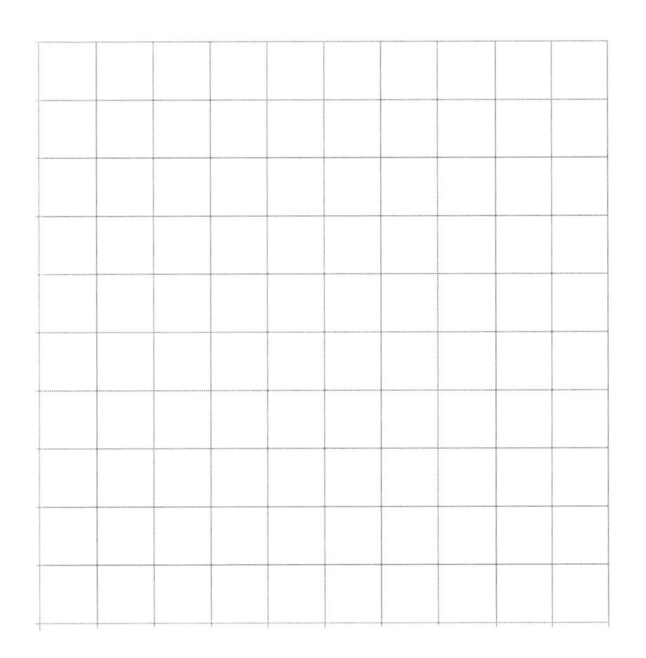

2. Graph the line by plotting points.

Study Tip: Not enough space is provided to adequately do the algebra necessary to compute the points for the graphs. Use lined paper to help organize your work.

a. $y=\frac{2}{3}x-7$

x	y	Point (x, y)

b. $8x - 3y = 24$

x	y	Point (x, y)

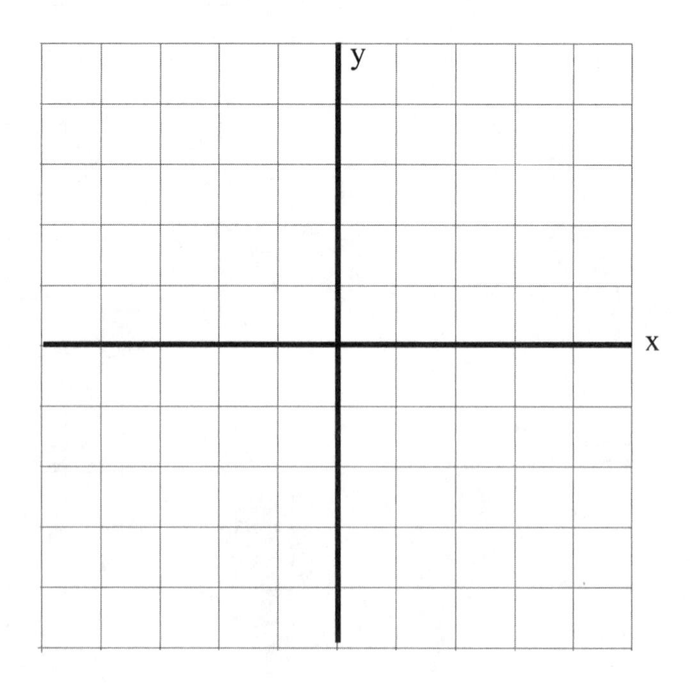

HOMEWORK EXERCISES

Study Tip: Necessary materials: pencils, colored pencils, ruler, eraser, graph paper, and note cards.

Skill Building Exercises

1. Plot the points (3, 5), (–2, –5), (2.3, 4.5), and (0, –2.75).

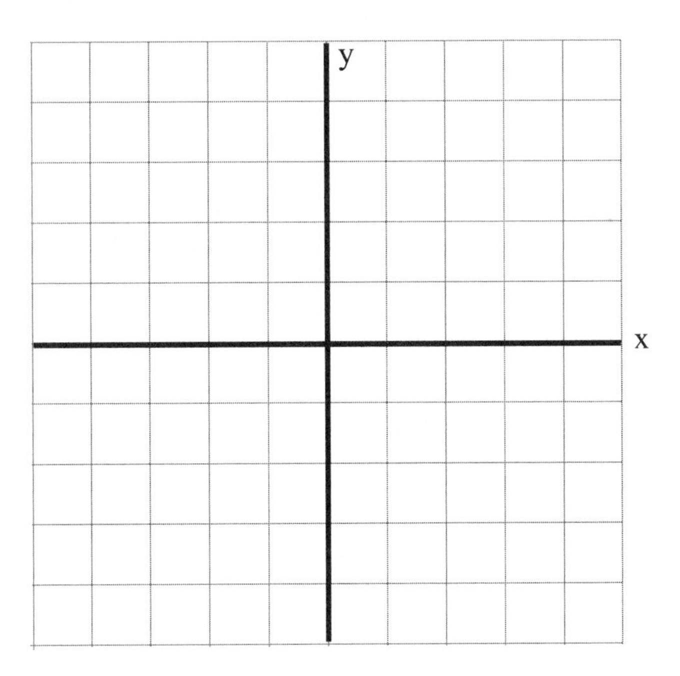

2. Complete the table for $y = -6x - 12$.

x	Calculation	y	(x, y)
–7			
0			
5			

3. Complete the table below for $y = \frac{-3}{4}x + 7$.

x	Calculation	y	(x, y)
–4			
0			
12			

4. a. Complete the table by solving the following equation for y given the particular value for x.

$$4x - 3y = 10$$

x	y	Point (x, y)

b. Use the algebra from Part a to help you solve $4x - 3y = 10$ for y. Similar problems were done in Section 1.6 "Literal Equations."

Practice Exercises

5. An internet provider, Wild Web, charges $15 per month plus 50 cents an hour.

a. Complete the table below.

Hours	**Calculation**	**Cost**	**Point (h, c)**
20			
50			
100			
h			

b. What is the equation that relates cost and hours?

d. Use the results in Part a. to graph the equation in Part b. Choose an appropriate scale and only graph the portion that makes sense to the problem. Label the axes.

Hours	**Cost**	**Point (h, c)**
20		
50		
100		

Study Tip: If you are having difficulties with the Practice Exercises, attempt the Reading and Writing Exercises first. Often reviewing the material in a different manner will result in better comprehension. Experiment, see what works for your unique learning style.

6. A printing press that costs $250,000 depreciates at a rate of $30,000 a year.

a. Complete the table below. (You must pick the years.)

Years	Calculation	Value
t		

b. What is the equation that relates value and years?

c. Use the results in Part a. to graph the equation in Part b. Choose an appropriate scale and only graph the portion that makes sense to the problem. Label the axes.

Years	Value	Point (t, v)

7. Graph the line by plotting points.

Study Tips: Use graph paper, colored pencils, and a ruler to create the graphs. Construct a table below for each problem. The table helps organize your work.

x	y	Point (x, y)

a. $y = 2x + 7$

b. $y = \frac{-1}{2}x + 5$

c. $3x - 8y = 32$

d. $6x + 4y = 18$

Reading and Writing Mathematics

8. In each problem, find the **mistake** and write a sentence describing the error. Also, write a suggestion so that any student who makes this type of mistake will have a way to remember not to make the error again.

Graph $y = 2x - 5$

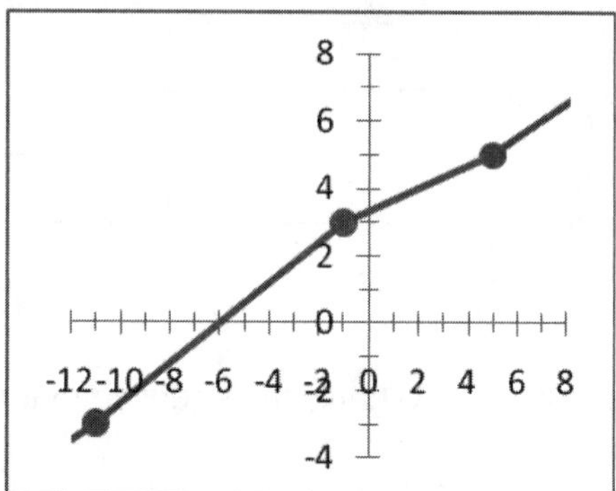

Let x = 3	*Let x = 5*	*Let x = -3*
y = 2(3)–5	*y = 2(5)–5*	*y = 2(-3)-5*
y = -1	*y = 5*	*y = -11*
(3, -1)	*(5, 5)*	*(-3, -11)*

9. A friend of yours misses class and wants to know how to graph $y = \frac{4}{7}x + 8$. Write a paragraph explaining the process of graphing the equation. Make sure you explain why you choose values for x that make the arithmetic easier.

10. A classmate asks you to look over her work. The mathematics is correct. Make 5 suggestions that would improve the presentation of the problem. Review the problem the way a teacher might look at it.

Graph the line $y = \frac{-3}{7}x + 12$ by plotting three points.

$y = \frac{-3}{7}(1) + 12$	$y = \frac{-3}{7}(5) + 12$	$y = \frac{-3}{7}(6) + 12$
$y = \frac{-3}{7} + 12$	$y = \frac{-15}{7} + 12$	$y = \frac{-18}{7} + 12$
11.57	9.8	$y = 9.4$

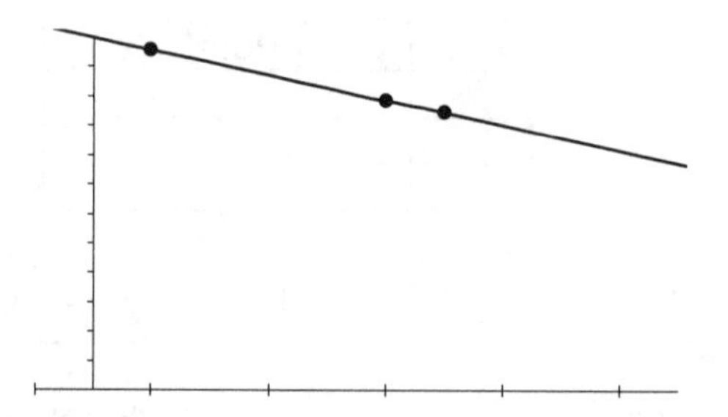

Study Tips:

1. Always check your homework by looking up the answers in the back of the book.
2. If you had difficulty with the homework, be prepared to ask your teacher for help. Ask your teacher to go over specific problems.
3. For further assistance:
   a. See your instructor during his/her office hours.
   b. Review the section using materials from the MAT 011 web page.
   c. Go to the L. A. L.
4. Detailed solutions to problems 1, 3, 5, 6, 8 b, d, 9, and 11 can be found on the MAT 011 Electronic Resource page. See page vii.

SECTION 2.6 GRAPHING LINES BY PLOTTING INTERCEPTS PREVIEW

Objectives: This section presents an additional way to graph a line. To graph a line, you need a minimum of two points. Two special points can be used. They are the intercepts of each axis. Often the intercepts have special meanings in a mathematical model. Also covered in this section are horizontal and vertical lines.

Example 1. An 8-year-old boy plans to open a lemonade stand. All of his supplies cost \$18.00, and he charges \$0.50 cents per glass. The equation that relates profit and number of glasses sold is

$$P = 0.50g - 18.00$$

a. What are the independent and dependent variables?

His profit depends on the number of glasses sold. So P is the dependent variable, and g is the independent variable. The points on the graph will have the form (g, P).

b. How many glasses does he have to sell to break even?

Breaking even means that his profit will be zero.

Find g when P = 0.

$0 = 0.50g - 18.00$	Substituted 0 for P.
$18.00 = 0.50g$	Added 18.00 to both sides.
$36 = g$	Divided both sides by 0.50.

He needs to sell 36 glasses to break even.
Graph the point (36, 0).

c. How much money will he make if he doesn't sell any lemonade?

If he doesn't sell any, then g = 0. Find P when g = 0.

$P = 0.50 \bullet 0 - 18.00$	Substituted 0 for g.
$P = -18.00$	Computed P.

He will lose \$18.00 if he doesn't sell any glasses of lemonade.
Graph the point (0, –18).

Explanation: Parts b and c are illustrated in the table below.

g	P	Point (g, P)
36	0	(36, 0)
0	–18	(0, –18)

d. Graph the line $P = 0.50g - 18.00$ by plotting the points obtained in Parts b and c. Choose an appropriate scale and only graph the portion which makes sense in the problem. Label the axes.

Vocabulary: The point (36, 0) is the **g intercept** because the point is on the g axis.

The point (0, –18) is the **P intercept** because the point is on the P axis.

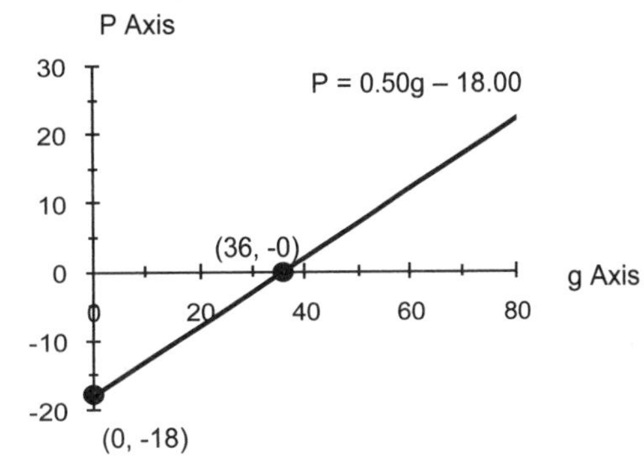

The significance of the previous example is:

The point (36, 0) is the **g intercept**. The P coordinate of the point (36, 0) is zero.

The point (0, –18) is the **P intercept**. The g coordinate of the point (0, –18) is zero.

To find the intercept of one of the axes, set the other variable equal to zero.

Example 2. Graph the line $25x + 0.04y = 50$ by finding the intercepts.

a. Find the y intercept. **Set x = 0**.

$25 \bullet 0 + 0.04y = 50$	Substituted x = 0.
$0.04y = 50$	Multiplied, $25 \bullet 0 = 0$.
$y = 1250$	Divided both sides by 0.04.

The y intercept is (0, 1250).

b. Find the x intercept. **Set y = 0**.

$25x + 0.04 \bullet 0 = 50$	Substituted y = 0.
$25x = 50$	Multiplied. $0.04 \bullet 0 = 0$.
$x = 2$	Divided both sides by 25.

The x intercept is (2, 0).

c. Graph the points (0, 1250) and (2, 0).

You have to think about the scale of the y axis. The scale of the y axis is 500. It is nice, but not necessary, to have the intercept correspond to an interval on the axis. Also, you don't want the intercept to be at the very top or bottom of the graph. There are other possibilities. Also, the scale of the x axis is different than the scale of the y axis.

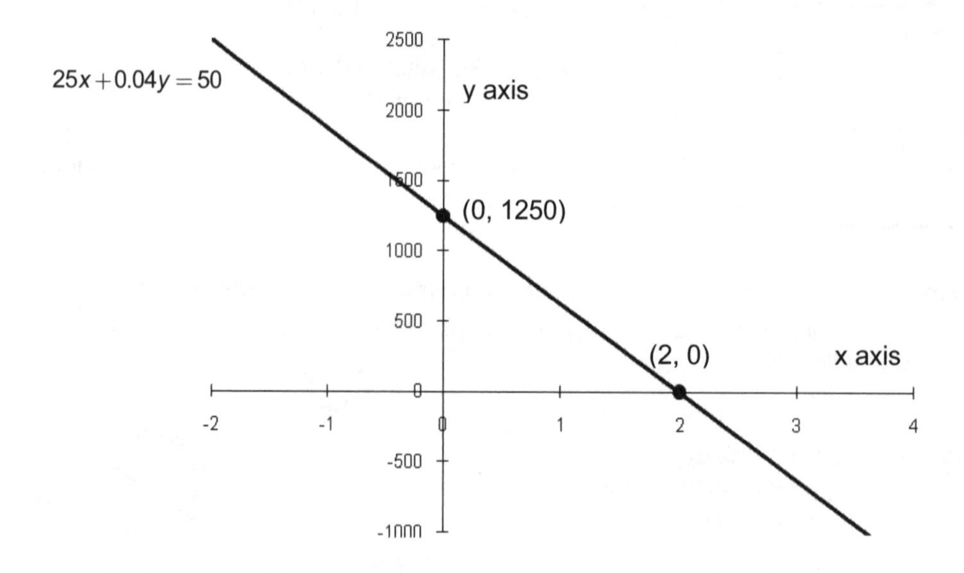

Study Tip: Write a note card describing the process of graphing by finding the intercepts. Review regularly.

Horizontal Lines:

Example 3. Today we will look at the cost of renting a car from three different rental companies. Elvis will rent us a car for \$35 plus \$0.25 a mile. Quartz rents the same model for \$25 plus \$0.50 a mile. AUTO will rent it to us for a flat daily rate of \$55 with no mileage charge.

(This is the group work problem from Introduction to Variables on page 29.)

The equations for the three companies are:

Elvis: $C_E = 0.25m + 35.00$

Quartz: $C_Q = 0.50m + 25.00$

AUTO: $C_A = 55.00$

The independent variable is m and the dependent variable is C.

The purpose of this example is to graph the cost equation for AUTO.
The company AUTO charges \$55.00 no matter how many miles you go.

If you drive, 10 miles it costs \$55. The ordered pair is (10, 55).
If you drive, 30 miles it costs \$55. The ordered pair is (30, 55).
If you drive, 90 miles it costs \$55. The ordered pair is (90, 55).

The graph of $C = 55.00$ is given below.

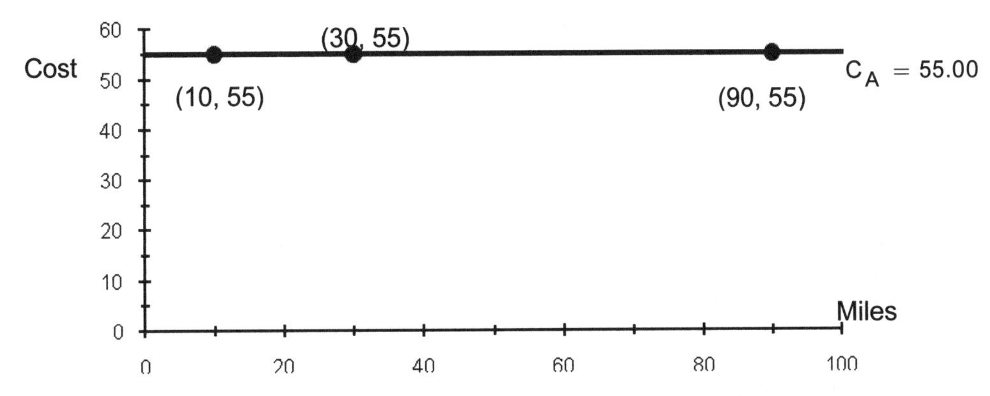

Vocabulary: The graph is **horizontal** or flat because the cost never changes.
The equation of a **horizontal** line is y equal to a constant, y = c.

Example 4. Graph y = –4.

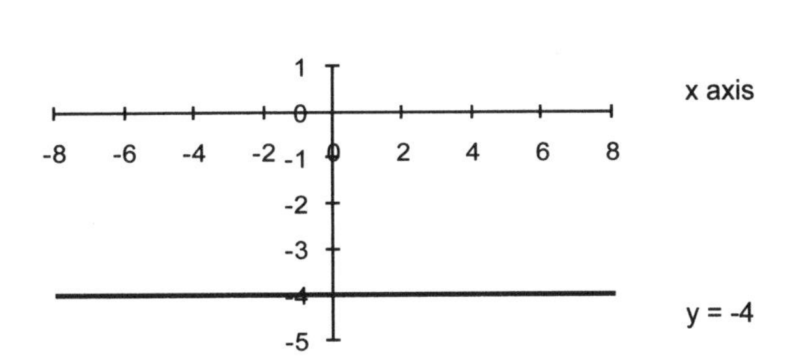

Explanation: Every point on the graph has a y coordinate of – 4.

Points on the graph:
(– 6, – 4), (0, – 4), (3, – 4).

Study Tip: You should write the equation for a horizontal line on a note card. You will need to graph horizontal lines in the Section 2.9 “Applications of Graphs”. You should review this card at least twice a week.

Vocabulary: The equation of a **vertical line** is the independent variable equal to a constant. The graph of x = h, h a constant, is a **vertical line**.

Example 5. Graph x = 3.

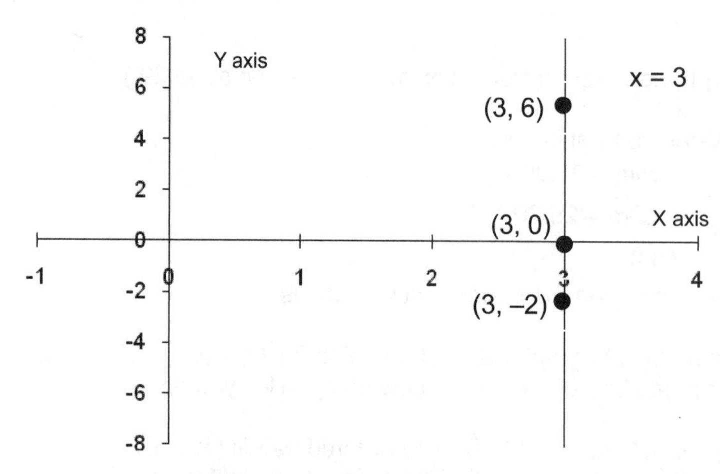

Explanation: Every point on the graph has an x coordinate of 3.

Points on the graph: (3, –2), (3, 0), (3, 6).

Study Tip: You should write the equation for a vertical line on a note card.

Summary: Graphs allow you to visualize the equation. You now know two ways to graph a line, plotting any three points or finding the intercepts. Sometimes you will have to decide which way is easier.

A. To graph a line by plotting three points.

1. Choose two values of the independent variable.
2. For each value of the independent variable, use algebra to find the value of the dependent variable.
3. Plot and connect the two points.
4. Choose a third value of the independent variable to check your work.

B. Graphing lines by finding the intercepts.

1. To find the x intercept, set y = 0 and solve for x.
2. To find the y intercept, set x = 0 and solve for y.

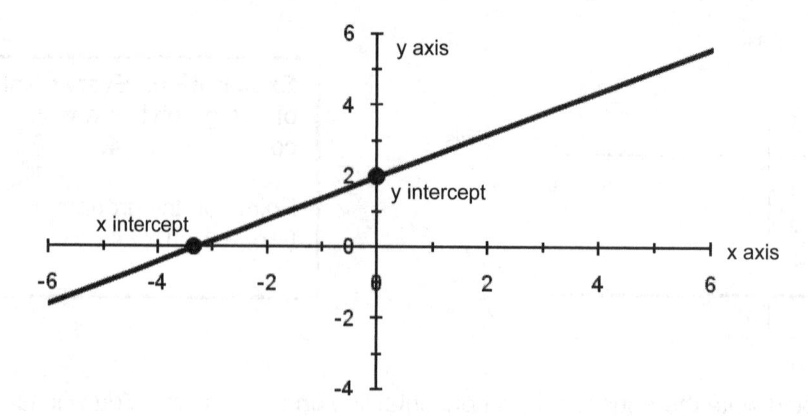

C. Horizontal lines.

1. The equation of a horizontal line is:

y = a number

2. The graph of a horizontal line:

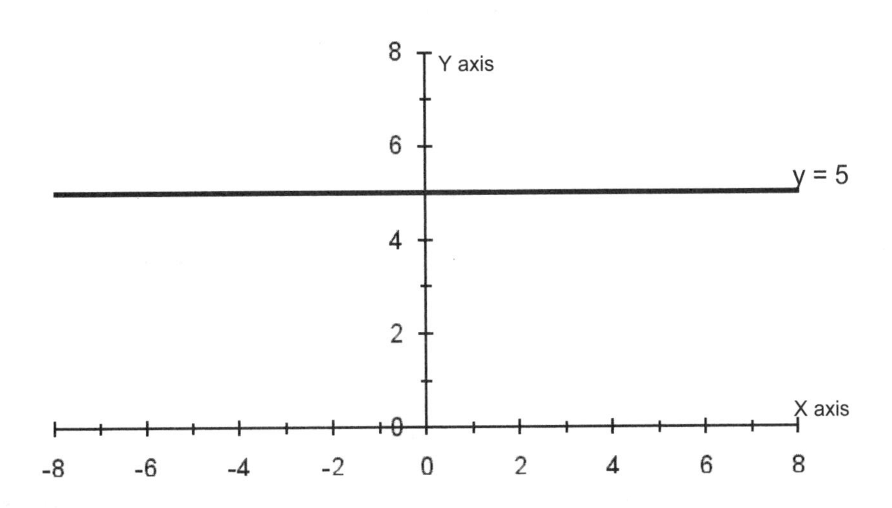

D. Vertical lines.

1. The equation of a vertical line is:

x = a number

2. The graph of a vertical line is:

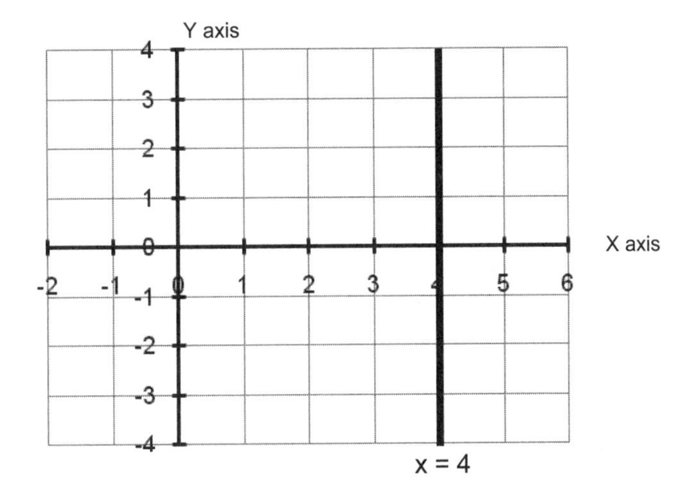

CLASS WORK

1. Sally started a lawn-mowing business for the summer. She bought a lawn mower for \$200, and she charges \$5 an hour. The equation that relates profit and hours worked is

$$p = 5h - 200$$

a. How many hours does she have to work to break even?

b. How much money will she make if she doesn't work any hours?

c. Graph the line $p = 5h - 200$ by plotting the points obtained in Parts a. and b. Choose an appropriate scale and only graph the portion that makes sense to the problem. Label the axes.

h intercept	
p intercept	

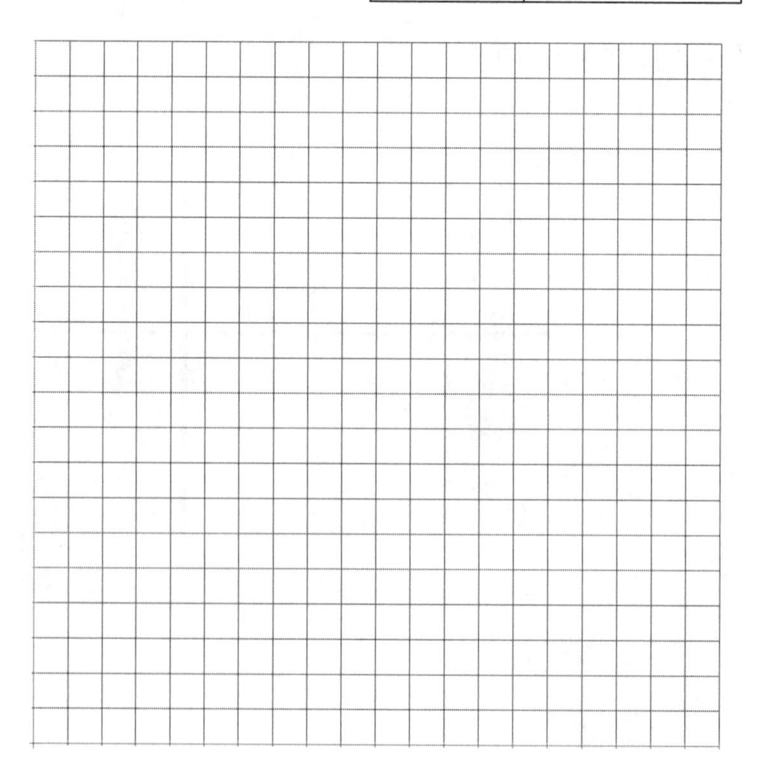

2. Graph the line by finding the **x and y intercepts**. Choose an appropriate scale and label the axes.

a. $y = \frac{2}{3}x - 5$

x intercept	
y intercept	

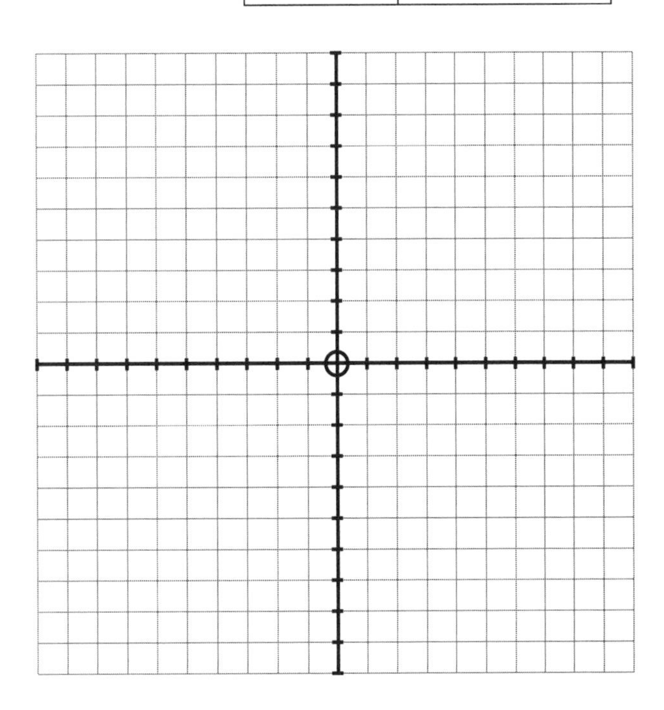

b. $0.03x - 4y = 16$

x intercept	
y intercept	

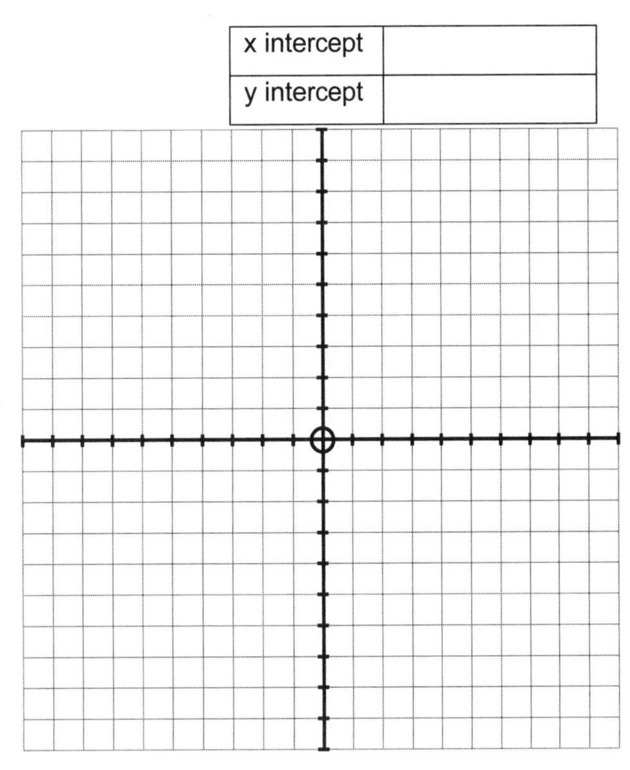

3. Define vertical and horizontal lines.

    a. Plot the points (3, 1) (3, –2) and (3, 5).

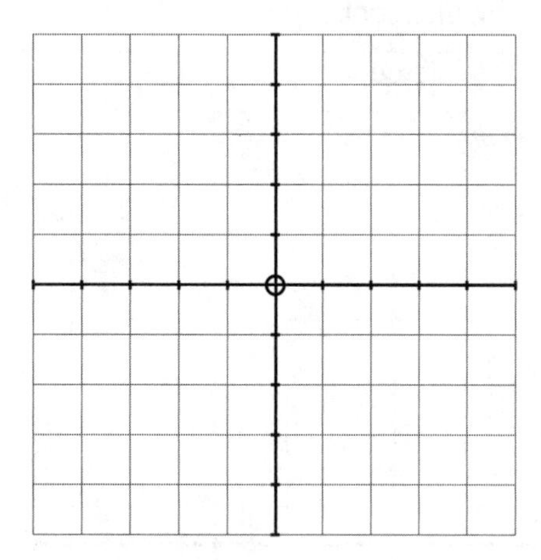

    b. Plot the points (5, 2) (4, 2) and (–3, 2).

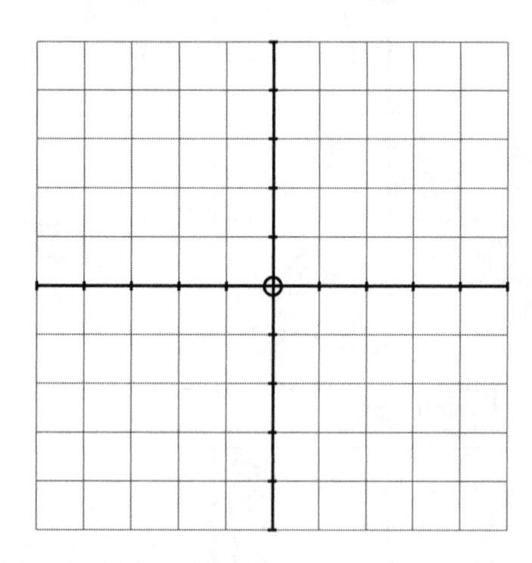

4. Graph the lines.

    a. $y = 18$

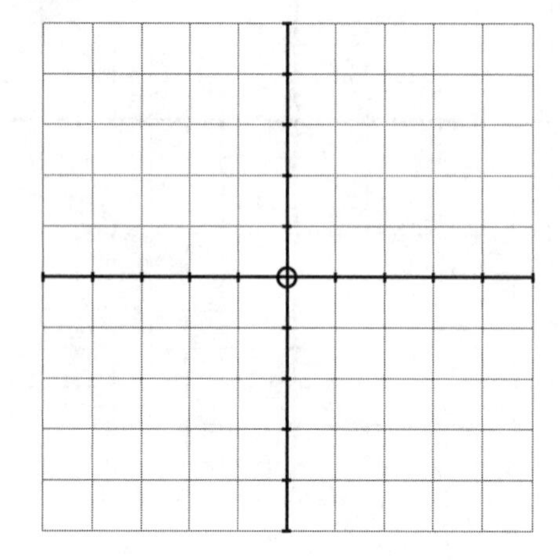

    b. $x = -4$

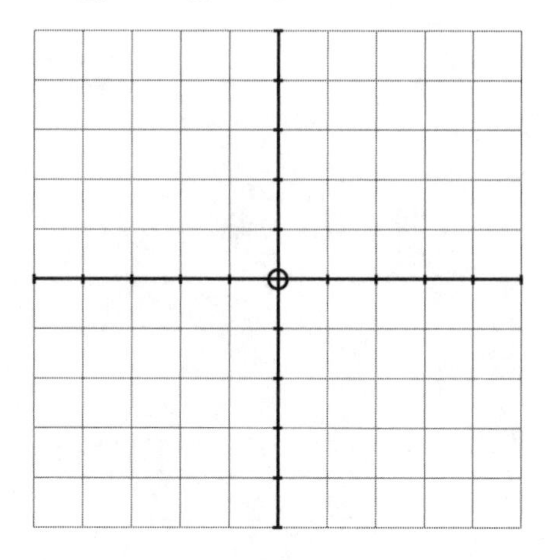

GROUP EXERCISES

Johnny Lift runs a snow clearing business for the winter. He bought a snow blower for $310 and charges $10 per hour. The equation that relates profit and hours is

$$p = 10h - 310$$

a. How many hours does he have to work to break even?

b. How much money will he make or lose if he doesn't work any hours?

c. Graph the line $p = 10h - 310$ by plotting the points obtained in Parts a. and b. Choose an appropriate scale and only graph the portion that makes sense to the problem. Label the axes.

p intercept	
h intercept	

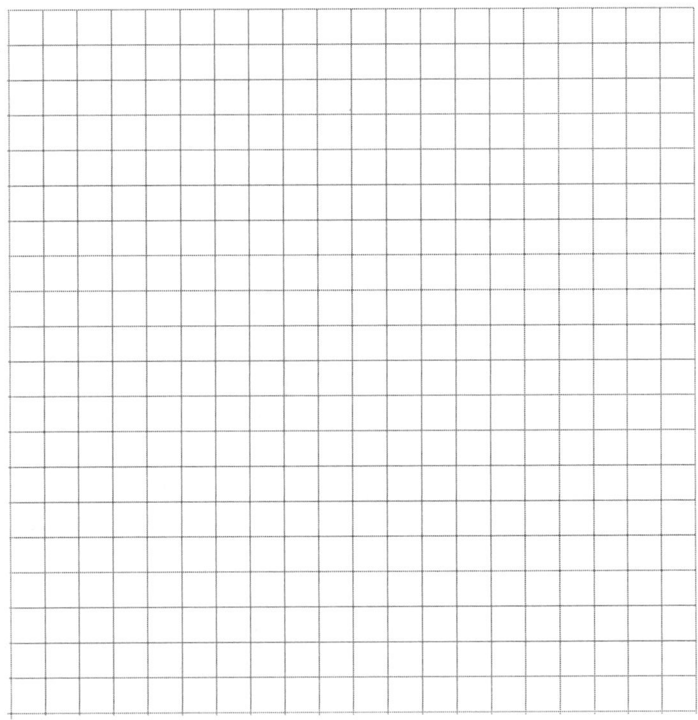

3. Graph the line. If possible, find the **x and y intercepts**. Choose an appropriate scale and label the axes.

a. $0.02x - 15y = 8$

x intercept	
y intercept	

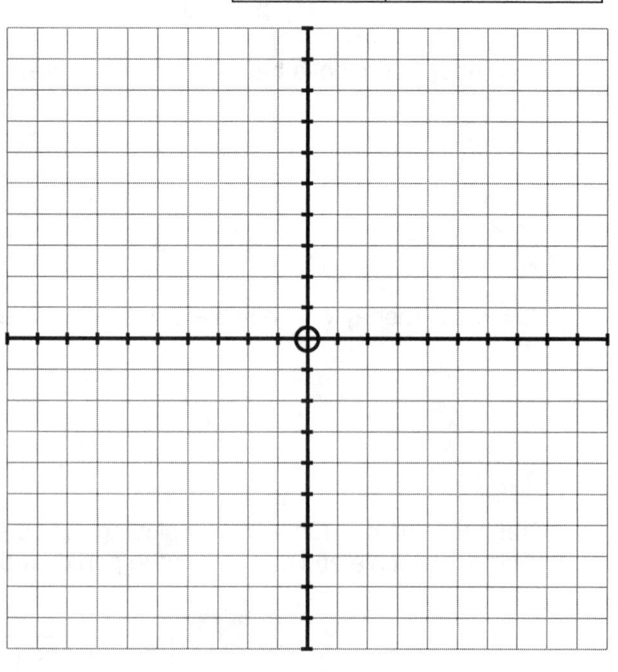

b. $y = 7$

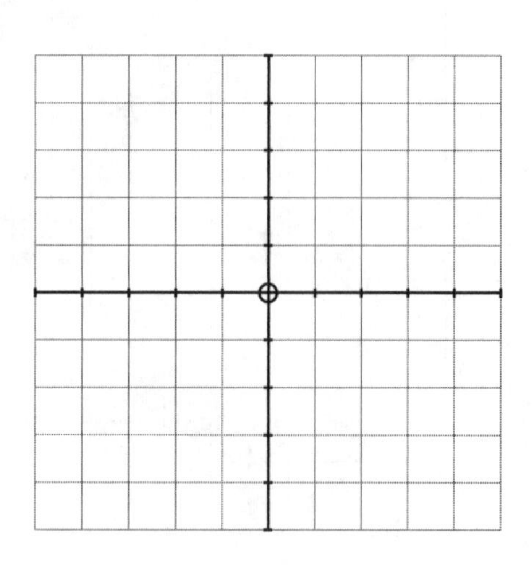

HOMEWORK EXERCISES

Study Tip: Necessary materials: pencils, colored pencils, ruler, eraser, graph paper, and note cards. Review the example on page 155.

Skill Building Exercises

1. Solve for x: $3x - 8 = 0$.

2. Find y when $x = 0$ in the equation $4x - 10y = 38$.

Practice Exercises

3. Joe Skuppy runs a pool cleaning service. The equipment costs $1095, and he charges $15 an hour. The equation that relates profit and hours is

$$p = 15h - 1095$$

   a. How many hours does he have to work to break even?

   b. How much money will he make if he doesn't work any hours?

   c.. Graph the line $p = 15h - 1095$ by plotting the points obtained in parts a. and b. Choose an appropriate scale and only graph the portion that makes sense to the problem. Label the axes.

4. The equation $V = -2{,}300t + 20{,}700$ represents the value of a 2007 minivan as it depreciates y years after it is bought.

   a. When will the minivan be worthless?

   b. How much was the minivan worth in 2007? (Hint: what value of t represents the year 2007?)

   c. Graph the line $V = -2{,}300t + 20{,}700$ by plotting the points obtained in parts a. and b. Choose an appropriate scale and only graph the portion that makes sense to the problem. Label the axes.

5. Graph each line by finding the **x and y intercepts**. Choose an appropriate scale and label the axes.

   a. $y=\frac{3}{5}x+11$

   b. $11x + 1{,}241y = 100$

   c. $3x - 0.02y = 12$

   d. $y = \frac{-3}{4}x-5$

6. a. Write an equation for a horizontal line.

   b. Write an equation for a vertical line.

7. Graph each line.

   a. $y = -3$

   b. $x = 6$

   c. $x = \frac{-1}{2}$

   d. $y = 8$

8. Graph the line y = 0.2x + 70 by finding the x and y intercepts. Use the scale from the two graphs below. Which graph is steeper? Should one graph be steeper than the other? Why or why not? (You will need to use graph paper.)

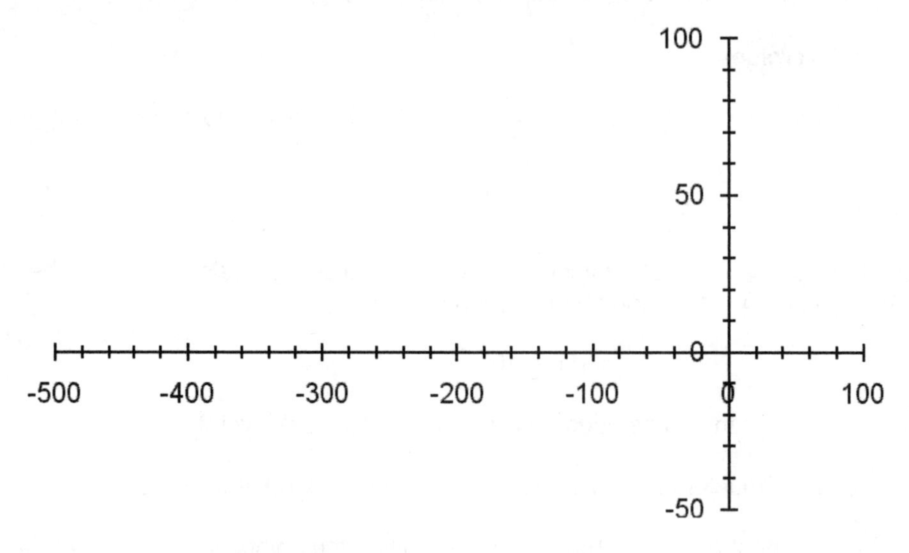

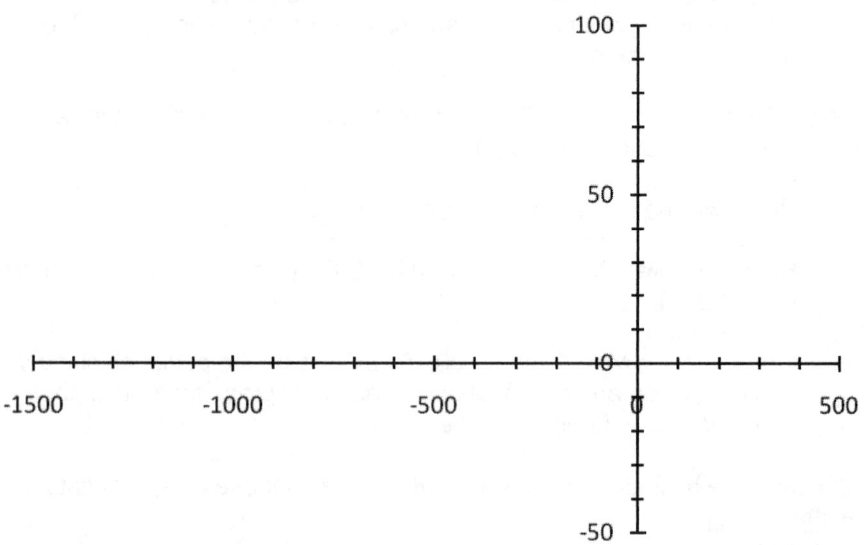

Reading and Writing Mathematics

9. In the problem below, find the **mistake** and write a sentence describing the error. Also, write a suggestion so that any student who makes this type of mistake will have a way to remember not to make the error again.

Graph 3x – 2y = 6

Let $x = 0$	*Let $y = 0$*
$3(0) - 2y = 6$	$3x - 2(0) = 6$
$-2y = 6$	$3x = 6$
$y = -3$	$x = 2$

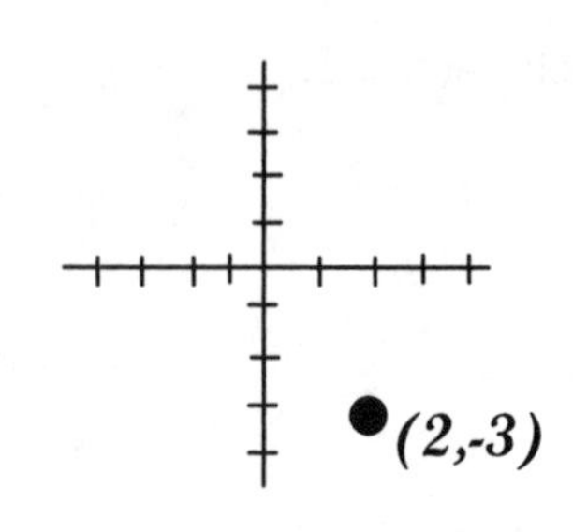

10. In the problem below, find the **mistake** and write a sentence describing the error. Also, write a suggestion so that any student who makes this type of mistake will have a way to remember not to make the error again.

Graph the line $y = \frac{2}{5}x - 22$ by finding the x and y intercepts.

$y = \frac{2}{5}(0) - 22$

$y = -22$

$0 = \frac{2}{5}x - 22$

$22 = \frac{2}{5}x$

$\frac{5}{2}22 = x$

$55 = x$

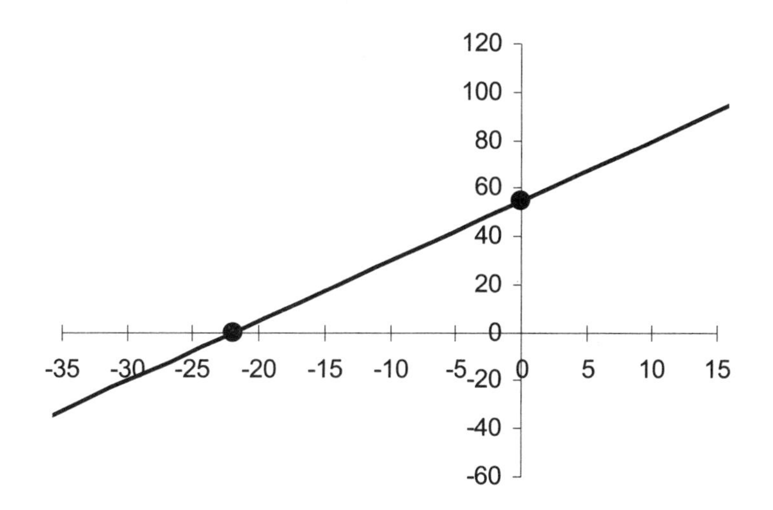

11. a. Write a sentence describing how you find the x intercept?

 b. Write a sentence describing how you find the y intercept?

12. A classmate asks you for help. He says that he doesn't know how to finish the problem. Look at his work below and decide what he did and why he did it. Write what steps he needs to complete in order to finish the problem.

Graph the line 0.25x + 12y = 44.

$0.25x + 12\,(0) = 44$

$0.25x = 44$

$x = 176$

Now what do I do?

Study Tip: Detailed solutions to problems 2, 3, 5 a, c, 7 a, c, and 9 can be found on the MAT 011 Electronic Resource page. See page vii.

SECTION 2.7 INTRODUCTION TO SLOPE
PREVIEW

Objectives: This section introduces the important concept of slope using applications from previous sections. Slope describes the rate at which a line either rises or falls.

Example 1. You need to rent a moving van. Class Movers charges a basic rate of \$24.95 plus 32 cents per mile.

(This example is from Graphing Lines by Plotting Points, page 140.)

a. Calculate the cost of renting a van if you drive the following number of miles.

MILES	CALCULATION	COST
10	0.32(10) + 24.95	28.15
20	0.32(20) + 24.95	31.35
30	0.32(30) +24.95	34.55
m	0.32m + 24.95	c

b. The graph of the equation $c = 0.32m + 24.95$ is presented below.

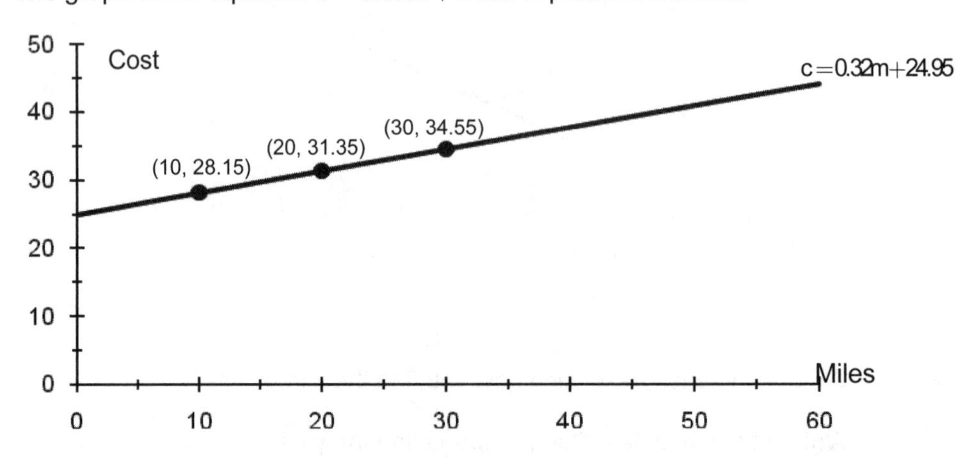

c. The **slope** of this line is computed by selecting any two points to find $\dfrac{\text{change in cost}}{\text{change in miles}}$.

For example, $\dfrac{34.55-28.15}{30-10}$.

This formula can be interpreted as:

- $\dfrac{\text{Change in Cost}}{\text{Change in Miles}}$
- $\dfrac{\text{Change in Dependent Variable}}{\text{Change in Independent Variable}}$
- $\dfrac{\text{Vertical Change}}{\text{Horizontal Change}}$
- $\dfrac{\text{Rise}}{\text{Run}}$

Explanation:
34.55 – 28.15, represents the change in cost. Cost is the dependent variable and the vertical axis.

30 – 10, represents the change in miles. Miles are the independent variable and the horizontal axis.

d. Compute $\frac{34.55-28.15}{30-10}$ and interpret what it means.

$$\frac{34.55-28.15}{30-10}=0.32$$

0.32 is the cost per mile and is the coefficient of m, the independent variable. This is not a coincidence. In this problem, **slope is the cost per mile**.

e. Suppose Class Movers begins to charge 55 cents per mile. Then the new equation is $c=0.55m+24.95$. The slope is still the cost per mile, so the slope of this line is 0.55. The graphs of both equations appear below.

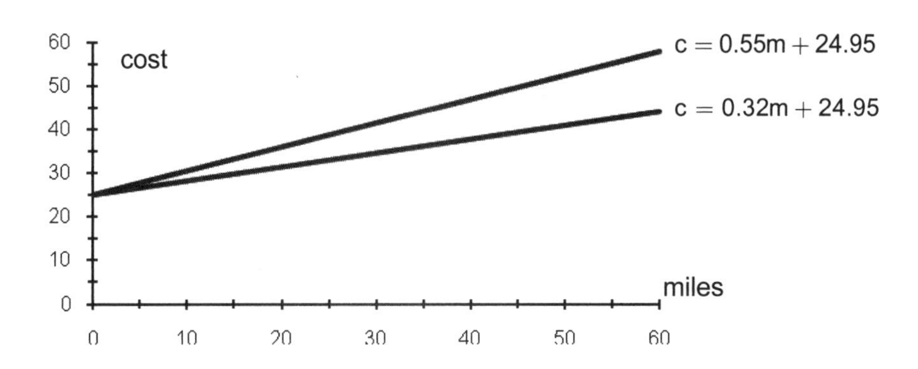

The line representing the equation $c=0.55m+24.95$ is steeper than the line representing $c=0.32m+24.95$ because Class Movers charge more per mile. The slope of the line $c=0.55m+24.95$ is greater than the slope of the line $c=0.32m+24.95$.

Slope measures the steepness of a line.

Example 2. Which plant grows faster: Hybrid A sunflower which grew 26 inches in 10 days or Hybrid B sunflower which grew 28 inches in 9 days?

To answer the question we will compute $\frac{\text{growth}}{\text{time}}$.

Hybrid A: $\frac{26}{10}=2.6$. Hybrid A grew 2.6 inches per day.

Hybrid B: $\frac{28}{9}=3.111$. Hybrid B grew 3.111 inches per day.

Hybrid B grew faster than Hybrid A. Since plants grow at different rates, the numbers 2.6 and 3.111 represent the average growth per day. The numbers 2.6 and 3.111 also represent the idea of slope,

$$\frac{\text{Change in Dependent Variable}}{\text{Change in independent variable}}=\frac{26}{10}=2.6.$$

Slope also means the average rate of change. The slope of Hybrid B is steeper than the slope of Hybrid A.

Example 3. The average cost of a personal computer is shown in the table below.

YEAR	COST
1987	$1,678
2001	$1,076

a. Make a graph of year versus cost.

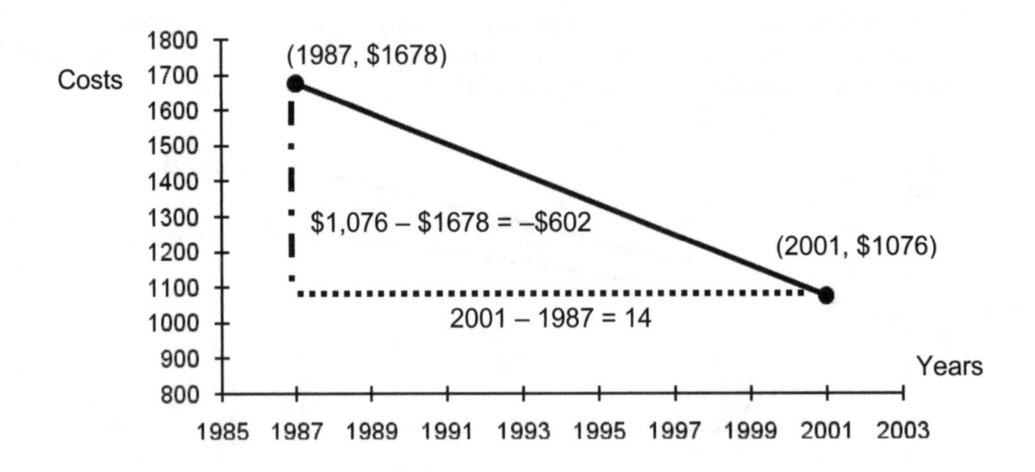

b. Calculate the average rate of change.

Average Rate of Change = slope

$$= \frac{\text{Vertical Change}}{\text{Horizontal Change}}$$

$$= \frac{\text{Change in Cost}}{\text{Change in Years}}$$

$$= \frac{1{,}076 - 1{,}678}{2001 - 1987}$$

$$= \frac{-602}{14}$$

$$= -43$$

Explanation: Look at the graph above:

1,076 – 1,678 represents the vertical change.

2001 – 1987 represents the horizontal change.

On the average, the cost of personal computers decreased $43 per year between 1987 and 2001.

If the slope of the line is negative, then the line is decreasing (moving down left to right).

Conversely, if the slope is positive then the line is increasing (moving up left to right).

Example 4. Use the data from Example 3 to calculate the percent change in the cost of personal computers.

Percent change is a similar idea to slope. It also measures how a quantity changes; however, percent change only involves one variable. In our problem, the change only involves the cost.

The formula for percent change is:

$$\text{Percent Change} = \frac{\text{New - Old}}{\text{Old}} \bullet 100$$

The variable New is the cost of personal computers in 2001, \$1,076.

The variable Old is the cost of personal computers in 1987, \$1,678.

$$\text{Percent Change} = \frac{1{,}076 - 1{,}678}{1{,}678} \bullet 100$$

$$\text{Percent Change} = -35.88$$

Explanation:
Notice that the numerator of the formula for percent change is the same as the numerator for the formula for slope.

The cost of personal computers decreased 35.88% from 1987 to 2001.
From example 3, the slope is –43, the cost of personnel computers decreased on average \$43 per year between 1987 and 2001.

Summary: Slope is a very important topic in algebra. It measures how things change. The following are different interpretations of slope:

Slope

- $\dfrac{\text{Change in dependent variable}}{\text{Change in independent variable}}$ or $\dfrac{\text{Change in y}}{\text{Change in x}}$
- $\dfrac{\text{Vertical Change}}{\text{Horizontal Change}}$
- $\dfrac{\text{Rise}}{\text{Run}}$
- Slope measures the steepness of a line.
- Slope is the average rate of change.
- If the slope of the line is **negative**, then the line is **decreasing** (moving down left to right).
- If the slope of the line is **positive**, then the line is **increasing** (moving up left to right.)

Percent Change also measures changes in a quantity. The formula for Percent Change is:

$$\text{Percent Change} = \frac{\text{New - Old}}{\text{Old}} \bullet 100$$

Study Tip: You should write this formula on a note card and memorize it.

CLASS WORK

1. A rental car company, Wrecker, charges $21.95 per day plus 41 cents a mile.

   a. Calculate the cost of renting a car for one day.

Miles	Calculation	Cost	(miles, cost)
10	0.41*10 + 21.95	26.05	(10, 26.05)
20	0.41*20 + 21.95	30.15	(20, 30.15)
30	0.41*30 + 21.95	34.25	(30, 34.25)
m	0.41*m + 21.95	c	(m, c)

   b. The graph of the equation c = 0.41m + 21.95 is shown below.

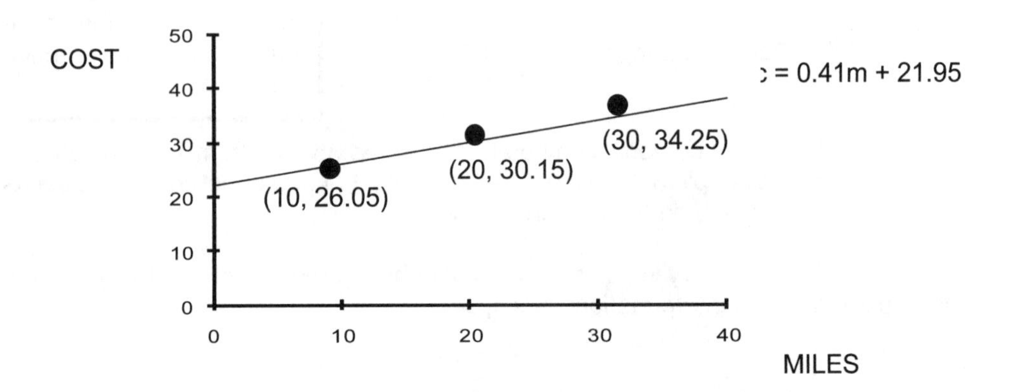

   c. What does $\frac{34.25 - 26.05}{30 - 10}$ mean?

   d. Suppose Wrecker starts charging $0.61 cents a mile. Graph the new cost equation c = 0 .61m + 21.95 using the axis in Part b.

2. Which grows faster: Hybrid A corn seedlings, which grow 14.6 centimeters in 15 days, or Hybrid B, which grow 11.2 centimeters in 12 days?

3. What does the highway sign mean?

Average Rate of Change and Percent Change

4. A public school district charts enrollment in first grade as follows:

Year 2000	276 students in first grade
Year 2004	320 students in first grade

A graphical representation of the data is shown below.

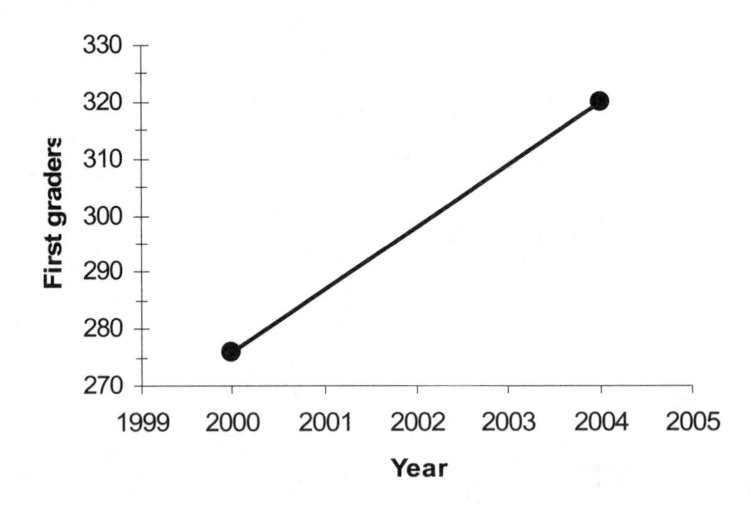

a. Calculate the average rate of change. (Be sure to include the correct units.)

b. What is the slope of the line through the two points?

c. Calculate the percent increase in enrollment.

$$\text{Percent Change} = \left(\frac{\text{New} - \text{Old}}{\text{Old}}\right) \times 100$$

5. The graph and table illustrate imports of Mexican products into the United States.

Year	Mexico imports to U. S. in Millions of Dollars
1999	109
2000	136
2001	131
2002	134
2003	138

Source: Mexican Chamber of Commerce

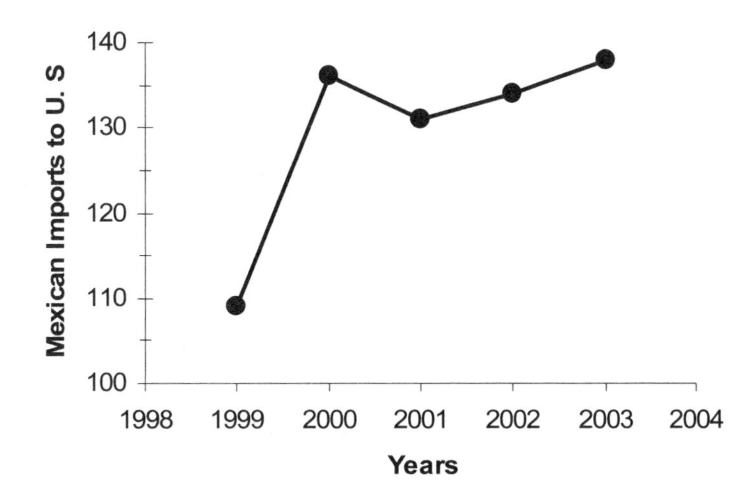

a. Calculate the average rate of change between 2000 and 2001 (include the correct units). Write a sentence describing your results.

b. What is the percent change between 2000 and 2001? Write a sentence describing your results.

c. Use the table and graph to predict the dollar amount of Mexican imports into the U. S. in the year 2004.

6. The graph and table illustrate men's average math SAT scores from 1970 to 2002.

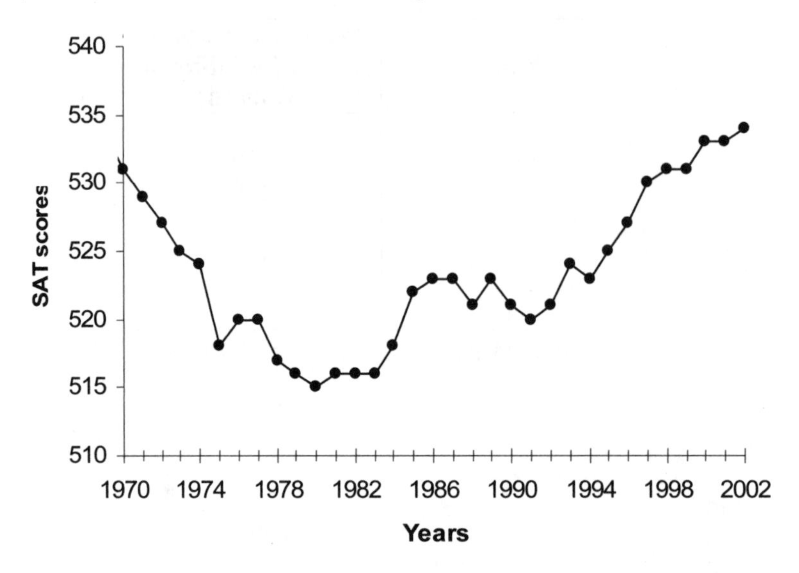

Year	SAT Score	Year	SAT Score	Year	SAT Score
1970	531	1981	516	1992	521
1971	529	1982	516	1993	524
1972	527	1983	516	1994	523
1973	525	1984	518	1995	525
1974	524	1985	522	1996	527
1975	517	1986	523	1997	530
1976	520	1987	523	1998	531
1977	520	1988	521	1999	531
1978	517	1989	523	2000	533
1979	516	1990	521	2001	533
1980	515	1991	520	2002	534

Source: Collegeboard.com

a. According to the graph, what was the longest time period for declining math SAT scores?

b. According to the graph, over what year did math SAT scores decrease the most?

c. Use the table to find the average rate of change for your answer in Part b.

d. According to the graph, over what year did the SAT scores increase the most?

e. Use the table to find the average rate of change for your answer in Part d.

f. According to the graph and chart, over for what three year period did the math SAT scores remain constant?

GROUP EXERCISE

Use the table below to make a very accurate graph of women's math SAT scores during the indicated years. Make sure you label your axes and choose a correct scale.

Study Tips: 1. Review the Class Work on page 175.
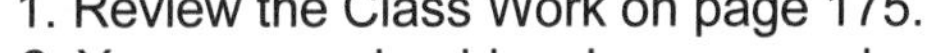
2. Your group should make one graph on graph paper.
3. Use a ruler and colored pencils.

Year	1992	1993	1994	1995	1996	1997	1998	1999	2000	2001	2002
SAT Score	484	484	487	490	492	494	496	495	498	498	500

A blank graph is provided for you on page 178, or use your own graph paper.

a. According to the graph, over what year did women's math SAT scores decline.?

b. Use the table to find the average rate of change for your answer in Part a.

c. Use the table to find the percent decrease for your answer in Part a.

d. According to the table, over what year did the math SAT scores increase the most? (There is more than one answer.)

e. Use the table to find the average rate of change for your answer in Part d.

f. Use the table to find the percent increase for your answer in Part d.

g. According to the graph, over what time period did women's math SAT scores remain constant?

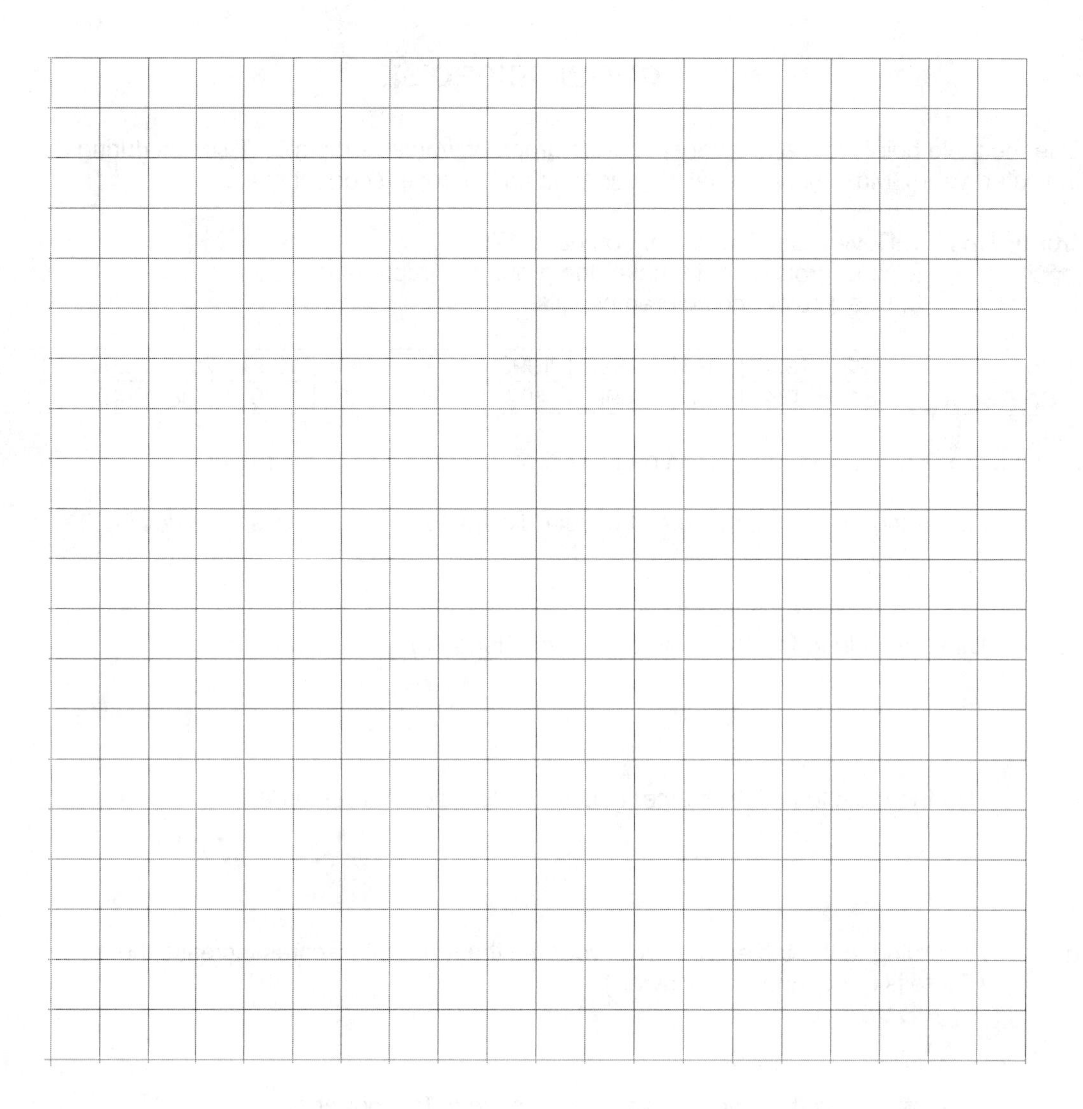

HOMEWORK EXERCISES

Study Tip: Do your homework every day but for short time periods.

Skill Building Exercises

1. The equation v = –25t + 346 models the depreciation of a copy machine t years after it was purchased. The graph is shown below. Identify the independent and dependent variables. Is the slope of the line positive or negative?

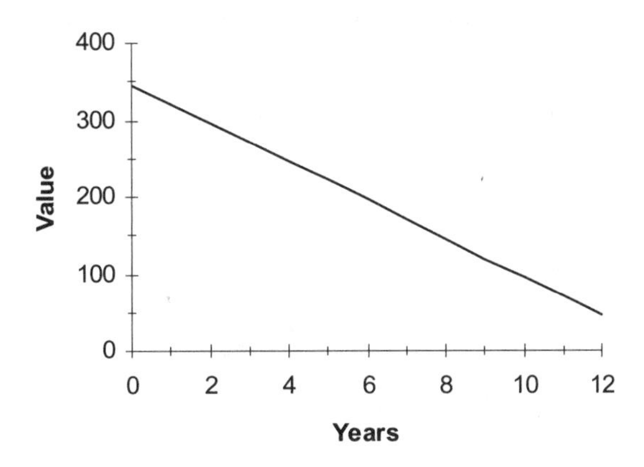

2. The table below shows the minimum wage adjusted for inflation.

Year	2000	2001	2002	2003	2004	2005
Min. Wage	$4.69	$4.56	$4.49	$4.39	$4.28	$4.15

Source: Infoplease .com

Identify the independent and dependent variables.

Practice Exercises

3. Little Haven grocery store sells a dozen grade A eggs for $1.89. The Fresh Stop sells 18 eggs for $2.68. Which store has the better buy?

4. Which is steeper, the car ramp for Take Away Rental Company, which rises 5 feet for every horizontal distance of 9 feet, or Darrel's toy garage which rises 3 inches for every horizontal distance of 8 inches?

Go Back: Questions 3 and 4 are similar to Example 2 page 169 and Problem 2 page 172.

5. The table below shows the minimum wage adjusted for inflation. Use the table to answer the following questions.

Year	2000	2001	2002	2003	2004	2005
Min. Wage	$4.69	$4.56	$4.49	$4.39	$4.28	$4.15

Source: Infoplease .com

Study Tip: You should use graph paper, a ruler, and colored pencils.

a. Make a graph of the minimum wage for the indicated years. Make sure you label your axes.

b. Calculate the average rate of change between 2000 and 2005 (include the correct units).

c. Calculate the average rate of change between 2004 and 2005 (include the correct units).

d. Use Parts b or c to estimate the minimum wage in 2006. Write a sentence that describes your logic.

Go Back: Review problem 5b on page 174.

e. What is the percent change between the years 2000 and 2005?

f. Write a topic sentence summarizing what you think is the central idea to be drawn from this data.

6. Use the table to answer the following questions.

Source: *2004 Statistical Yearbook by the United Nations Educational, Scientific and Cultural Organization*

Year	Number of Daily Newspapers in the U.S.
1997	1,509
1998	1,489
1999	1,483
2000	1,471

a. Make a graph of the number of newspapers in the indicated years.

b. Calculate the average rate of change between the years 1997 and 2000 (include the correct units).

c. Calculate the average rate of change between the years 1999 and 2000 (include the correct units).

d. What is the percent change between the years 1999 and 2000?

e. Write a topic sentence summarizing what you think is the central idea to be drawn from this data.

7. Use the table below to make a very accurate graph of men's average age of first marriage during the indicated years. Make sure you label your axes and choose a correct scale.

Year	Men's Average age of First Marriage
1890	26.1
1900	25.9
1910	25.1
1920	24.6
1930	24.3
1940	24.3
1950	22.8
1960	22.8
1970	23.2
1980	24.7
1990	26.1
2000	26.4

a. According to the graph, over what 10 year period was there the greatest decrease in men's average age of first marriage?

b. Use the table to find the average rate of change over the 10 year period for your answer in Part a.

c. According to the graph, over what 10 year period did the greatest increase in men's average age of first marriage occur? Why are you not sure you have the correct answer?

d. Use the table to find the average rate of change over the 10 year period for your answer in Part c. Find the average rate of change over the 10 year period in men's average age of first marriage for your "other" answer in Part c.

e. According to the graph, over what 10 year period was there no change in men's average age of first marriage?

f. What does the slope tell you about how the average age of when a man first marries is changing in 2000?

g. Use slope to predict men's average age of first marriage in the year 2010. Write a sentence explaining what you did.

8. Below is an approximation of the cost of doctors' bills and Medicare between 1963 and 1979.

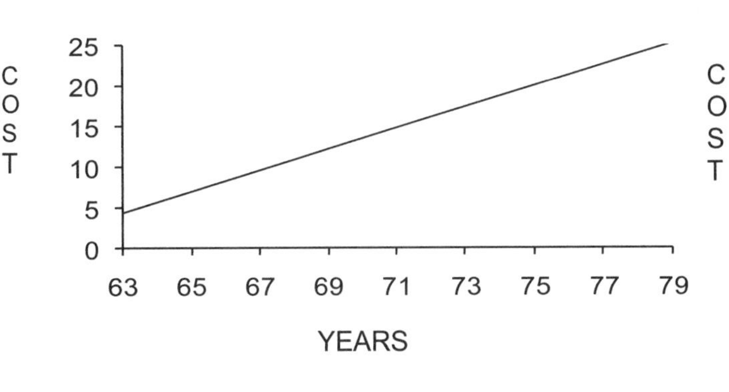

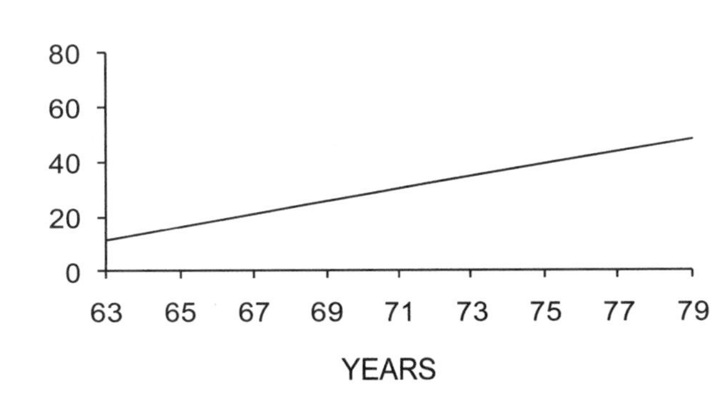

Study Tip: Review slope and pay attention to the scales.

a. Which *appears* to have been growing at a faster rate: doctors' bills or Medicare costs? Why?

b. Which actually grew at a faster rate, and how can you tell?

9. Use the two graphs below to answer the questions.

   a. Which line appears to have the greater slope?

   b. Estimate the slope of both lines by finding two points from each line.

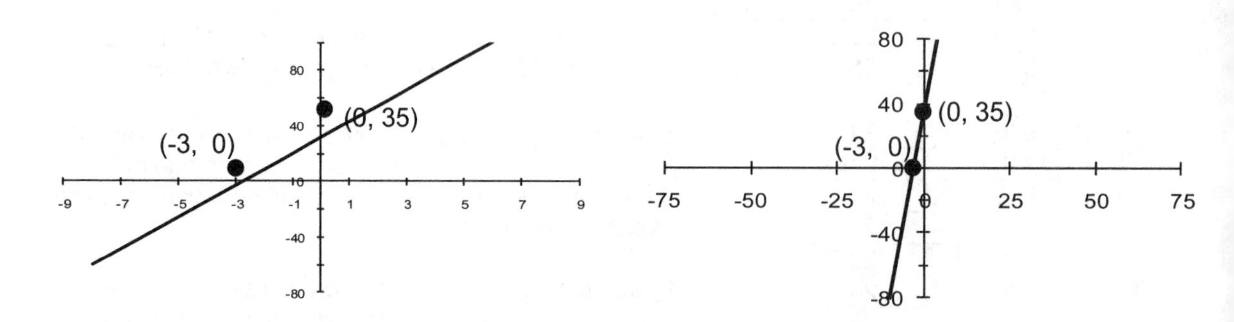

10. The table below appeared in the *Morning Call* newspaper on Sunday, October 16, 2000.

Study Tip: Review the percent change formula.

UTILITY COMPLAINTS RISE Change in "justified" consumer complaints from 1998 to 1999 for selected utilities:			
	COMPLAINTS		
UTILITY	**1998**	**1999**	**INCREASE**
PPL	55	390	Up 609%
BELL ATLANTIC	1,078	3,443	Up 219%
COMMONWEALTH TELEPHONE	28	44	Up 57%
GTE	163	227	Up 39%

How did the newspaper compute the increase column?

Reading and Writing Mathematics

11. List 3 meanings or definitions of slope.

12. How is slope different from percent change?

13. How is slope similar to percent change?

14. Find 3 articles from newspapers that used slope or percent change in them.

15. In the problem below, find the **mistakes** and write a sentence describing each error. Also, write a suggestion so that any student who makes this type of mistake will have a way to remember not to make it again. The student made two errors in the problem.

Use the table below to make an accurate graph of the average starting salary of accountants in the indicated years.

Year	1980	1985	1990	1995	2000
Salary	$23,500	$25,600	$28,400	$31,100	$34,000

I made the graph below.

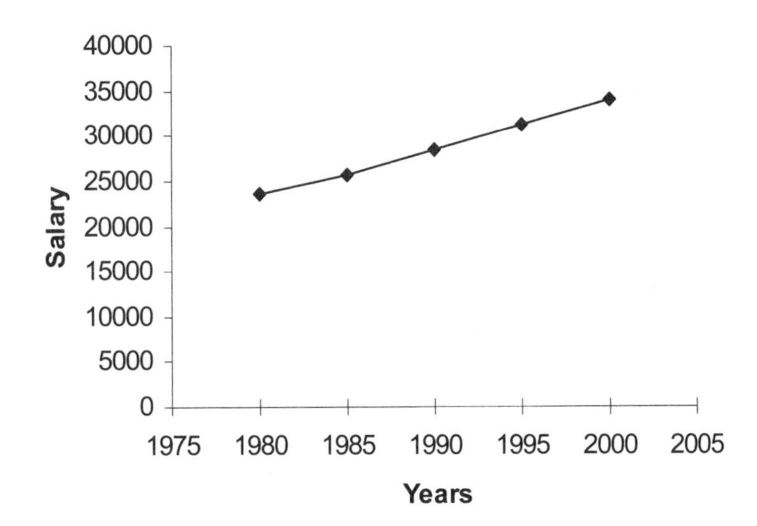

a. Calculate the average rate of change between the years 1980 and 2000.

(23,500 – 34,000) / (2000 – 1980) =
-10,500/ 20 =
-525
The salaries decrease $525 per year.

b. Calculate the percent change between 1985 and 1995.

(31,100 – 25,600) / 31,100 =
5,500 / 31,100 =
0.1768 or 17.68%

c. Use the graph and the data to predict the average salary in the year 2005.

I noticed that the salary went up $2,900 between 1995 and 2000, so I added 2,900 to 34,000 and got $36,900.

Study Tip: Registration for next semester will begin soon, page viii contains advising information for MAT 011 students.

16. A classmate asks you to look over her work. The mathematics is correct. Make five suggestions that would improve the presentation of the problem. Review the problem the way an instructor might look at it.

Use the table below to make an accurate graph of the U. S. population (in millions) in the indicated years.

Year	1985	1990	1995	1998	2000
Population	238	250	263	271	281

Source: U. S. Census Bureau

I made the graph below.

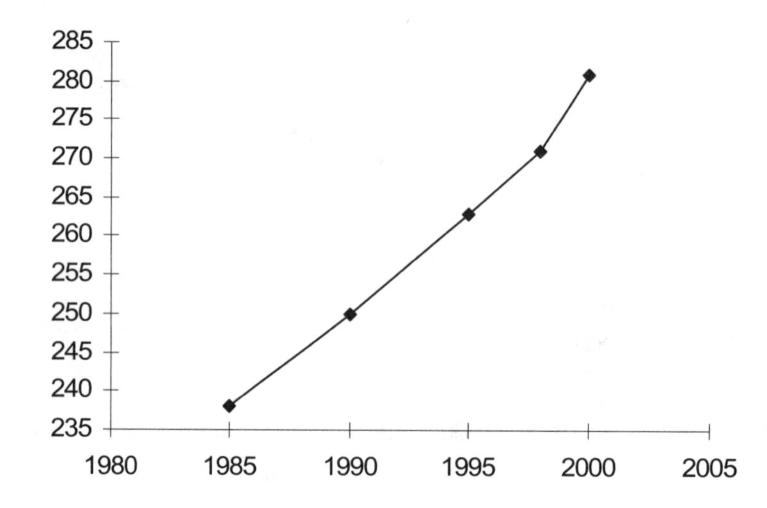

a. Calculate the average rate of change between the years 1985 and 1998. (Be sure to include the correct units.)

271 - 238 = 33
33/13 = 2.5

b. Calculate the percent change between the years 1990 and 2000.

281 - 250 / 250 *100 = 12.4%

c. Use the table and graph to estimate the population in the year 2005. Write a sentence that describes your logic.

10/2 = 5
25 + 281 = 306

I found the slope for the years 1998 and 2000 then multiplied that number by 5 and added to 281.

Study Tip: Detailed solutions to problems 1, 3, 5, 7, 9, and 15 can be found on the MAT 011 Electronic Resource page. See page vii.

SECTION 2.8 SLOPE
PREVIEW

Objective: This section will cover the algebraic formula for slope, including the slopes of horizontal and vertical lines, and the slope-intercept equation of a line.

Algebraic formula for slope:

Let (x_1, y_1) and (x_2, y_2) be any two points on the line; then the formula for slope is:

$$m = \frac{y_2 - y_1}{x_2 - x_1}.$$

Explanation: Slope is $\frac{\text{vertical change}}{\text{horizontal change}}$.

$y_2 - y_1$ represents the vertical change.

$x_2 - x_1$ represents the horizontal change.

Study Tip: Write the formula on a note card for easy reference.

Example 1. Graph the line that passes through the two points (–2, –1), (3, 5) and find the slope.

a. To graph the line, just plot the two points.

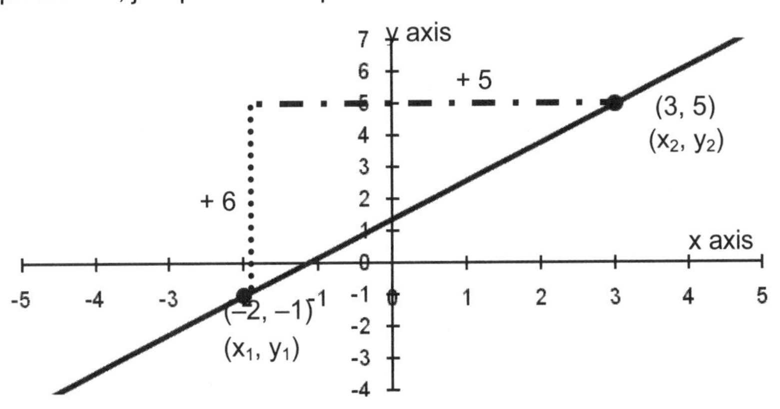

b. Use the formula $m = \frac{y_2 - y_1}{x_2 - x_1}$ to find the slope.

$y_2 = 5$
$y_1 = -1$
$x_2 = 3$
$x_1 = -2$

Explanation: It doesn't matter which y value you choose to equal y_1 as long as you are consistent. If $y_1 = 5$, then x_1 has to be 3. (3, 5) is a point on the graph.

$$m = \frac{y_2 - y_1}{x_2 - x_1} = \frac{5-(-1)}{3-(-2)}$$

$$m = \frac{5+1}{3+2}$$

$m = \frac{6}{5}$, The slope of the line is $\frac{6}{5}$.

Explanation:
$-(-1) = +1$

$-(-2) = +2$

Since the slope is positive, the line is increasing or rising from left to right.

Example 2. Given the graph below, find the slope.

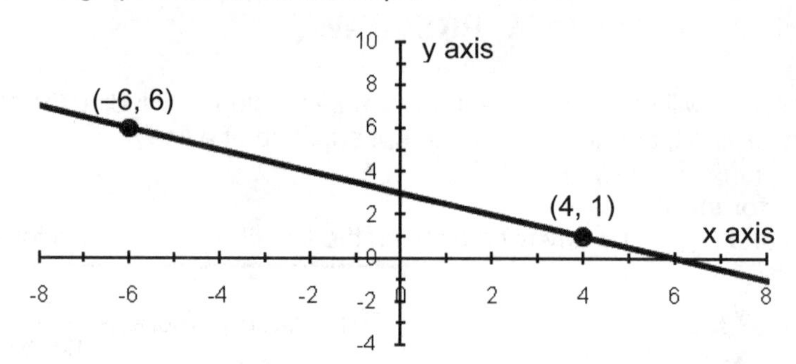

Use the formula $m = \dfrac{y_2 - y_1}{x_2 - x_1}$ to find the slope.

$y_2 = 6$ $\quad y_1 = 1$

$x_2 = -6$ $\quad x_1 = 4$ $\quad m = \dfrac{y_2 - y_1}{x_2 - x_1} = \dfrac{6 - 1}{-6 - 4}$

$$m = \frac{5}{-10}$$

$m = -\dfrac{1}{2}$, The slope of the line is $-\dfrac{1}{2}$.

Since the slope is negative, the line is decreasing or falling from left to right.

Example 3. Graph the line that passes through the two points (–3, 4), (5, 4) and find the slope.

a. To graph the line, just plot the two points.

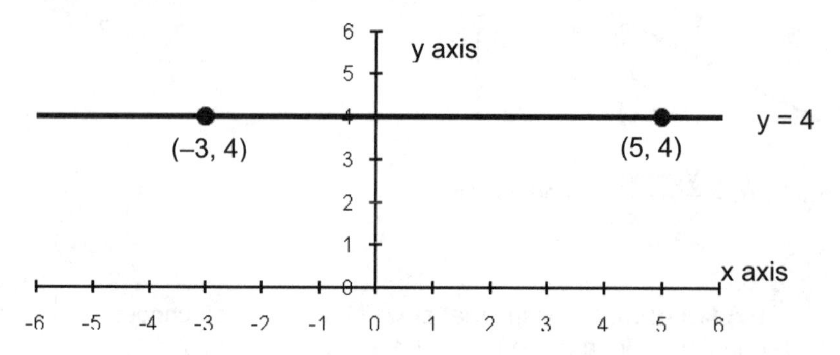

b. Use the formula $m = \dfrac{y_2 - y_1}{x_2 - x_1}$ to find the slope.

$y_2 = 4$ $\quad y_1 = 4$

$x_2 = -3$ $\quad x_1 = 5$ $\quad m = \dfrac{y_2 - y_1}{x_2 - x_1} = \dfrac{4 - 4}{-3 - 5}$

$$m = \frac{0}{-8}$$

$$m = 0$$

The slope of a horizontal line is zero.

Explanation: The slope of a horizontal line is zero because there is no vertical change.

Study Tip: This is an important fact that will be significant in a later section.

Example 4. Graph the line that passes through the two points (3, –4), (3, 2) and find the slope.

a. To graph the line just plot the two points.

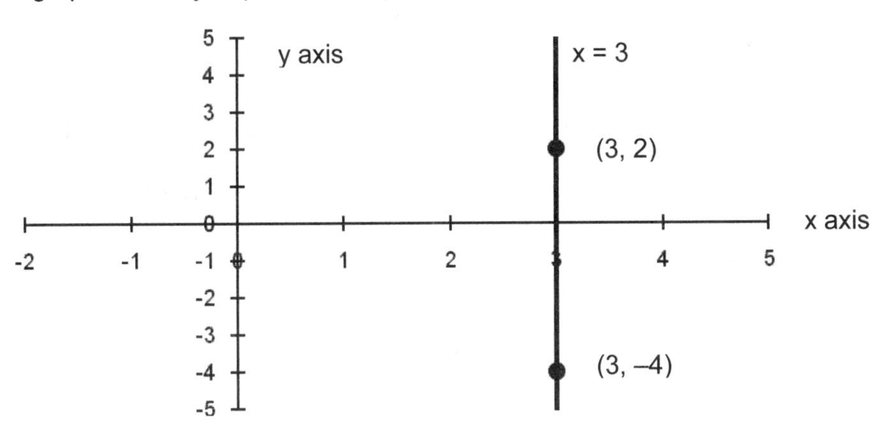

b. Use the formula $m = \frac{y_2 - y_1}{x_2 - x_1}$ to find the slope.

$y_2 = -4 \quad y_1 = 2$

$x_2 = 3 \quad x_1 = 3$

$$m = \frac{y_1 - y_0}{x_1 - x_0} = \frac{-4-2}{3-3}$$

$$m = \frac{-6}{0}$$

The slope of a vertical line is undefined since division by zero is undefined.

The Slope-Intercept Equation of a Line

Vocabulary: The equation **y = mx + b** is called the **slope-intercep**t equation of a line. The coefficient of x, **m**, is the **slope** and **(0, b)** is the **y intercept**. The equation is called a first degree polynomial because x is raised to the first power.

All of the applications in this section are in the form of the **slope-intercept** equation.

Example 5. You need to rent a moving van. Class Movers charges a basic rate of $24.95 plus 32 cents per mile.

This is the basic problem for the first half of the course, and we know the equation relating cost and miles is:

$c = 0.32m + 24.95$

The slope of the line is 0.32 since 0.32 is the coefficient of variable m, miles.

> **Explanation:** The letter m is used differently in the definition than it is used in the application. In the definition, m represents slope. In the example, m is the variable for the number of miles.

The c intercept is (0, 24.95).

Study Tip: y = mx + b is an important equation you need to know. Write it on an index card for further reference. Know that **m** is the slope and **(0, b)** is the y intercept.

Summary: Slope is a fundamental concept in mathematics. It measures how things change.

The basic ideas in this section are:

- The formula for the slope of a line is $m = \dfrac{y_2 - y_1}{x_2 - x_1}$.
- If the slope of a line is positive, then the line is increasing or rising from left to right.
- If the slope of a line is negative, then the line is decreasing or falling from left to right.
- The slope of a horizontal line is zero.
- The slope of a vertical line is undefined.
- In the slope-intercept equation, $y = mx + b$, m is the slope, and $(0,b)$ is the y intercept.

CLASS WORK

Definition: a. $m = \dfrac{\text{Change in } y}{\text{Change in } x}$

b. $m = \dfrac{y_2 - y_1}{x_2 - x_1}$ (x_2, y_2) and (x_1, y_1) are any two points on the line.

Graph the line that passes through the two given points and find the slope of the line.

1. (6, –2) and (5, 7)

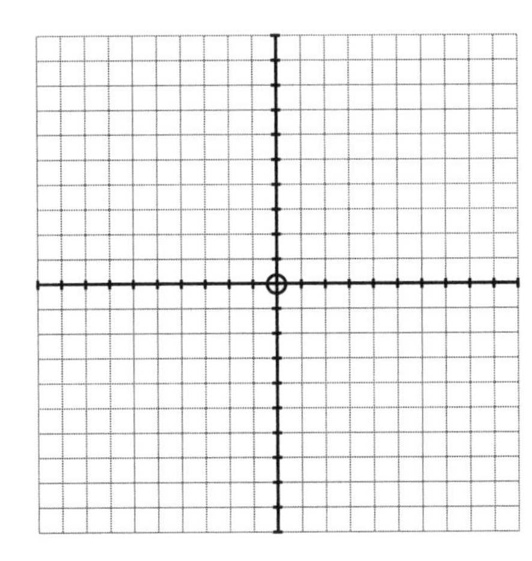

2. (8, 2) and (4, –12)

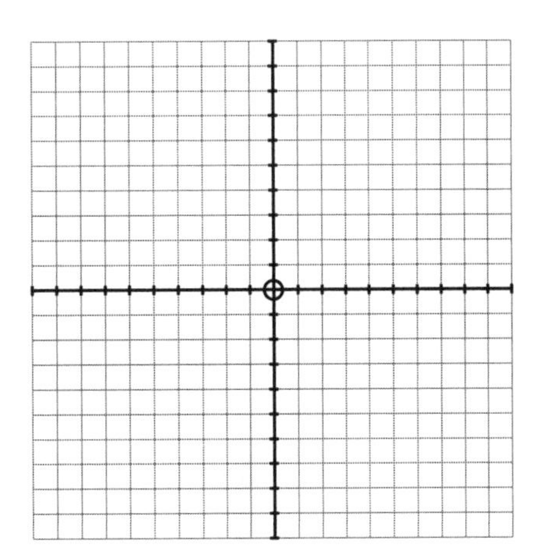

3. (2, 4) and (2, –5)

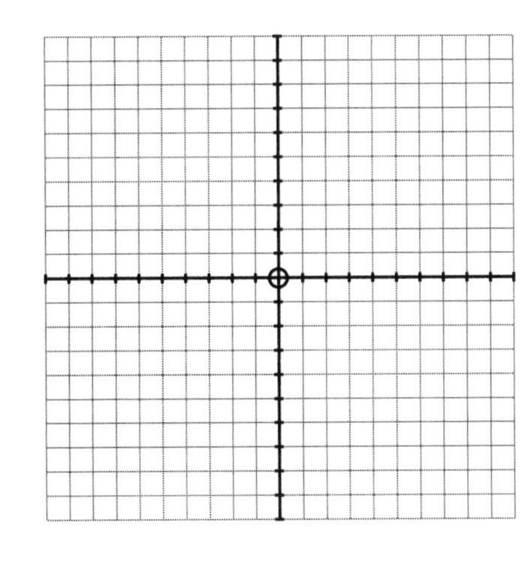

4. (7, –3) and (–2, –3)

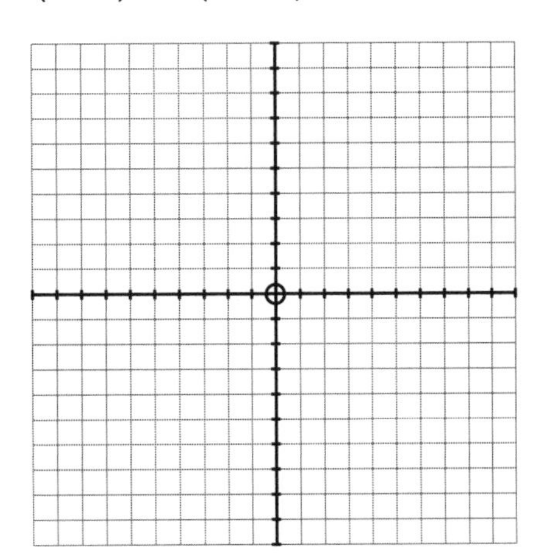

The equation **y = mx + b** is called the slope-intercept equation of a line. The coefficient of x, m, is the slope of the line and (0, b) is the y intercept. The slope and y-intercept are easy to identify because the given line is in the slope-intercept pattern of equation of a line.

5. Identify the slope and y-intercept of the equation of the line. Graph the line.

a. $y = -\frac{3}{4}x - 5$

b. $y = 4x + 5$

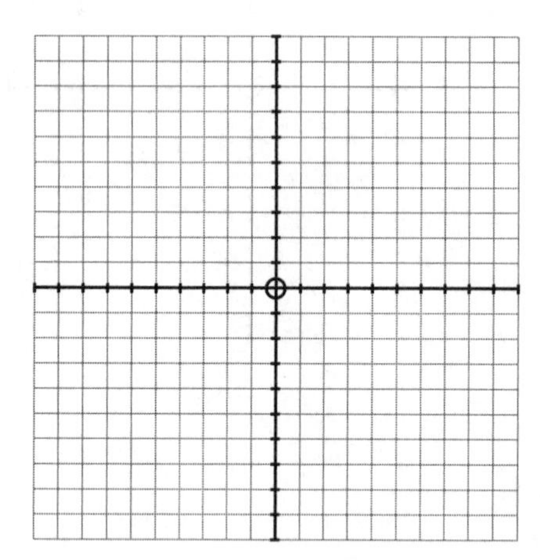

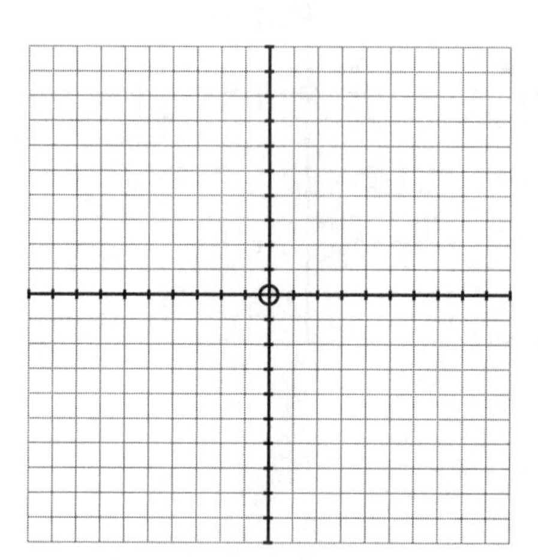

6. Mr. McNab started a lawn-mowing business for the summer. He bought a lawn mower for $350, and he charges $6.50 an hour. The equation that relates profit and hours worked is

$$p = 6.50h - 350$$

Identify the slope and p intercept of the equation above.

Study Tip: New students must learn to budget their time in order to be successful in college. It is especially important when you have a test. See page iv and complete a weekly planner for the week of your second MAT 011 test. Make sure you include three one hour blocks to study for your upcoming MAT 011 test.

GROUP EXERCISE

Study Tips:
1. Discuss the problem. Don't have each person solve it separately.
2. Review the slope formula.
3. Review addition/subtraction of signed numbers.
4. Use one sheet of paper per group.

1. Find the mistake in the problems below. Write a sentence describing the error.

a. (6, 4) and (–7, 2)

$$m = \frac{6-(-7)}{4-2}$$

$$m = \frac{13}{2}$$

b. (–3, 5) and (2, 6)

$$m = \frac{5-6}{2-(-3)}$$

$$m = \frac{-1}{5}$$

c. (4, –2) and (–5, 1)

$$m = \frac{-2-1}{4-5}$$

$$m = \frac{-3}{-1}$$

2. Graph the line that passes through the two points and find the slope of the line.

a. (–1, 5) and (3, –2)

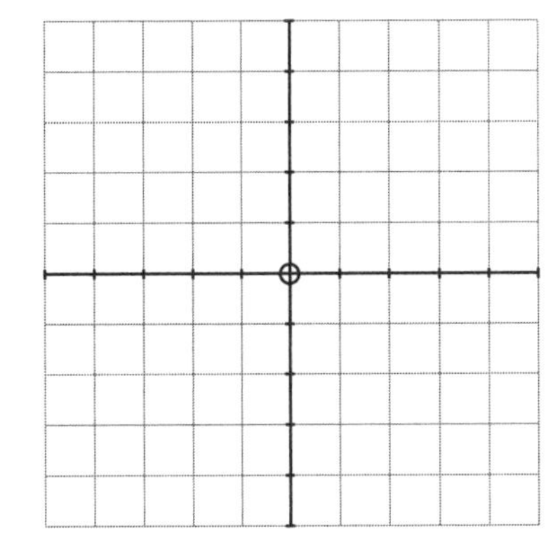

b. (–2, 4) and (5, 4)

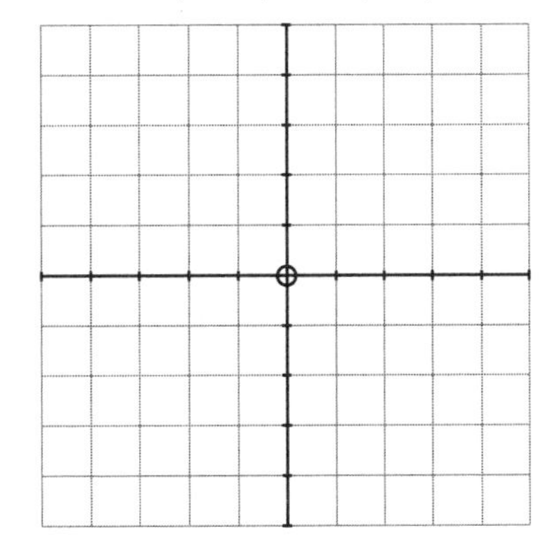

c. Which line is increasing?

d. Which line is decreasing?

HOMEWORK EXERCISES

Go Back: Review group work on page 191.

Skill Building Exercises

1. Simplify the arithmetic problem.

   a. $-2 - 3$ b. $5 - (-4)$ c. $-6 -(-2)$

2. For the point (5, 9), which coordinate is the x coordinate and which is the y?

Practice Exercises

3. Find the slope of the lines.

   a.
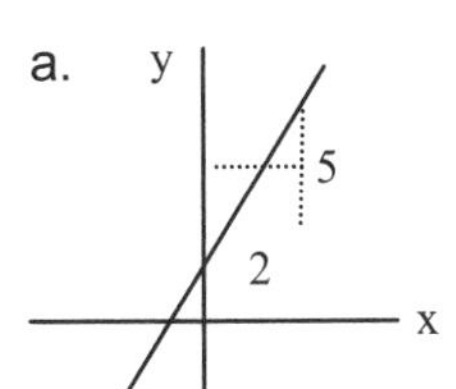

   b.
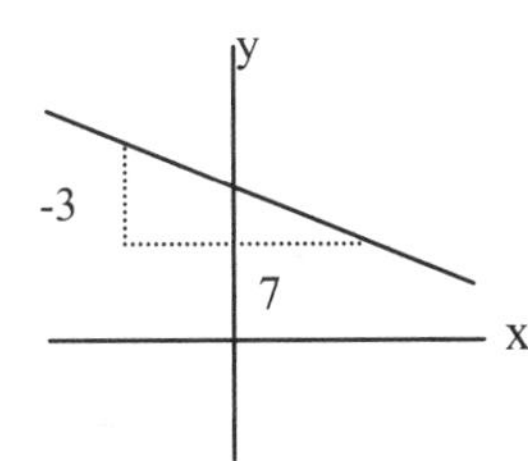

   c.
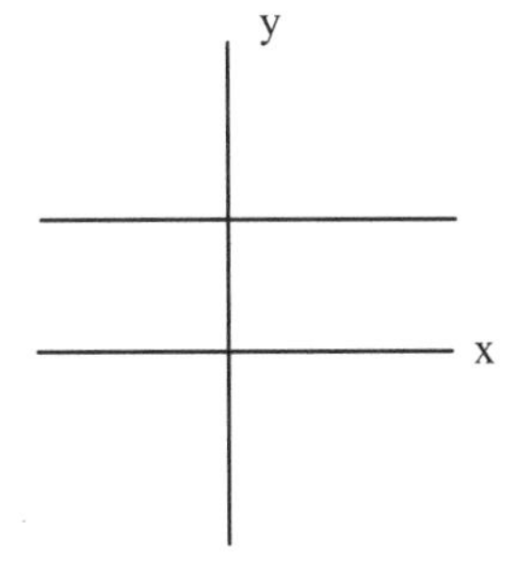

4. Graph the line that passes through the two points and find the slope of the line.

   a. (8, –1) and (–2, 4) b. (3, 5) and (7, 5)

   c. (–3, 1) and (6, 5) d. (6, –2) and (6, 4)

   e. (9, 6) and (–1, –2)

5. Identify the slope and y intercept of the equation of the line.

   a. $y = 7x + 5$ b. $y = \frac{-2}{3}x - 2$

6. The equation $v = -1{,}825t + 73{,}250$ indicates the value of a truck t years after it is purchased

   a. Identify the slope and v intercept. What do they mean in terms of the value of the truck?

   b. Graph the equation.

7. The equation $w = 0.10s + 22{,}000$ indicates the wages of someone who makes 10% commission on sales of an item.

   a. Identify the slope and the w intercept. What do they mean in terms of the wages of the employee?

   b. Graph the equation.

Reading and Writing Mathematics

8. The table below indicates the U. S. Governments yearly deficit or surplus (in billions).

Year	2000	2001	2002	2003	2004
Deficit or Surplus	237	127	-159	-374	-455

Source: Budget of the United States Government

The equation d = –188t + 250 can be used to model or approximate the deficit or surplus. T is the number of years since 2000, and d is the deficit or surplus in billions of dollars.

a. Assume that you are an economist and create a graph of d = –188t + 250 that is very steep by picking an appropriate scale for the vertical or d – axis. The d – axis should go from -600 to 400.

Go Back: See problems 8 and 9 on page 181 and 182.

b. Assume that you are an economist and create a graph of d = –188t + 250 that is flat by picking an appropriate scale for the vertical or d – axis. The d – axis should go from -1,000 to 1,000.

c. What are the slope and d intercept of the line d = –188t + 250? What do they mean? Are they the same as in parts a and b?

d. Write a paragraph about how the scale of a graph can make the slope appear to be large or small.

9. In each problem below, find the **mistake** and write a sentence describing the error. Also, write a suggestion so that any student who makes this type of mistake will have a way to remember not to make the error again.

a. (–6, 1) and (–2, 3)

$m = \frac{1-(-2)}{3-(-6)}$

$m = 3/9$

$m = 1/3$

b. (5, –1) and (3, 7)

$m = \frac{5-3}{-1-7}$

$m = 2/-8$

$m = -1/4$

Study Tip: Don't wait until the night before to study for a test. Begin to review now. The next section is extremely important as it summarizes the material you <u>must</u> <u>know</u> for the test on Chapter 2.

Study Tip: Registration for next semester will begin soon, page viii contains advising information for MAT 011 students.

Study Tip: Detailed solutions to problems 3, 4a, c, e, 5, 7, and 9 can be found on the MAT 011 Electronic Resource page. See page vii.

SECTION 2.9 APPLICATION OF GRAPHS
PREVIEW

Objectives: This section summarizes the course thus far. You will create **tables** to find equations, apply your knowledge of graphing lines by finding the **intercepts** and **plotting points**, interpret **slope**, understand **inequalities** graphically, and **solve equations**.

Vocabulary Review

- **Tables:** A systematic arrangement of information using rows and columns. (Section 1.2 "Introduction to Variables")

- **Solving Equations:** Algebraic technique used to determine the point when two quantities are equal. (Section 1.4 "Solving Equations")

- **Inequalities:** The use of less than (<) and greater than (>) symbols to show relationships. (Section 2.2 "Applications of Inequalities")

- **Plotting Points:** Using numbers generated by the table to graph the line. (Section 2.5: "Graphing Lines by Plotting Points")

- **Intercept:** The point where the graph crosses either the x or y axis. (Section 2.6: "Graphing Lines by Plotting Intercepts")

- **Slope:** (Steepness of a line.) Change in the dependent variable divided by change in the independent variable. Often slope is described by cost per mile or something similar. ("Section 2.7 Introduction to Slope")

Example. You are going to rent a car for a day. You have two choices, Speed Car Rental and Honest Car Rental. Speed charges $18 plus $0.85 per mile while Honest charges $42 plus $0.45 per mile.

a. Develop an equation for the cost of renting a car from Speed.

Miles	**Calculation**	**Cost**
10	$0.85 \bullet 10 + 18$	$26.50
30	$0.85 \bullet 30 + 18$	$43.50
m	$0.85m + 18$	c

Suggestion: By now, you may be able to derive the cost equation by reading the problem. Using descriptive variable names like "m" for the number of miles driven and "c" for cost should help you interpret what the formula means.

The equation for Speed is $\mathbf{c = 0.85m + 18}$.

b. Develop an equation for the cost of renting a car from Honest.

Miles	Calculation	Cost
10	$0.45 \bullet 10 + 42$	$46.50
30	$0.45 \bullet 30 + 42$	$55.50
m	0.45m + 42	c

Suggestion: Instead of making a table, you could have recognized that the cost per mile is multiplied by the variable m, and the flat cost is the constant.

The equation for Honest is **c =0.45m + 42.**

c. Find the intersection of two lines. Label the point.

Study tip: Question c is similar to calculating how many miles you have to drive for the two companies to charge the same. This was covered in Section 1.5 "Applications of Linear Equations."

Step 1. Find the number of miles that result in the same cost.

Cost of Speed = Cost of Honest

0.85m + 18 = 0.45m + 42	Set the cost equations equal to each other.
0.40m+18 = 42	Subtracted 0.45m from both sides.
0.40m = 24	Subtracted 18 from both sides.
m = 60	Divided both sides by 0.40

The two companies charge the same when you drive 60 miles.

Step 2. Find the cost of going 60 miles

Choose one of the equations and plug in 60 for m.
Speed: $C = .85 \bullet 60 + 18$
$C = 69$

Explanation: It doesn't matter which company you choose to substitute 60 for miles; you will get the same cost.

The two lines intersect at (60, 69).

d. Graph both equations on the same set of axes. Label each axis and choose an appropriate scale. Only graph the portion that is relevant to the problem.

Step 1. We need to decide which variable is the independent variable and which is the dependent variable.

Since cost depends on miles, cost is the dependent variable, and miles are the independent variable. So we will write our points as (miles, cost), and our graph will be:

Step 2. Find at least two points for each line, Speed and Honest.

Point 1. From Part c, we know that the lines intersect at (60, 69). This point will be used to graph both lines.

Point 2. Find the cost intercept for Speed and Honest. We find the cost intercept by letting m = 0.

SPEED				HONEST			
Miles	**Calculation**	**Cost**	**Point**	**Miles**	**Calculation**	**Cost**	**Point**
60	$0.85 \bullet 60 + 18$	\$69.0	(60, 69)	60	$0.45 \bullet 60 + 42$	\$69.00	(60, 69)
0	$0.85 \bullet 0 + 18$	\$18.00	(0, 18)	0	$0.45 \bullet 0 + 42$	\$45.00	(0, 42)

Study Tip: 1. Organize your work in tables to see this more easily.

2. Note that the intersection and the intercept for each company are two different points.

Step 3. Plot the points and label the graph.

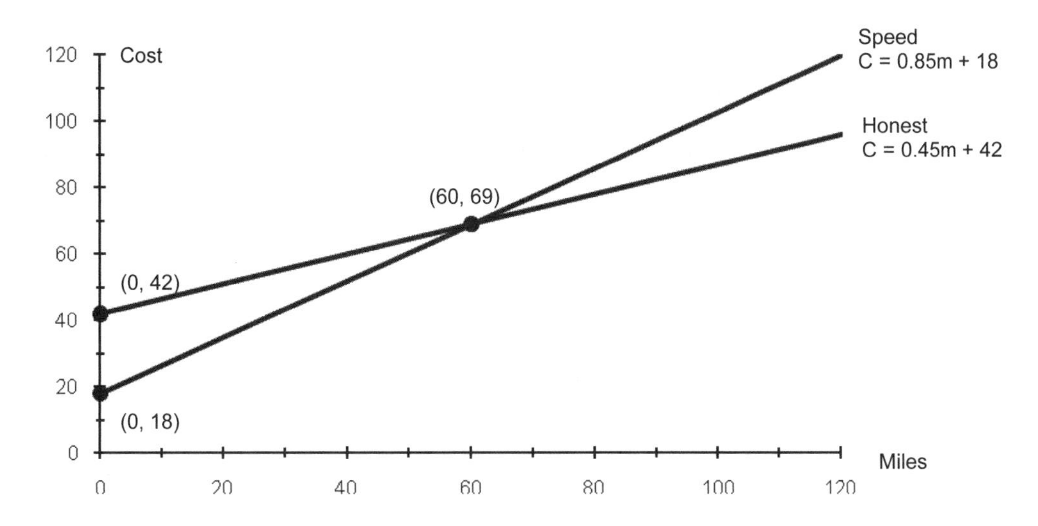

Study Tips 1. You should use graph paper and a ruler when you make a graph.

2. You should use different colored pencils, and you should label each line, the intersection, and the cost intercepts.

e. Use the graph to determine when Speed costs more than Honest.

Speed is more expensive than Honest when the graph of Speed is above the graph of Honest. This is when m is greater than 60, ($m > 60$) . So Speed costs more than Honest when miles is greater than 60.

f. Use the graph to determine when Honest costs more than Speed.

Honest is more expensive than Speed when the graph of Honest is above the graph of Speed. This is when m is less than 60, ($0 < m < 60$). So Honest costs more than Speed between 0 and 60 miles.

g. What do the cost intercepts mean in terms of the problems?

The cost intercept of Speed is where the line for Speed crosses the Cost axis. This is the point (0, 18). The cost of going zero miles is $18.

The cost intercept of Honest is where the line for Honest crosses the Cost axis. This is the point (0, 42). The cost of going zero miles is $42.

h. What does the slope of each line mean in terms of the problem?

We can find the slope of each line by using the **slope-intercept** equation

$$y = mx + b.$$

The number multiplying x (the coefficient) is the slope of the line.

For Speed, $c = 0.85m + 18$, so the slope of the line is 0.85.
For Honest, $c = 0.40\,m + 42$, so the slope of the line is 0.40.

In both cases, the slope of the line is the cost per mile and indicates the steepness of the line and how fast the cost is increasing per mile.

Summary: This section reviews most of the material presented thus far in the course. You should be able to look at the equation

$$c = 0.85m + 18$$

and understand:

a. 0.85 is the **slope** of the line, measures its steepness, and the cost per mile.

b. 18 is the cost **intercept,** and it represents the cost of going 0 miles.

c. **Intersection** and **intercept** are two different terms.

The **intersection** is where two lines cross. The intersection is found by setting the two equations equal to each other and solving algebraically for x (or the independent variable). Then find the y coordinate (or dependent variable) by substituting the solution into one of the equations.

An **intercept** is where the line touches one of the axes. The x intercept of an equation is found by setting y = 0. The y intercept is found by setting x = 0.

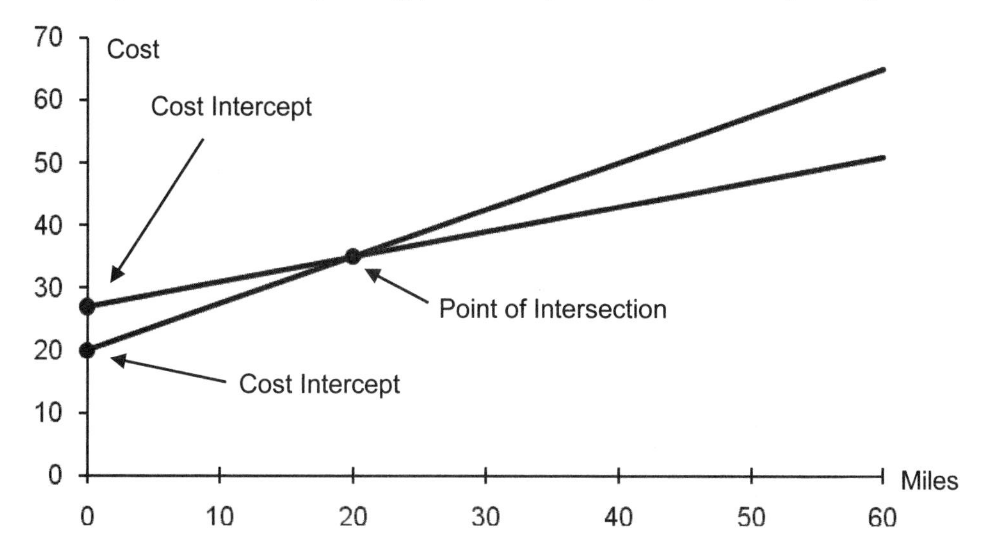

Study tip: Write the definitions of intercept and intersection along with a graph on the same note card so that you realize that they are different.

CLASS WORK

1. Two women want to start a lawn mowing business for the summer. They buy a lawn mower for $400 and plan to charge $8.75 an hour.

    a. Write an equation for the amount of profit they plan to make in terms of the number of hours they work.

    b. Graph the equation. Label your axes and use an appropriate scale. Only graph the portion that is relevant to the problem.

Hours	Profit	(h, P)

c. What is the profit intercept? Label the point on the graph. What does the profit intercept mean? What does it mean in terms of the problem?

d. What is the hour intercept? Label the point on the graph. What does the hour intercept mean? What does it mean in terms of the problem?

e. What is the slope? What does it mean in terms of the problem?

f. Graph the line P = 300. Use the equation to determine how many hours they have to work to make $300.

2. Two companies, ACME and EMAC, offer you very similar sales positions. ACME pays $25,000 a year while EMAC pays $10,000 a year plus 10% commission.

a. Write an equation for your yearly wages from ACME.

Write an equation for your yearly wages from EMAC.

b. Where do the two lines intersect? This is the same as finding the sales amount when each company pays the same, however, you have to also find the wage. Label this point.

c. Graph both equations on the same set of axes. Label your axes and choose an appropriate scale. Only graph the portion that is relevant to the problem.

ACME	**EMAC**
Intersection	
W intercept	

d. Use the graph to determine when ACME pays more than EMAC.

e. Use the graph to determine when EMAC pays more than ACME.

f. What are the wage intercepts for ACME and EMAC? Label the points on the graph. What does the wages intercept mean in terms of the problem?

g. What is the slope for each line? What does the slope of each line mean in terms of the problem?

3. You are going to rent a car for a day. You have two choices, Lemon Car Rental and Go Kart Car Rental. Lemon charges $20 a day and 75 cents a mile while Go Kart charges $27 a day and 40 cents a mile.

   a. Write an equation for the cost of renting a car from Lemon.

      Write an equation for the cost of renting a car from Go Kart.

   b. Where do the two lines intersect? This is the exact problem as finding how many miles you have to drive for the two companies to charge the same, except you have to also find the cost. Label the point.

   c. Graph both equations on the same set of axes. Label each axis and choose an appropriate scale. Only graph the portion that is relevant to the problem.

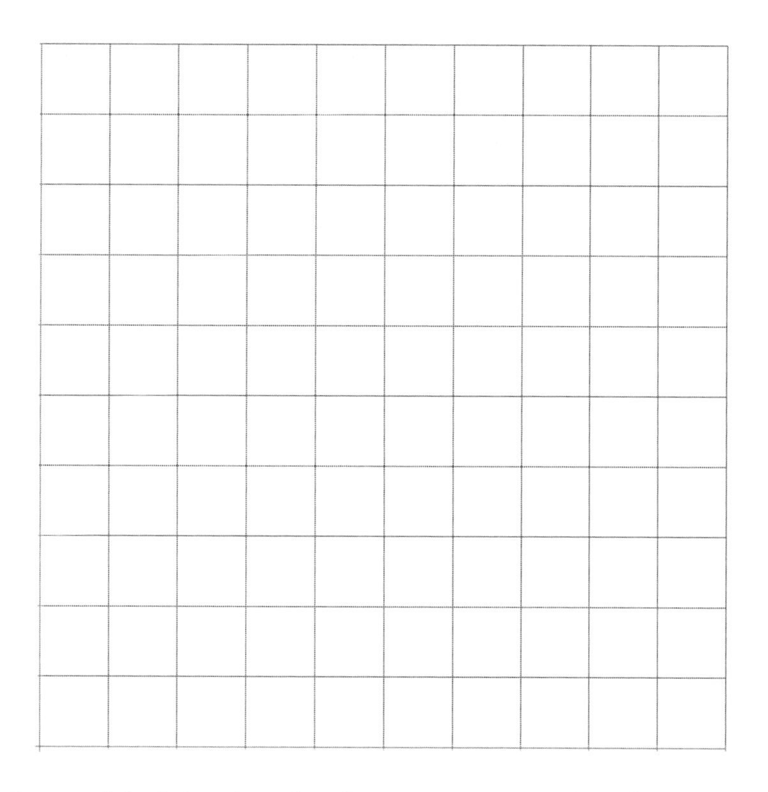

d. Use the graph to determine when Lemon costs more than Go Kart.

e. Use the graph to determine when Go Kart costs more than Lemon.

f. What are the cost intercepts for Lemon and Go Kart? Label the points on the graph. What does the cost intercept mean in terms of the problem?

g. What is the slope for each line? What does the slope of each line mean in terms of the problem?

4. A phone company, DADBELL, charges 75 cents a phone call and 15 cents per minute **after** the first three minutes.

a. Write an equation for the cost of a phone call that lasts longer than 3 minutes.

b. What is the cost of a phone call 2 minutes long?

c. What is the cost of a phone call 1 minute long?

d. What is the cost of a phone call 10 minutes long?

e. What is the equation of a phone call that lasts fewer than 3 minutes?

f. Graph the cost of a phone call. Make sure you include the first three minutes in your graph. Label the axes and choose an appropriate scale.

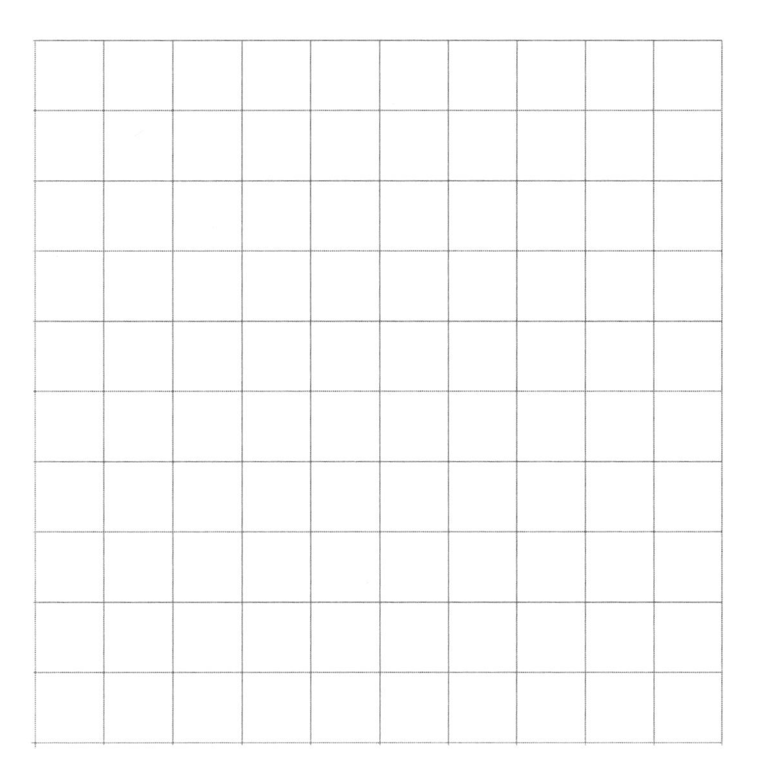

Study Tip: Registration for next semester will begin soon, page viii contains advising information for MAT 011 students.

GROUP EXERCISE

Study Tip: 1. Construct a table for the information.
2. Have all of your graphing materials available.

Two companies offer you a similar sales position. Brisk Inc. will pay you $40,000 a year while Bipton Tea Co. will pay you $18,000 plus 8.8% commission.

a. Write 8.8% as a decimal. Verify with the teacher that you are correct.

b. Write an equation for your yearly wages from Brisk Inc.

Write an equation for your yearly wages from Bipton Tea Co.

c. Where do the two lines intersect? This is the exact problem as finding the sales amount when each company pays the same wage, except you also have to find the wage. Label this point.

d. Graph both equations on the same set of axes. Label your axes and choose an appropriate scale. Only graph the portion that is relevant to the problem. (Graph paper is on the next page.)

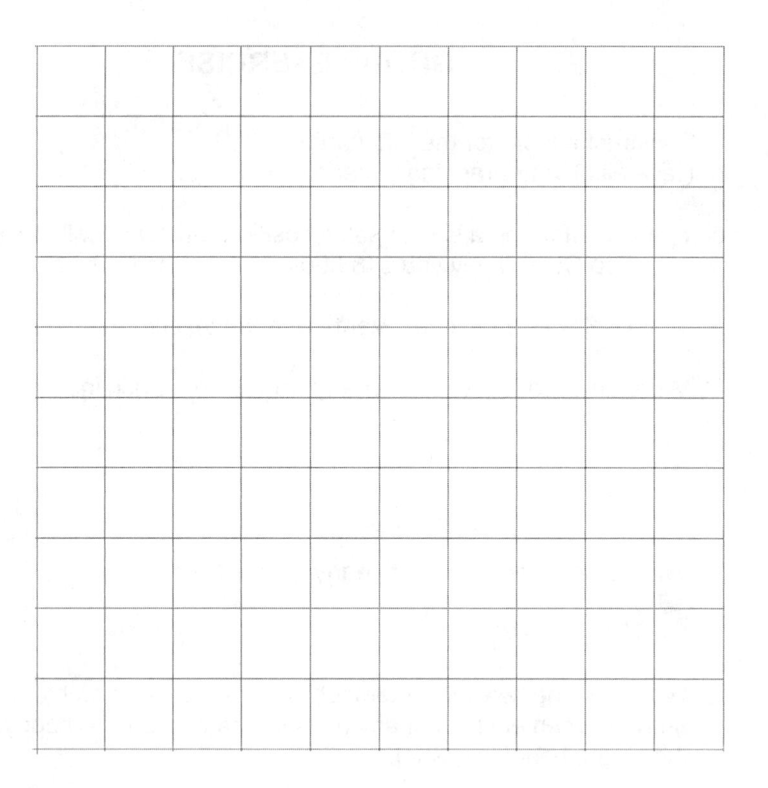

d. Use the graph to determine when Brisk Inc. pays more than Bipton Tea Co.

e. Use the graph to determine when Bipton Tea Co. pays more than Brisk Inc.

f. What are the wage intercepts for Brisk and Bipton? Label the points on the graph. What does the wage intercept mean in terms of the problem?

g. What is the slope for each line? What does the slope of each line mean in terms of the problem?

HOMEWORK EXERCISES

Study Tip: Necessary materials: pencils, colored pencils, ruler, eraser, graph paper, and note cards

Skill Building Exercises

1. Solve $7x + 54 = 3x + 187$

2. For $y = 0.5x + 20$:

   a. What is the slope of the line?

   b. What is the y intercept?

   c. Graph the line.

3. For $y = 15$:

   a. What is the slope of the line?

   b. What is the y intercept?

   c. Graph the line.

4. What is the difference between the intersection of two lines and an intercept of a line?

Practice Exercises

5. Darrel plants sunflower seedlings, each 4 inches tall. With plenty of water and sunlight, they will grow approximately 1.7 inches a day.

   a. Write an equation for the height, h, of the plants in terms of the number of days, d, since they were planted. (If you don't recognize the equation, construct a table.)

   b. Graph the equation. Label your axes and use an appropriate scale. Only graph the portion that is relevant to the problem.

   c. How tall are the sunflowers after two weeks? (14 days)

   d. How tall are the sunflowers after two months? (60 days)

   e. How tall are the sunflowers after four months (120 days)? Why does this not make sense? How can your graph reflect this idea? What additional information would you need?

   f. Use the equation to find out how long it will take before the sunflower is 5 feet tall. Does your answer agree with your graph?

Study Tip: If you are having difficulties with the Practice Exercises, attempt the Reading and Writing Exercises first. Often reviewing the material in a different manner will result in better comprehension. Experiment – see what works for your unique learning style.

6. You are going to rent a car for a day. You have two choices, Golden Car Rental and Classic Car Rental. Golden Car Rental will rent you the car for $35 a day and unlimited mileage while Classic Car Rental will rent you the car for $15 a day plus $0.80 a mile.

a. Write an equation for the cost of renting a car from Golden Car Rental. Write an equation for the cost of renting from Classic Car Rental.

Go Back: 1. Review a similar problem on page 204.
2. Construct tables before deriving equations and before graphing.
3. Remember to use graph paper, ruler, and colored pencils.

b. Use the equation to find the point where the two lines intersect. This is the exact problem as finding how many miles you have to drive for the two companies to charge the same, except you also have to find the cost. Label this point on the graph.

c. Graph both equations on the same set of axes. Label your axes and choose an appropriate scale. Only graph the portion that is relevant to the problem.

d. Use the graph to find when Golden Car Rental is more expensive than Classic Car Rental.

e. Use the graph to find when Classic Car Rental is more expensive than Golden Car Rental.

f. What are the cost intercepts for Golden and Classic? Label the points on the graph. What does the cost intercept mean?

g. What is the slope of each line? What does the slope of each line mean in this problem situation?

Study Tip: Detailed solutions to problems 2, 3, 5, 7, 9, 11, 13 can be found on the MAT 011 Electronic Resource page. See page vii.

7. You have a choice of two cell phone companies, Ringer and Buzz. Ringer charges 50 cents a phone call and 18 cents a minute. Buzz charges 25 cents a phone call and 27 cents a minute.

Go Back: Refer to the example from the Class Work section on page 204.

a. Write an equation for the cost of making a phone call using Ringer. Write an equation for the cost of making a phone call using Buzz. (If you don't recognize the equations, construct a table.)

b. Use the equations to find the point where the two lines intersect. This is the exact problem as finding how many minutes you have to be on the phone for the two companies to charge the same, except you also have to find the cost. Label this point on the graph.

c. Graph both equations on the same set of axes. Label your axes and choose an appropriate scale. Only graph the portion that is relevant to the problem.

d. Use the graph to determine when Ringer is more expensive than Buzz.

e. Use the graph to determine when Buzz is more expensive than Ringer.

f. What are the cost intercepts for Ringer and Buzz? Label the points on the graph. What does the cost intercept mean in terms of the problem?

g. What is the slope of each line? What does the slope of each line mean in terms of the problem?

8. Two companies offer you very similar sales positions, MATHCO and CALCCO. MATHCO will pay $5,000 a year and 8% commission while CALCCO will pay $10,000 a year and 4% commission.

Go Back: Refer to your Group Work notes on page 209 or example 2 on page 202.

a. Write an equation for your yearly wages from MATHCO. Write an equation for your yearly wages from CALCCO.

b. Use the equations to determine where the two lines intersect. This is the exact problem as finding the sales amount where each company pays the same salary, except you also have to find the wage. Label this point on the graph.

c. Graph both equations on the same set of axes. Label your axes and choose an appropriate scale. Only graph the portion that is relevant to the problem.

d. Use the graph to determine when MATHCO will pay more than CALCCO.

e. Use the graph to determine when CALCCO will pay more than MATHCO.

f. What are the wage intercepts for MATHCO and CALCCO? Label the points on the graph. What does the wages intercept mean in terms of the problem?

g. What is the slope of each line? What does the slope of each line mean in terms of the problem?

9. A company has a choice of two copy machines. One, made by Duplicate Company, charges $32,000 for a new copier. This machine depreciates $2,000 a year. A second company, Multiview, charges $42,000 for a new copier. This machine depreciates $3,000 a year. The company is interested in determining which copy machine will have the most value after it is bought. For example the value of the copy machine bought from Duplicate Company one year after purchase is $30,000 (32,000 – 2,000).

a. Write an equation for the value of the copy machine from Duplicate Company. Write an equation for the value of the copy machine from Multiview.

b. Use the equations to determine where the two lines intersect. Find a value for both variables. Label this point on the graph.

c. Graph both equations on the same set of axes. Label your axes and choose an appropriate scale. Find the intercepts. Only graph the portion that is relevant to the problem.

d. Use the graph to determine when the copy machine from Duplicate Company is worth more than the one from Multiview.

e. Use the graph to determine when the copy machine from Multiview is worth more than the one from Duplicate Company.

f. What are the value intercepts for Duplicate Company and Multiview? Label the points on the graph. What does the value intercept mean in terms of the problem?

g. What are the year intercepts for Duplicate Company and Multiview? Label the points on the graph. What does the value intercept mean in terms of the problem?

h. What is the slope of each line? What does the slope of each line mean in terms of the problem?

10. The cell phone company, Hook, charges 50 cents a call and 20 cents per minute **after** the first three minutes.

Go Back: Refer to your notes about example 4 on page 206 from Class Work.

a. Write an equation for the cost of a phone call. (You may need to make a table.)

b. When is the formula in Part a. not valid?

c. What is the cost of a phone call for the first three minutes?

d. Graph the cost of a phone call. Make sure you include the first three minutes in your graph. Label the axes and choose an appropriate scale.

11. A company, Mathematics, Inc., will pay you $10,000 a year plus 10% commission on sales **over** $50,000.

a. Write an equation for your yearly wages. (You may need to make a table.)

b. When is the formula in Part a. not valid?

c. What are your wages if you sell under $50,000 worth of merchandise?

d. Graph your wages for the year. Make sure you include the possibility of selling less than $50,000 worth of merchandise. Label the axes and choose an appropriate scale.

Reading and Writing Mathematics

12. In the problem below, find the **mistakes** and write a sentence describing each error. Also, write a suggestion so that any student who makes this type of mistake will have a way to remember not to make the error again. The student made at least four errors in the problem.

Two companies offer you very similar sales positions, LAXCO and Reality Inc. LAXCO will pay $10,000 a year and 6% commission while Reality Inc. will pay $25,000 a year and 4% commission.

a. Write an equation for your yearly wages from LAXCO. Write an equation for your yearly wages from Reality Inc.

LAXCO: $w = 0.6s + 10{,}000$

Reality Inc $w = 0.4s + 25{,}000$

b. Use the equations to determine where the two lines intersect. This is the same problem as finding the sales amount when each company pays the same wage, except you also have to find the wage. Label this point on the graph.

$0.6s + 10{,}000 = 0.4s + 25{,}000$
$0.2s = 15{,}000$
$s = 75{,}000$

Find w when $s = 75{,}000$
$w = 0.4(75{,}000) + 25{,}000$
$w = 55{,}000$

c. Graph both equations on the same set of axes. Label your axes and choose an appropriate scale. Only graph the portion that is relevant to the problem. (Answering question c before question b may be helpful.)

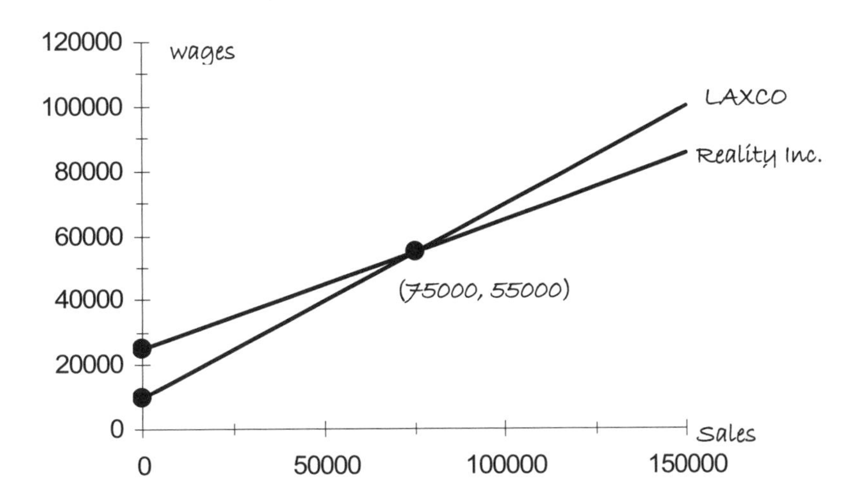

d. Use the graph to determine when LAXCO will pay more than Reality Inc.

LAXCO will pay more than Reality Inc. when $s < 75{,}000$.

e. Use the graph to determine when Reality Inc. will pay more than LAXCO.

Reality Inc will pay more than LAXCO Inc. when $s < 75{,}000$.

f. What are the wage intercepts for LAXCO and Reality Inc.? Label the points on the graph. What does the wages intercept mean in terms of the problem?

(75000, 55000) This is where the two companies will pay the same.

g. What is the slope of each line? What does the slope of each line mean in terms of the problem?

The slope for LAXCO is .6 and for Reality Inc it is .4.
The slope is how much the ir pay increases per year.

13. A classmate asks you to look over her work. The mathematics is correct. Make five suggestions that would improve the presentation of the problem. Review the problem the way an instructor might look at it.

You are going to rent a car for a day. You have two choices, Always Ready Car Rental and Speedy Car Rental. Always Ready charges \$35 a day and \$0.85 a mile while Speedy charges \$45 a day and 0.50 cents a mile.

a. Write an equation for the cost of renting a car from Always Ready.

$0.85m + 35$

Write an equation for the cost of renting a car from Speedy.

$0.50m + 45$

b. Where do the two lines intersect? This is the exact problem as finding how many miles you have to drive for the two companies to charge the same, except you also have to find the cost. Label the point.

$0.85m + 35 = 0.50m + 45$

$0.35m = 10$

$m = 28.57$

c. Graph both equations on the same set of axes. Label each axis and choose an appropriate scale. Only graph the portion that is relevant to the problem. (Answering question c before question b may be helpful.)

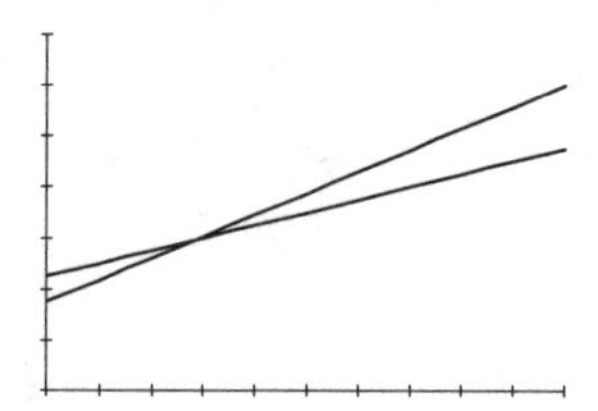

d. Use the graph to determine when Always Ready costs more than Speedy.

$m > 28$

e. Use the graph to determine when Speedy costs more than Always Ready.

$M < 28$

f. What are the cost intercepts for Always Ready and Speedy? Label the points on the graph. What does the cost intercept mean in terms of the problems?

Always Ready: 35, Speedy: 45

It is the cost of going zero miles.

g. What is the slope for each line? What does the slope of each line mean in terms of the problem?

Always Ready: .85, Speedy: .5

It is the cost per mile.

CHAPTER 2 REVIEW

This unit interprets algebra and inequalities graphically. You should be able to read a problem and construct a graph that displays all of the important features of the problem.

Section 2.1 Inequalities:

Solving equations of inequalities is similar to solving traditional algebraic equations except, when you multiply or divide by a negative, you must change the direction of the inequality symbol.

Example 1. Solve. $12 - 3x \le 27$

$$-3x \le 15$$
$$x \ge -5$$

Some inequality equations have three parts. The variable is to be isolated in the middle.

Example 2. Solve. $-5 \le 7 + 2x < 15$

$$-12 \le 2x < 8$$
$$-6 \le x < 4$$

When graphing inequalities on the number line use a shaded circle, •, for $\le$ or $\ge$ and an open circle, ○, for $<$ or $>$.

Example 3. Graph $-4 \le x < 3$.

-6 -4 -2 0 2 4

Section 2.2 Applications of Inequalities:

Inequalities interpret phrases like “more than” and “less than” in mathematical models studied in the previous unit.

Example 4. The equation C=0.12m+.40 represents the cost of making a long distance phone call. M is the number of minutes on the phone. If the cost was more than \$1.25 and less than \$1.40, how long were you on the phone?

$$1.25 < C < 1.40$$
$$1.25 < 0.12m + .40 < 1.40$$
$$.85 < 0.12m < 1.00$$
$$7.08 < m < 8.333$$

If the phone call cost between \$1.25 and \$1.40, then you were on the phone between 7.08 minutes and 8.333 minutes.

Section 2.3 Plotting Plots:

Important vocabulary words:

The **independent variable** is the one represented by the first column of a table and is the horizontal axis. In equations involving x and y, x is the independent variable.

The **dependent variable** is the one represented by the last column of the tables and is the vertical axis. In equations involving x and y, y is the dependent variable.

Since there are two variables on our graph, we must be consistent in how we describe a point on the graph. An **ordered pair** describes this point. It always has the form (independent variable, dependent variable) or in a nonapplication problem (x, y).

Example 5. The equation $c = 0.12m + 0.40$ represents the cost of making a long distance phone call. M is the number of minutes on the phone.

Construct a table.

Minutes	Calculation	Cost
10	$0.12 \bullet 10 + 0.40$	\$1.60
20	$0.12 \bullet 20 + 0.40$	\$2.80
30	$0.12 \bullet 30 + 0.40$	\$4.00
m	$0.12 \bullet m + 0.40$	c

Since the cost of making a phone call depends on how long you were on the phone, c is the dependent variable, and m is the independent variable.

An ordered pair will have the form (m, c).

The graph has the form

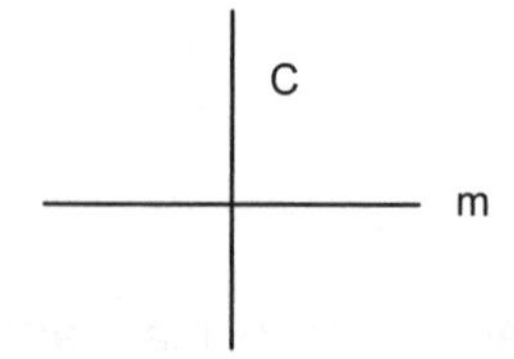

Section 2.4 Interpreting Graphs:

The important features of a graph are:

- **Vertex:** The high or low point.
- **Intercept:** The point at which the graph crosses the horizontal or vertical axis.
- **Intersection:** The point where two graphs meet.
- **Slope:** Measures the steepness of a line of the average rate of change.

Section 2.5 Graphing Lines By Plotting Points:

Use the points from a table to generate a graph.

Example 6. A math textbook company, Calculate Inc., offers you a job selling textbooks. They pay \$15,000 plus 9% commission. Complete the table below and make a graph of your possible wages.

Sales	Calculation	Wages
50,000	$0.09 \bullet 50,000 + 15,000$	19,500
100,000	$0.09 \bullet 100,000 + 15,000$	24,000
200,000	$0.09 \bullet 200,000 + 15,000$	33,000
S	$0.09S + 15,000$	W

Graph the points (50000, 19500), (100000, 24000), and (200000, 33000).

Choosing the scale of the graph:

For the Sales axis:

Start at zero and go past \$200,000. Perhaps \$250,000.
Count by ten thousands.

For the Wages axes:

Start at zero and go past \$33,000. Perhaps \$40,000.
Count by five thousands.

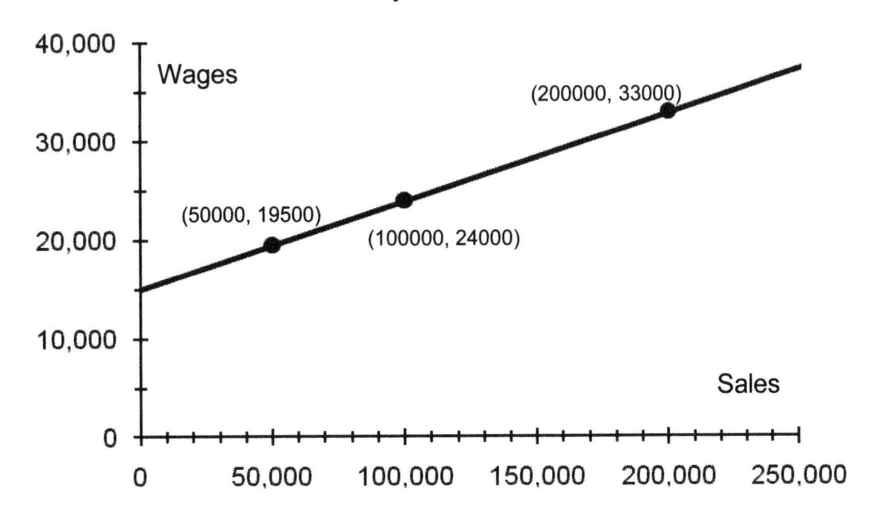

Section 2.6 Graphing Lines by Finding Their Intercepts:

To find the x intercept, set y = 0.
To find the y intercept, set x = 0.

Example 7. Graph $0.02x + 30y = 15$

Find the x intercept; set y = 0.

$$0.02x + 30 \bullet 0 = 15$$
$$0.02x = 15$$
$$x = 750$$

The x intercept is (750, 0).
Find the y intercept; set x = 0.

$$0.02 \bullet 0 + 30y = 15$$
$$30y = 15$$
$$y = 0.5$$

The y intercept is (0, 0.5).

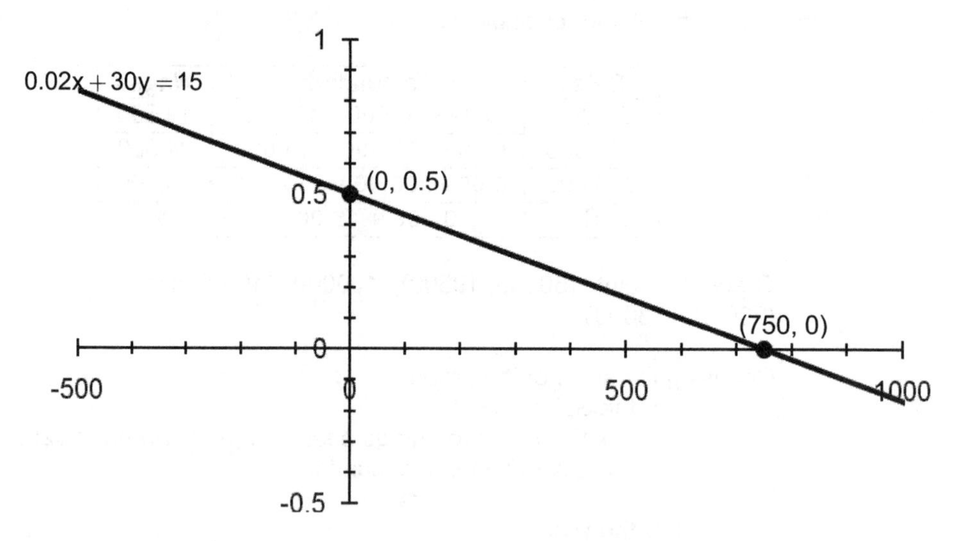

Section 2.7 Introduction to Slope:

Slope measures how quantities change. Slope is:

- $\frac{\text{Change in Dependent Variable}}{\text{Change in Independent Variable}}$
- $\frac{\text{Vertical Change}}{\text{Horizontal Change}}$
- $\frac{\text{Rise}}{\text{Run}}$

- Slope measures the steepness of a line.
- Slope is the average rate of change.
- If the slope of the line is negative, then the line is decreasing left to right.
- If the slope of the line is positive, then the line is increasing left to right.

Percent Change also measures how a quantity changes. The formula for Percent Change is:

$$\text{Percent Change} = \frac{\text{New - Old}}{\text{Old}} \bullet 100$$

Example 8. Use the information in the table below to answer the questions.

Year	Number of Radio Stations with a Jazz Format
1999	243
2001	213

a. Find the average rate of change.
(This is the same as the slope of a line.)

Year is the independent variable, and number of stations is the dependent variable.

$$\text{Average Rate of Change} = \frac{213-243}{2001-1999}$$

Average Rate of Change = –15.

On the average, there was a decrease of 15 radio stations per year.

b. Find the percent change.

$$\text{Percent Change} = \frac{\text{New - Old}}{\text{Old}} \bullet 100$$

$$\text{Percent Change} = \frac{213 - 243}{243} \bullet 100$$

$$\text{Percent Change} = -12.35$$

The number of jazz radio stations decreased by 12.35% between 1999 and 2001.

Section 2.9 Slope:

The algebraic formula for slope is $m = \frac{y_2 - y_1}{x_2 - x_1}$.

The slope of a horizontal line is zero.

The slope of a vertical line is undefined.

The slope-intercept equation is y = mx + b.

Example 9. Find the slope of the line that contains the points (–3, 5) and (2, –1).

$$m = \frac{5-(-1)}{-3-2}$$

$$m = \frac{-6}{5}$$

The slope of the line is $\frac{-6}{5}$ or –1.2.

Section 2.9 Applications of Graphs:

This section summarizes the major concepts of the course thus far.

Example 10. You need to rent a moving van. One company, Quick Movers, charges a basic rate of \$24.95 plus \$0.32 a mile. A second company, Silver Glove Movers, charges a basic rate of \$19.95 plus \$0.40 a mile.

The equations are: Quick: $c = 0.32m + 24.95$
Silver: $c = 0.40m + 19.95$

To find where the two lines intersect:

$$0.40m + 19.95 = 0.32m + 24.95$$
$$0.40m = 0.32m + 5.00$$
$$0.08m = 5.00$$
$$m = 62.5$$

Find C when m = 62.5.

$$c = 0.32 \bullet 62.5 + 24.95$$
$$c = 44.95$$

The two lines intersect at (62.5, 44.95).

Explanation: You can use either company's equation.

Graph the two equations.

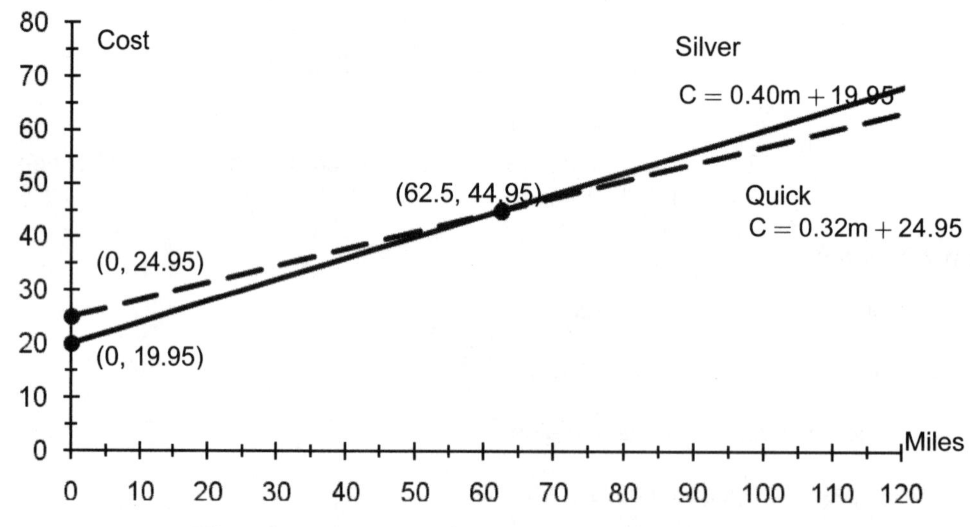

Silver Co. costs more if you drive over 62.5 miles.
Quick costs more if you drive under 62.5 miles.

The cost intercept of Quick is (0, 24.95). It will cost you \$24.95 to drive nowhere.

The slope of $c = 0.40m + 19.95$ is 0.40. Silver company charges 40 cents per mile.

Study Tips:

1. Make sure you have done all of the homework exercises.
2. Practice the review test starting on the next page by placing yourself under realistic exam conditions.
3. Find a quiet place and use a timer to simulate the class length.
4. Write your answers in your homework notebook or make a copy of the test. You may then re-take the exam for extra practice.
5. Check your answers. The answers to the review test are on page 465.
6. There is an additional exam available on the Beginning Algebra web page, **www.mc3.edu/aa/career/MATHSCI/mathprog/mat011/mat011.htm**
7. Review often. Do NOT wait until the night before to study.

CHAPTER 2 REVIEW TEST

1. Solve and graph each solution on the number line.

   a. $8x - 3 \le 7$ b. $4 - 2x \ge -2$ c. $-3 \le 7x - 15 < 10$

2. An electric company has a fleet of trucks. The annual operating cost per truck is

$$c = 0.26m + 3{,}100$$

where m is the number of miles traveled in a year.

   a. How many miles can a truck travel in a year and still cost less than $4,000 to operate?

   b. How many miles can a truck travel in a year and still cost between $3,500 and $5,000 to operate? (You must set up an inequality and then solve it.)

Study Tip: Detailed solutions to all the problems can be found on the MAT 011 Electronic Resource page. See page vii.

3. The following table shows the temperature, in Celsius, of a frozen dinner while it is in the freezer, taken out to defrost, cooked in the oven, and served at the table. The food was removed from the freezer at t = 0 min.

Time in Minutes	Temperature Celsius
–15	–10°
0	–10°
10	-5°
20	3°
25	23°
30	45°
35	90°
50	125°
60	160°
65	90°
70	55°
75	40°

a. Make a graph of temperature versus time. Make sure you label your axes and choose an appropriate scale. (Use graph paper.)

b. Approximately when do you think the frozen dinner was placed in the oven?

c. When do you think the frozen dinner was taken out of the oven?

d. From the graph, approximately when was the frozen dinner 100°?

4. Graph the lines.

a. $y = -4$

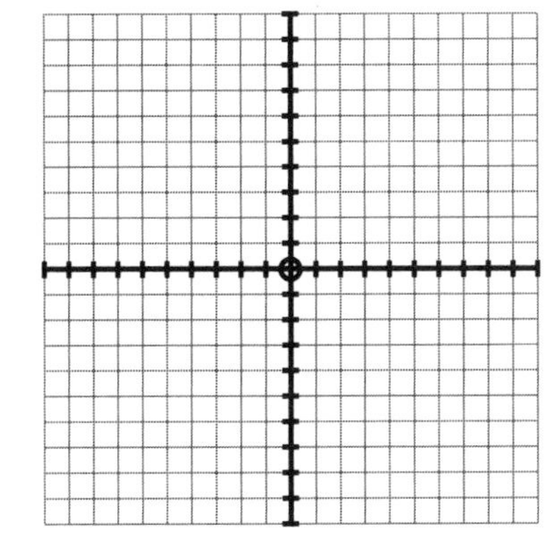

b. $x = 7$

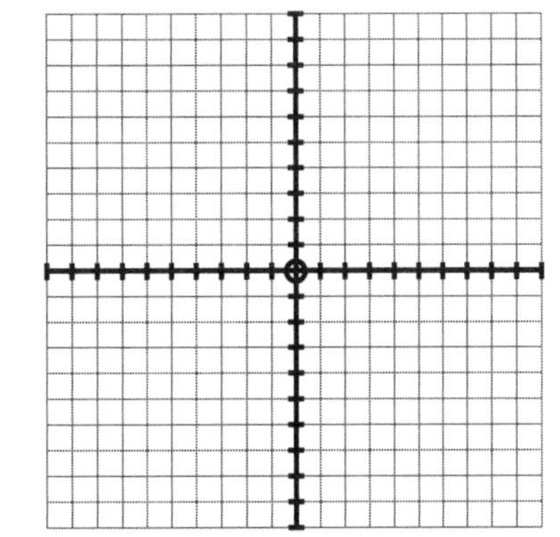

5. Find the **x and y intercepts** and graph the following lines. Label your axes and choose an appropriate scale.

a. $y = 0.1x + 210$

b. $76x + 2y = 4$

c. $4x + 7y = 20$

d. $y = \frac{4}{3}x + 8$

6. SITUATION: The following diagram shows the temperature in Frostburg, Maryland, for a typical December day. The temperature is a function of the time of day.

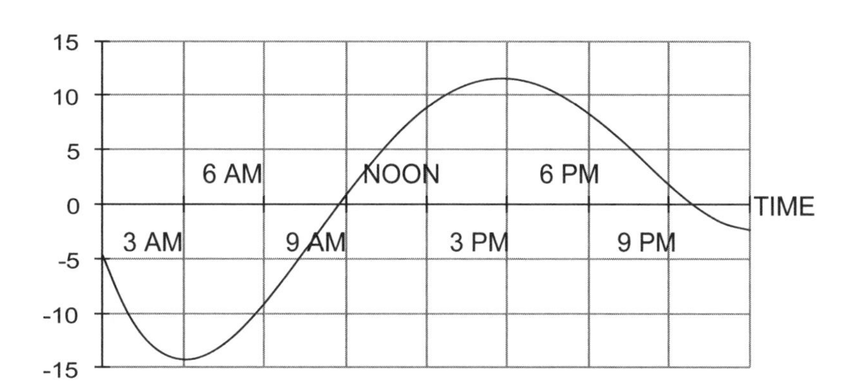

For each of the following questions, list the coordinates of the point(s) that give the answer. Then write your answer in a sentence. Estimate where necessary.

a. What was the temperature at 3 a.m.?

b. What was the temperature at 9 p.m.?

c. When was the temperature –7°C?

d. When was the temperature 5°C?

e. What was the maximum temperature, and when did it occur?

f. What was the minimum temperature, and when did it occur?

g. When was the temperature rising?

h. When was the temperature falling?

Study Tip: If you don't remember how to do a problem, review an example similar to the one which is giving you difficulty.

7. Use the table to answer the following questions.

Year	Millions of Tons of Corn Produced in Nebraska
1980	62.4
1984	78.5

a. Find the average rate of change of corn produced in Nebraska between 1980 and 1984.

b. Find the percent increase of corn produced in Nebraska between 1980 and 1984.

c. Find the slope of the line created by the data.

8. Given the equation, find the slope and y the intercept.

a. $y = -3x + 7$

b. $y = 0.15x - 6$

9. Graph the line indicated by the two points. Find the slope of the line containing the two points. Check that the slope agrees with whether the line is increasing or decreasing.

a. $(5, -8)$ and $(-3, 5)$

b. $(2, 6)$ and $(-9, 6)$

10. P.M.A. offers you a sales position. They pay 10% commission plus $20,000 a year. The equation that models this situation is $w = 0.10S + 20000$. W is your wages for the year, and S is the dollar amount of your sales.

a. What is the slope of the line? What does the slope mean in terms of the problem?

b. If you don't sell anything for P.M.A., how much money will you make for the year? If you were to graph this point, what would it be called?

11. In the problem below, find the **mistake** and write a sentence describing the error.

Graph the equation $y = 4x + 12$ by finding the intercepts.

Pick $x = 3$, $y = 4(3) + 12$ Pick $x = -2$, $y = 4(-2) + 12$ Pick $x = 5$, $y = 4(5) + 12$

$y = 24$ $y = 4$ $y = 32$

(3, 24) (-2, 4) (5, 32)

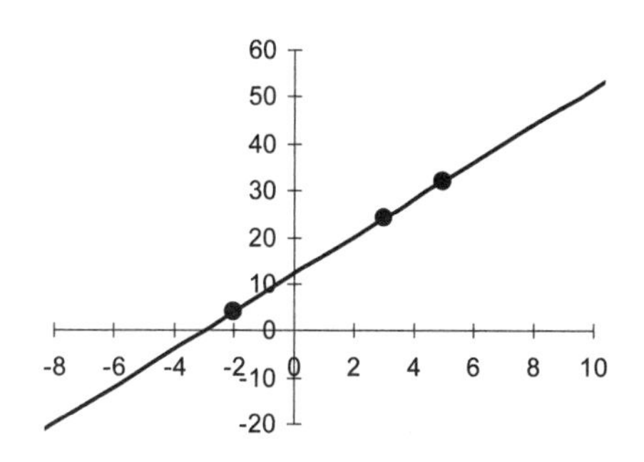

12. You want to rent a car for a day. Limo will charge you $32.00 for the day while Ultra will charge you $19 for the day plus 26 cents a mile.

a. Write an equation for the cost of renting a car from Limo. Write an equation for the cost of renting a car from Ultra.

b. Use the equations to find where the two lines intersect. This is the same question as finding how many miles you have to drive for the two companies to charge the same; however, you have to also find the cost. Label this point on the graph.

c. Graph both equations on the same set of axes. Label your axes and choose an appropriate scale. Only graph the portion that is relevant to the problem.

d. Use the graph to find when Limo is more expensive than Ultra.

e. Use the graph to find when Ultra is more expensive than Limo.

f. What are the cost intercepts for Limo and Ultra? Label the points on the graph. What do the intercepts mean in terms of renting a car?

g. What is the slope of each line and explain what each means in terms of the problem.

CHAPTER 3

EXPONENTS AND ALGEBRAIC FRACTIONS

SECTION 3.1 INTRODUCTION TO POSITIVE EXPONENTS PREVIEIW

Objectives: In this section, you will define exponents and perform computations with a calculator. In addition, you will solve problems using the formula for compound interest and tables for demonstrating bacteria growth to illustrate the applications of exponents.

Vocabulary: $\mathbf{b^n}$ means **b** times itself **n** times; **b** is called the **base** and **n** is called the **exponent**.

Example 1. Write 3^5 using the definition of exponents.

Three is the base and five is the exponent.

$3^5 = 3 \bullet 3 \bullet 3 \bullet 3 \bullet 3$

Example 2. Use a calculator to compute the following.

The exponent key for the TI-30x II S, the recommended calculator for the course, is ^. For other calculators, the exponent key is y^x. The explanation below is for the TI-30x II S.

a. 7.6^8

Type 7.6, then the ^ key. Press 8 and ENTER =

$7.6^8 = 11{,}130{,}347.87$

b. -6.2^4

Use the (–) key. Press 6.2, then the ^ key. Press 4 and ENTER =

$-6.2^4 = -1{,}477.6336$

c. $(-6.2)^4$

Use the (key then the (–) key; press 6.2,) key, then the ^ key. Press 4, and ENTER =

$(-6.2)^4 = 1{,}477.6336$

Explanation: Why is -6.2^4 negative while $(-6.2)^4$ is positive?

$-6.2^4 = -1 \bullet 6.2 \bullet 6.2 \bullet 6.2 \bullet 6.2$
Recall the order of operations: compute exponents before multiplication.
So -6.2^4 means $(-1) \bullet 6.2^4$.

$(-6.2)^4 = (-6.2) \bullet (-6.2) \bullet (-6.2) \bullet (-6.2)$
A negative times a negative four times is positive. Generally any number raised to an even power will be positive.

d. -5.6^3

$-5.6^3 = -175.616$

e. $(-5.6)^3$

$(-5.6)^3 = -175.616$

Explanation: Why are both answers negative?
$-5.6^3 = (-1) \bullet 5.6 \bullet 5.6 \bullet 5.6$

$(-5.6)^3 = (-5.6) \bullet (-5.6) \bullet (-5.6)$
A negative times a negative three times is negative. Generally, a negative number raised to an odd power will be negative.

Study Tip: Parentheses often make a difference in the answer. Make a note card showing examples with and without parentheses and with even and odd exponents. Review the card as homework.

For many transactions, interest is added to the principal, the amount invested, at regular time intervals, so that the interest itself earns interest. Examples of accounts that use compound interest are: savings accounts, certificates of deposit, savings bonds, and money market accounts.

Example 3. When the interest is compounded monthly, the formula below computes how much money will be in your account at sometime in the future.

$$F = P(1 + i)^n$$

where: F is Future value
P is amount invested or Principal
i is interest rate per month
n is the number of times compounded

a. If you invest $3,500 at an annual interest rate of 6%, how much money will you have after 20 years?

Make a table of the information and variables in the problem.

Variables	Values
F	What you need to find.
P	$3,500
i	$\frac{0.06}{12} = 0.005$
n	$20 \bullet 12 = 240$

Explanation:
You need to divide 0.06 by 12 because annual interest is per year and the formula is per month.

You need to multiply 20 by 12 because there are 12 months in a year.

Substitute the values into the formula, $F = P(1 + i)^n$.

$F = 3{,}500(1 + 0.005)^{240}$	Substituted the values into the variables.
$F = 3{,}500(1.005)^{240}$	Added inside parentheses.
$F = 3{,}500(3.310)$	Computed the exponent.
$F = 11{,}585$	Multiplied.

You will have $11,585 in twenty years.

b. How much money should you invest at an annual interest rate of 3% if you want $15,000 in 10 years?

Make a table of the information and variables in the problem.

Variables	Values
F	15,000
P	What you need to find.
i	$\frac{0.03}{12} = 0.0025$
n	$10 \bullet 12 = 120$

Substitute the values into the formula, $F = P(1 + i)^n$.

$15,000 = P(1+.0025)^{120}$	Substituted the values into the variables.
$15,000 = P(1.0025)^{120}$	Added inside parentheses.
$15,000 = P(1.349)$	Computed the exponent.
$11,119.35 = P$	Divided both sides by 1.349.

You need to invest $11,119.35 now in order to have $15,000 in ten years.

Example 4. There are 5,000 bacteria initially present in a culture. The culture grows at a rate of 8% each day. Find an equation that relates number of bacteria and days.

a. First find how many bacteria will be present one day later?

The number of bacteria present one day later is equal to the initial amount plus how many grew in one day or the increase.

Number of bacteria = Initial amount + increase
= 5,000 + 0.08(5,000) The increase is 8% of 5,000.
= (**1**)(5,000) + 0.08(5,000) **1** means 100% of the initial amount
= $5,000 \bullet 1.08$

The new amount of bacteria is all of the initial amount, 100%, plus 8% of the initial amount or 108% of the initial amount.

$$5,000 \bullet 1.08 = 5,400.$$

5,400 is 108% of 5,000.

There are 5,400 bacteria after one day.

b. How many bacteria will be present two days later?

The number of bacteria two days later is equal to 108% of the of the number of bacteria present one day later, or

Number of bacteria = 108% of 5,400.	
$= 1.08 \bullet 5,400$	
$= 1.08 \bullet (1.08 \bullet 5,000)$	Replaced 5,400 with $5,000 \bullet 1.08$
$= 5,000 \bullet 1.08^2$	Replaced $1.08 \bullet 1.08$ with 1.08^2
$= 5,832$	

There will be 5,832 bacteria two days later.

c. How many bacteria will be present three days later?

Number of bacteria = 108% of 5,832.	
$= 1.08 \bullet 5,832$	
$= 1.08 \bullet (1.08^2 \bullet 5,000)$	Replaced 5,832 with $5,000 \bullet 1.08^2$
$= 1.08^3 \bullet 5,000$	Replaced $1.08 \bullet 1.08^2$ with 1.08^3
$= 6,299$	

There will be 6,299 bacteria three days later.

d. Use the results from above to complete the table below.

Time	Calculation	Number Of Bacteria
Initial day		5,000
1 day later	$5,000 \bullet 1.08$	5,400
2 days later	$5,000 \bullet 1.08^2$	5,832
3 days later	$5,000 \bullet 1.08^3$	6,299
4 days later	$5,000 \bullet 1.08^4$	6,802
N days later	$5,000 \bullet 1.08^n$	B

Explanation: The results from parts a, b, and c were inserted into the calculation column. This suggests the pattern that on the fourth day the number of bacteria is found by computing 5,000 times 1.08 raised to the fourth power.

e. What is the equation that relates the number of bacteria to time?

$B = 5,000 \bullet 1.08^n$, where n is the number of days.

f. Use the equation to calculate the number of bacteria present after 35 days.

$B = 5,000 \bullet 1.08^{35}$	Substitute 35 into n.
$B = 5,000 \bullet 14.79$	Compute the exponent.
$B = 73,950$	Multiply.

There will be 73,950 bacteria in 35 days.

Study Tip: It is important to see the logic of the calculation column.

Summary: Not everything grows at a constant rate as shown in Chapter 2. In this section, we examined what happens when something grows exponentially. Savings accounts, populations, and radioactive decay all change in this way. Equations with the variable as an exponent model this behavior. Such equations are called exponential equations.

Vocabulary: b^n means **b** times itself **n** times; **b** is called the **base** and **n** is called the **exponent**.

When computing exponents:

Know why -6.7^8 is negative.

Know why $(-6.7)^8$ is positive.

Know why the answer doesn't change if the exponent is odd whether or not you have parentheses.

Know how to use your calculator.

Know the logic of how the equation in Example 4 was derived.

CLASS WORK

1. What is the definition of an exponent?

2. Compute the following using a calculator.

a. $(-6)^2$

b. $(-8.2)^4$

c. 7^0

d. -6^2

e. -8.2^4

f. 8.6^0

g. $(-3.1)^3$

h. -3.1^3

Compound Interest For many transactions, interest is added to the principal, the amount invested, at regular time intervals, so that the interest itself earns interest. Examples of accounts that use compound interest are: savings accounts, certificates of deposit, savings bonds, and money market accounts.

3. Assuming that the interest is compounded monthly, the formula below computes how much money will be in your account at sometime in the future.

$$F = P(1 + i)^n$$

where: F is Future Value
P is amount invested or principal
i is interest rate per month
n is the number of months

a. A couple invests $2000 at an annual interest rate of 12%. How much money will they have after 10 years?

b. How much money should you invest now at an annual interest rate of 6% if you want $10,000 twenty years in the future?

4. a. An orange growing on a tree weighs 8 grams and is increasing in weight by 1% per day. Complete the table below.

Compute the weight of the orange 1 day later.

Compute the weight of the orange 2 days later.

DAY	CALCULATION	WEIGHT
Initial		8 gm
1 day later		
2 days later		
3 days later		
4 days later		
d days later		

b. What is the equation that relates the weight of the orange and days?

c. Use the equation to find the weight of the orange in 25 days.

5. a. Six milliliters of a drug are injected into the bloodstream. After one hour, 75% of the original amount remains in the bloodstream. For each succeeding hour, 75% of the new amount present remains in the bloodstream. Complete the table below.

Hour	CALCULATION	Milliliters
Initial		6 ml
1 hour later		
2 hours later		
3 hours later		
4 hours later		
h hours later		

b. What is the equation that relates the amount of the drug to the number of hours in the bloodstream?

c. Use the equation to calculate the number of milliliters in the blood stream after 6 hours?

Study Tip: Many students find Chapter 3 to be the hardest chapter in the course. For this reason, you must follow all of the Note Taking Tips on page 27 and Homework Suggestions on page 15, **and** create Weekly Time Sheets that are presented on page v.

GROUP EXERCISE

1. There are 2,000 bacteria present initially in a culture. The culture grows at 13% each day.

Go Back: Review example 4 on page 235 or problem 4 on page 239. Without disturbing the class, do this table on the board. Ask the teacher first.

a. Complete the table.

TIME	CALCULATION	NUMBER OF BACTERIA
Initial Day		2000
1 Day Later		
2 Days Later		
3 Days Later		
4 Days Later		
n Days Later		

b. What is the equation that relates number of bacteria to time?

c. Use the equation in 1b to find how many bacteria there will be in

1) 15 days

2) 20 days

d. Use the table below to find out when there will be 16,000 bacteria.

TIME (GUESS)	CALCULATION	NUMBER OF BACTERIA	TOO LOW/ TOO HIGH

HOMEWORK EXERCISES

Study Tip: Review pertinent note cards first.
Refer to Appendix C and MAT 011's web page to learn how to use the TI-30x IIS calculator.

Skill Building Exercises

1. Compute the following without using a calculator.

a. $(-3)(-3)$ b. $-(3 \bullet 3)$

Practice Excercises

2. Use a calculator to compute the following.

a.	6^5	b.	7.82^3	c.	8.51^4
d.	0.6^7	e.	0.25^4	f.	0.37^5

3. Use a calculator to compute the following. First decide if the answers should be positive or negative.

a.	$(-6)^2$	b.	$(-7.4)^6$	c.	$(-3.2)^4$
d.	$(-8.1)^2$	e.	$(-6.8)^4$	f.	$(-2.4)^8$
g.	-8.2^2	h.	-6.7^4	i.	-2.5^2
j.	-6^3	k.	$(-6)^3$	l.	-7^5
m.	$(-7)^5$	n	$(-0.9)^3$	o.	$(-0.4)^6$

4. Many MAT 011 students take AST 120, Introduction to Astronomy, to satisfy their science requirement at MCCC. The following problem comes from AST 120.

The formula below is used to approximate a star's luminosity (the total amount of energy a star radiates in 1 second) in terms of the sun's luminosity:

$$L = M^{3.5}$$

M is called solar mass and L is luminosity of a star in terms of the sun's luminosity. For example, the luminosity of a star two times the mass of the sun, M = 2 and $L = 2^{3.5}$ or 11.3. So the luminosity of a star with twice the mass of the sun will be 11.3 times the luminosity of the sun.

a. Approximate the luminosity of a star five times the mass of the sun. (M = 5.)

b. Approximate the luminosity of a star half the mass of the sun. (M = 0.5)

5. There are 1000 bacteria present initially in a culture. The culture grows at 5% each day.

Go Back: Review example 4 on page 235 or problem 4 on page 239.

a. Complete the table.

TIME	CALCULATION	NUMBER OF BACTERIA
Initial day		1000
1 day later	1000(1.05)	1050
2 days later		
3 days later		
4 days later		
n days later		

b. What is the equation that relates number of bacteria to time?

c. Use the equation in 4b. to calculate how many bacteria there will be 20 days later. (Round to the nearest whole number.)

d. Use the equation in 4b. to calculate how many bacteria there will be 40 days later. (Round to the nearest whole number.)

e. Use the table below to estimate when there will be 2000 bacteria.

TIME (GUESS)	CALCULATION	NUMBER OF BACTERIA	TOO LOW/ TOO HIGH

6. 14 milliliters of a drug are injected into the bloodstream. After one hour, 60% of the original amount remains in the bloodstream. For each succeeding hour, 60% of the new amount present remains in the bloodstream.

a. Complete the table below.

Hour	CALCULATION	Milliliters
initial		14 ml
1 hour later		
2 hours later		
3 hours later		
4 hours later		
h hours later		

b. What is the equation that relates the amount of the drug to the number of hours in the bloodstream?

c. Use the equation to calculate the number of milliliters in the blood stream after 8 hours?

d. Use the table below to estimate when there will be 4 milliliters in the bloodstream.

HOUR (GUESS)	CALCULATION	MILLILITERS	TOO HIGH/ TOO LOW

7. Assuming that the interest is compounded monthly, the formula below computes how much money will be in your account at sometime in the future.

$$F = P(1 + i)^n$$

where: F is Future Value
P is the amount invested or principal
i is the interest per period
n is the number of times compounded

a. Find the Future Value of a $1,000 deposit if the annual rate is 8% compounded monthly for 20 years. $(\text{Hint: } i = 0.08/12,\ n = 12 \bullet 20)$

b. Find the Future Value of a $3,000 deposit if the annual rate is 7.5% compounded monthly for 10 years. $(\text{Hint: } i = 0.075/12,\ n = 12 \bullet 10)$

c. Determine how much money must be invested today at an annual rate of 6% compounded monthly if the sum of $15,000 is desired fifteen years from now. (Hint: $i = 0.06/12$, $n = 12 \bullet 15$)

d. Determine how much money must be invested today at an annual rate of 7.5% compounded monthly if the sum of $10,000 is desired 20 years from now. ($i = 0.075/12$, $n = 12 \bullet 20$)

e. Use the table below to calculate how long it will take for $5,000 to grow to $15,000 if it is invested at an annual rate of 9.5% compounded monthly. (Hint: $i = 0.095/12$)

GUESS N	$\mathbf{5000(1+0.007917)^n}$	**TOO HIGH/TOO LOW (COMPARE TO 15,000)**
10 months		

Reading and Writing Mathematics

8. Explain why $(-5)^6$ is positive and -5^6 is negative.

9. Explain the difference between $-b^n$ and $(-b)^n$

10. For what values of b will b^n be larger than b? Only consider $b > 0$.

11. For what values of b will b^n be smaller than b? Only consider $b > 0$.

12. A friend from class asks how you got $1000(1.05^2)$ in the second line of the table from Practice exercise 5. Write a paragraph explaining your answer.

13. For the problem below, describe each step.

    Assuming that the interest is compounded monthly, the formula below computes how much money will be in your account at some time in the future.

$$F = P(1 + i)^n$$

    where: F is Future Value
    P is the amount invested or principal
    i is the interest per period
    n is the number of times compounded

    Determine how much money must be invested today at an annual rate of 8% compounded monthly if the sum of $20,000 is desired fifteen years from now. (Hint: $i = 0.08/12$, $n = 12 \bullet 15$)

    $20{,}000 = P(1 + 0.006667)^{180}$ ________________________

    $20{,}000 = P(1.006667)^{180}$ ________________________

    $20{,}000 = P(3.307)$ ________________________

    $6{,}048 = P$ ________________________

Study Tip: Detailed solutions to problems 3 a, c, e, g, I, k, m, o, 5, 6, 7a, c, e, 12 can be found on the MAT 011 Electronic Resource page. See page vii.

SECTION 3.2 NEGATIVE EXPONENTS AND SCIENTIFIC NOTATION PREVIEW

Objectives: This section will introduce negative exponents and scientific notation. We will use negative exponents to compute monthly mortgage payments. Scientific notation is used to write very large or very small numbers in a convenient and informative way especially by health professionals, scientists and engineers.

Vocabulary: A base with a **negative exponent** must be changed to its reciprocal to make the exponent positive.

$b^{-n}=\frac{1}{b^n}$ or

$\frac{1}{b^{-n}}=b^n$

> **Explanation:** Two numbers are **reciprocals** if their product is one.
>
> The reciprocal of $\frac{8}{3}$ is $\frac{3}{8}$

Example 1. Compute 5^{-2} using the definition and a calculator and.
(The explanation is for the TI-30X II S calculator.)

By the definition: $5^{-2}=\frac{1}{5^2}$

$=\frac{1}{25}$

$=0.04$

With your calculator: Press 5, the exponent key ^, the opposite key (−), and then 2, ENTER = .

$5^{-2}=0.04$

Example 2. Compute the following using your calculator.

a. -4.2^{-6}

Start with the opposite key (−), press 4.2, ^, (−), 6, ENTER = .

$-4.2^{-6}=-0.0001822$

b. $(-4.2)^{-6}$

Start with the parentheses key (; then enter –4.2, close parentheses, then enter the exponent, ^, (−), 6 and ENTER =.

$(-4.2)^{-6}=0.0001822$

Parts a and b illustrate the importance of parentheses when you have even exponents.

c. 0.24^{-5}

$0.24^{-5}=1{,}256$

If the base is less than one and the exponent is negative, then the answer will be large.

Example 3. Use the following formula to find the monthly payment of a loan.

$$P = A\left[\frac{i}{1-(1+i)^{-n}}\right]$$

P is the monthly payment

A is the amount of the loan

n is the number of monthly payments
i is the interest rate per month

Find the monthly payments on a 48-month car loan of $14,500 at 3% annual interest.

Make a table of the information and variables in the problem.

Variables	Values
P	What you need to find.
A	$14,500
i	$\frac{0.03}{12} = 0.0025$
n	48

Explanation: All the problems in this section are given as annual interest and monthly payments. You will always need to divide the interest rate by 12.

Substitute values into the formula $P = A\left[\frac{i}{1-(1+i)^{-n}}\right]$.

$$P = 14{,}500\left[\frac{0.0025}{1-(1+0.0025)^{-48}}\right]$$ Substituted values into the formula.

$$P = 14{,}500\left[\frac{0.0025}{1-(1.0025)^{-48}}\right]$$ Added inside the parentheses.

$$P = 14{,}500\left[\frac{0.0025}{1-0.8871}\right]$$ Computed the exponent.

$$P = 14{,}500\left[\frac{0.0025}{0.1129}\right]$$ Simplified the denominator by subtracting.

$$P = 14{,}500 \bullet 0.0221$$ Divided to obtain 0.0221.

$$P = 320.45$$ Multiplied to obtain 320.45.

The monthly payments are $320.45.

Study Tip: You do not have to memorize the formula to find the monthly payment. You do need to know how to use the formula.

Scientific Notation: Scientific notation indicates very large or extremely small numbers conveniently.

Example 4. How far can you see at night?

The farthest object that can be seen with the naked eye from North America is in the Andromeda Galaxy. The Andromeda Galaxy is 2,300,000 light years away. A light year is 10,000,000,000,000 kilometers. To answer the question, multiply the two numbers together. The zeros are can be confusing. Writing the numbers in scientific notation eliminates the need to write all the zeros.

$10{,}000{,}000{,}000{,}000 = 1.0 \bullet 10^{13}$ in scientific notation.

$2{,}300{,}000 = 2.3 \bullet 10^{6}$

The farthest you can see at night is

$(1.0 \bullet 10^{13})(2.3 \bullet 10^{6}) = 2.3 \bullet 10^{19}$ km.

Scientific notation is an easy way to indicate the answer.

Vocabulary: A number is in **scientific notation** if it is in the form

$$P \bullet 10^{n}$$

where $1 \leq P < 10$ and n is an integer.
An integer is one of the following numbers ….–3, –2, –1, 0, 1, 2, 3, …..

The idea of scientific notation is based on our number system being base 10. Consider the number 2,453.9678

Each digit has its own value depending on its position.

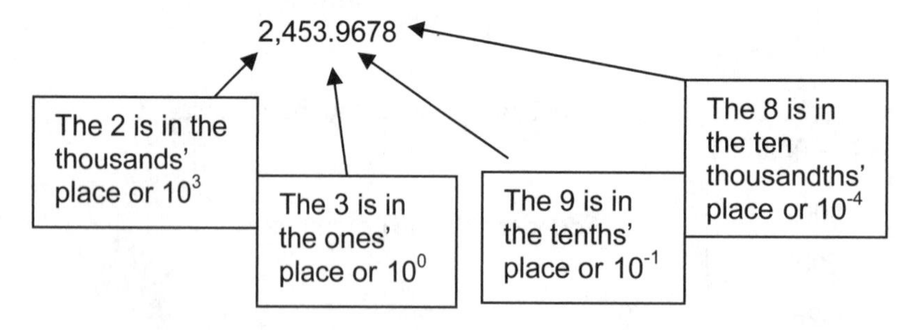

Example 5. Convert each number to scientific notation.

a. 2,340,000,000

Using the definition above, P = 2.34.
The 2 is in the 10^{9} place. Remember that the ones' place (the first zero) is 10^{0}.
$2{,}340{,}000{,}000 = 2.34 \bullet 10^{9}$

b. 0.0000967

Using the definition above, P = 9.67.
The 9 is in the 10^{-5} place. Remember that the first zero to the right of the decimal point is 10^{-1}.
$0.0000967 = 9.67 \bullet 10^{-5}$

Example 6. Convert from scientific notation to decimal notation.

a. $5.97 \bullet 10^6$

The 5 is in the 10^6 place.
$5.97 \bullet 10^6 = 5,970,000$

b. $2.53 \bullet 10^{-6}$
The 2 is in the 10^{-6} place.
$2.53 \bullet 10^{-6} = 0.00000253$

Example 7. Use your calculator to multiply $(6.732 \bullet 10^8)(4.67 \bullet 10^{12})$.

We use the EE command to enter a scientific notation number into your calculator. This key is equivalent to $\bullet 10$.

The EE compand is located above the x^{-1} button, use the 2nd EE x^{-1} keys

To enter the number $6.732 \bullet 10^8$, type 6.732, then the EE command, EE x^{-1} key, followed by the exponent, 8.

The display in your calculator should look like $6.732_{X10}8$.

Repeat the process for $4.67 \cdot 10^{12}$.

$(6.732 \bullet 10^8)(4.67 \bullet 10^{12}) = 3.144 \bullet 10^{21}$

Summary: Negative exponents and scientific notation play key roles in the fields of business and science. You must feel comfortable manipulating these principles to solve very important practical problems.

Remember:

A base with a negative exponent must be changed to its reciprocal to make the exponent positive..

$$a^{-n} = \frac{1}{a^n} \text{ or } \frac{1}{a^{-n}} = a^n$$

Scientific notation is in the form of $P \bullet 10^n$ where $1 \leq P < 10$ and n is an integer.

To enter a number in scientific notation into your calculator, use the EE command, the EE x^{-1} key.

Study Tip: Record on notecards the keys for computing exponents on your calculator and the key to compute arithmetic with numbers in scientific notation. For the TI-30x II S, the ^ is used to compute exponents, and the EE x^{-1} is used for scientific notation.

CLASS WORK

1. What does a negative exponent mean?

2. Use a calculator to compute the following.

   a. 8^{-2}

   b. -6^{-4}

   c. $(-6)^{-4}$

   d. 0.08^{-5}

3. Use the following formula to find the monthly payment of a loan.

$$P = A\left[\frac{i}{1-(1+i)^{-n}}\right]$$

P is the monthly payment
A is the amount of the loan
n is the number of monthly payments
i is the interest rate per month

   a. Find the monthly payments on a 48-month car loan of $18,000 at 3% annual interest. (Hint i = 0.03/12).

b. The Clintons can afford a $1,000 monthly payment for a house. They find a loan for 7.2% annual interest rate for 360 months. What price home can they afford? (Hint: i = 0.072/12)

$$P = A\left[\frac{i}{1-(1+i)^{-n}}\right]$$

P is the monthly payment
A is the amount of the loan
n is the number of monthly payments
i is the interest rate per month

A number in **scientific notation** has the form

$$P \bullet 10^{n}$$

where $1 \leq P < 10$ and n is an integer.

4. Write the number in scientific notation.

a) 8,200,000

b) 0.000517

c) The weight of an oxygen atom is 0.000000000000000000000026561 grams. Write this weight in scientific notation.

5. Write the number in decimal form.

a) $7.3 \bullet 10^{6}$

b) $3.141 \bullet 10^{-4}$

c) $8.14 \bullet 10^{3}$

6. Use your calculator to compute the following.

a) $(6.3 \bullet 10^{8})(4.2 \bullet 10^{9})$

b) $\dfrac{2.8 \bullet 10^{-5}}{8.6 \bullet 10^{-3}}$

c. Light travels at a rate of 1.86×10^{5} miles per second. How far does light travel in a day? (There are 8.64×10^{4} seconds in a day.)

d. The distance from the sun to the earth is 93,000,000 miles. How long does it take for the light of the sun to reach the earth? Recall that light travels at a rate of 1.86×10^{5} miles per second.

GROUP EXERCISE

1. Compute the following using your calculator

   a. 2^{-4} b. -2^{-4} c. $(-2)^{-4}$

2. Use the following formula to find the monthly payment of a loan.

$$P = A\left[\frac{i}{1-(1+i)^{-n}}\right]$$

P is the monthly payment

A is the amount of the loan

n is the number of monthly payments
i is the interest rate per month

Go Back: Review problem 3 on page 252 or example 3 on page 249.

   a. Find the monthly payments on a 36-month car loan of $7,800 at 4% annual interest. (Hint: i = .04/12)

   b. Eddie Nerder can afford a $250 car payment at 6% annual interest for 36 months. What price is the price of the car he can he afford? (Hint: i = .06/12)

3. The average amount of water flowing past the mouth of the Amazon River is 4.2×10^6 cubic feet per second. How much water flows past in a day?
(Hint: there are 8.64×10^4 seconds in a day.)

Names for Large Numbers

1×10^{3} = 1 thousand

1×10^{6} = 1 million

1×10^{9} = 1 billion

1×10^{12} = 1 trillion

1×10^{15} = 1 quadrillion

1×10^{18} = 1 quintillion

1×10^{21} = 1 sextillion

1×10^{24} = 1 septillion

1×10^{27} = 1 octillion

1×10^{30} = 1 nonillion

1×10^{33} = 1 decillion

1×10^{36} = 1 undecillion

1×10^{39} = 1 duodecillion

1×10^{42} = 1 tredecillion

1×10^{45} = 1 quattuordecillion

1×10^{48} = 1 quindecillion

1×10^{51} = 1 sexdecillion

1×10^{54} = 1 septendecillion

1×10^{57} = 1 octodecillion

1×10^{60} = 1 novemdecillion

1×10^{63} = 1 vigintillion

1×10^{66} = 1 unvigintillion

1×10^{69} = 1 duovigintillion

1×10^{72} = 1 trevigintillion

1×10^{75} = 1 quattuorvigintillion

1×10^{78} = 1 quinvigintillion

1×10^{81} = 1 sexvigintillion

1×10^{84} = 1 septenvigintillion

1×10^{87} = 1 octovigintillion

1×10^{90} = 1 novemvigintillion

1×10^{93} = 1 trigintillion

1×10^{96} = 1 untrigintillion

1×10^{99} = 1 duotrigintillion

1×10^{100} = 1 googol

HOMEWORK EXERCISES

Study Tips: Refer to Appendix C and the MAT 011 web page to learn how to use the TI-30x IIS calculator.

Skill Building Exercises

1. Compute the following using your calculator.

   a. 2^4 b. -2^4 c. $(-2)^4$

Practice Exercises

2. Compute the following using your calculator.

   a. 8^{-3} b. 3.1^{-2} c. $\left(\frac{1}{5}\right)^{-4}$ d. -3^{-4}

   e. $(-3)^{-4}$ f. -8^{-3} g. $(-8)^{-3}$ h. 0.2^{-5}

3. Compute using your calculator.

   a. $(3.8\text{x}10^5)(6.2\text{x}10^7)$ b. $\frac{8.7\text{x}10^{-3}}{2\text{x}10^5}$ c. $(7.3\text{x}10^{-8})(9.3\text{x}10^{20})$

4. Use the following formula to find the monthly payments of a loan.

   Payment of debts $$P = A\left[\frac{i}{1-(1+i)^{-n}}\right]$$

   P is the monthly payment
   A is the amount of the loan
   n is the number of monthly payments
   i is the interest rate per month

   a. Find the monthly payments on a 36-month auto loan of $25,000 at 15% annual interest compounded monthly. (Hint: i = 0.15/12)

   b. Jackson Pollock can afford a $300 a month car payment at 12% annual interest for 36 months. What price car can he afford? (Hint: i = 0.12/12, find A.)

   c. Find the monthly payments of a 30-year home mortgage of $100,000 at 9% annual interest compounded monthly. (Hint: i = 0.09/12, and *n* = 30(12).)

   d. The Bushes can afford a $1,000 monthly mortgage payment for a house. How large a 15-year mortgage can they afford at 8% annual interest compounded monthly. Hint: i = 0.08/12 and *n* = 15(12). Suppose they have a 30-year mortgage?

Go Back: Refer to problem 3b on page 252 for help with part d.

5. Write each number in scientific notation.

   a. 78,000 b. 0.00000167 c. 0.00635 d. 1,160,000

6. Write each number in decimal notation.

   a. $7.86 \bullet 10^8$ b. $8.673 \bullet 10^{-10}$ c. $3.3 \bullet 10^{-2}$ d. $2.032 \bullet 10^4$

7. The distance light travels in 1 year is 9.460×10^{12} kilometers. Write this number in decimal notation.

8. A beam of light travels 9.460×10^{12} kilometers in one year. How far does it travel in 10,000 years?

Reading and Writing Mathematics

9. Describe the steps in the problem below.

   Use the following formula to find the monthly payment of a loan.

$$P = A\left[\frac{i}{1-(1+i)^{-n}}\right]$$

   P is the monthly payment

   A is the amount of the loan

   n is the number of monthly payments
   i is the interest rate per month

   If a couple can afford a $320 monthly car payment on a five year loan, what price can they afford at 6% annual interest?

   i = 0.06/12 n = 5(12)
   i = 0.005 n = 60 ____________________

$$320 = A\left[\frac{0.005}{1-(1+0.005)^{-60}}\right]$$ ____________________

$$320 = A\left[\frac{0.005}{1-(1.005)^{-60}}\right]$$ ____________________

$$320 = A\left[\frac{0.005}{1-0.7414}\right]$$ ____________________

$$320 = A\left[\frac{0.005}{0.2586}\right]$$ ____________________

$$320 = A[0.01933]$$ ____________________

$$16,555 = A$$ ____________________

   The couple can afford a $16,555 car loan.

10. Write a sentence describing what a negative exponent means.

11. Write a sentence explaining why 2,300,000,000 is written as 2.3×10^9 in scientific notation.

12. If a positive number is less than one, what sign will the exponent be when the number is written in scientific notation?

13. Explain the difference between EE , , and carat, , commands on the TI 30XII S calculator.

14. What does $2.983_{\times 10}12$ mean when you see it on your calculator?

Study Tip: Detailed solutions to problems 2a, c,e, g,3a, b, c, 4a, c, 5a, c, 6a, c, and 8 can be found on the MAT 011 Electronic Resource page. See page vii.

SECTION 3.3 PROPERTIES OF EXPONENTS PREVIEW

Objectives: This section examines the algebraic properties of exponents. This is an important section for students who plan to take Intermediate Algebra, MAT 100.

Properties of Exponents:

Property		English Description
Property 1.	$a^n \bullet a^m = a^{n+m}$	When multiplying with the same bases, add the exponents.
Property 2.	$(a^n)^m = a^{nm}$	When there is an exponent raised to a power, multiply the exponents.
Property 3.	$(ab)^n = a^n b^n$	When two bases are being multiplied and are raised to the same power, then each base is raised to that power.
Property 4.	$a^{-n} = \frac{1}{a^n}$	A negative exponent means to use the reciprocal. If the base is in the numerator, then when you compute the reciprocal the base goes to the denominator.
Property 5.	$\frac{1}{a^{-n}} = a^n$	A negative exponent means to use the reciprocal. If the base is in the denominator, then when you compute the reciprocal the base goes to the numerator.
Property 6.	$\frac{a^n}{a^m} = a^{n-m}$	When dividing with the same bases, subtract the exponents.
Property 7.	$a^0 = 1$	Any base other than zero raised to the zero power is one.
Property 8.	$\left(\frac{a}{b}\right)^n = \frac{a^n}{b^n}$	When two bases are being divided and are raised to the same power, then each base is raised to that power.

The following examples illustrate how the properties are used.

Example 1. Simplify. $x^3 \bullet x$.

$x^3 \bullet x = x^4$ Added the exponents. Remember $x = x^1$.

Example 2. Simplify $(x^3y)^5$

$(x^3y)^5 = (x^3)^5(y^1)^5$ Wrote y as y^1

$= (x^3)^5 y^5$ Used the property $(ab)^n = a^n b^n$.

$= x^{15}y^5$ Multiplied the exponents.

Example 3. Simplify $(5x^4)^3$

$(5x^4)^3 = 5^3(x^4)^3$ Used property $(ab)^n = a^n b^n$

$= 125x^{12}$ Multiplied the exponents and computed 5^3.

Study Tip: Write the properties on separate note cards and review them frequently.

Example 4. Simplify $9x^{-4}$. Write the expression with positive exponents.

$9x^{-4} = \frac{9}{x^4}$ Only x was raised to the –4 power because no parentheses were present .

Example 5. Simplify $\frac{1}{(5x^3)^{-7}}$. Write the expression with positive exponents.

$\frac{1}{(5x^3)^{-7}} = (5x^3)^7$ Raised the entire denominator to the numerator because of the negative exponent.

$= 5^7(x^3)^7$ Used property $(ab)^n = a^n b^n$

$= 78{,}125x^{21}$ Used property $(a^n)^m = a^{nm}$

Example 6. Simplify $\frac{x^3}{x^7}$. Write the expression with positive exponents.

$\frac{x^3}{x^7} = x^{3-7}$ Used property $\frac{a^n}{a^m} = a^{n-m}$

$= x^{-4}$ Subtracted exponents.

$= \frac{1}{x^4}$ Used property $a^{-n} = \frac{1}{a^n}$

Example 7. Simplify $\frac{2x^{-3}}{5x^{-9}}$. Write the expression with positive exponents.

$\frac{2x^{-3}}{5x^{-9}} = \frac{2x^9}{5x^3}$ Used properties $a^{-n} = \frac{1}{a^n}$ and $\frac{1}{a^{-n}} = a^n$. Only the variables are raised to the negative exponents.

$= \frac{2x^{9-3}}{5}$ Used property $\frac{a^n}{a^m} = a^{n-m}$

$= \frac{2x^6}{5}$ Subtracted the exponents.

Summary: Manipulating exponents is an important skill in MAT 100, Intermediate Algebra. In MAT 011 you are expected to memorize the properties of exponents and how to apply them to solve basic problems.

CLASS WORK

Property 1. $a^n \bullet a^m = a^{n+m}$

Simplify each expression.

1. $x^5 \bullet x^3$

2. $x^4 \bullet x^2$

Property 2. $(a^n)^m = a^{nm}$

Simplify each expression.

3. $\left(x^3\right)^4$

4. $\left(x^5\right)^3$

Property 3. $(ab)^n = a^n b^n$

Simplify each expression.

5. $\left(3x^2\right)^4$

6. $\left(x^2y^5\right)^3$

Property 4. $a^{-n} = \dfrac{1}{a^n}$

Simplify each expression. Write the expression with positive exponents only.

7. $8x^{-3}$

8. $(2x)^{-4}$

Property 5. $\frac{1}{a^{-n}} = a^n$

Simplify each expression. Write the expression with positive exponents only.

9. $\frac{1}{4x^{-3}}$

10. $\frac{1}{(7x^2)^{-3}}$

Property 6. $\frac{a^n}{a^m} = a^{n-m}$

Simplify each expression. Write the expression with positive exponents only.

11. $\frac{x^8}{x^3}$

12. $\frac{x^2}{x^5}$

Property 7. $a^0 = 1$

Simplify each expression.

13. $8x^0$

14. $(7x^3)^0$

Property 8. $\left(\frac{a}{b}\right)^n = \frac{a^n}{b^n}$

Simplify each expression.

15. $\left(\frac{4}{x^2}\right)^3$

16. $\left(\frac{x^2}{3}\right)^2$

Simplify each expression. Write the expression with positive exponents only.

17. $3x^2x^3$

18. $4\left(-3x^2\right)^2$

19. $6xy^2\left(-2x^2y\right)^3$

20. $\dfrac{8x^5}{x^{-3}}$

21. $\dfrac{4x^{-3}}{8x^{-1}}$

22. $\left(\dfrac{-2xy^4}{x^2y}\right)^3$

GROUP EXERCISE

Study Tip: Review your exponent note cards first.

1. Find the **mistake**.

   Simplify each expression. Write the expression with positive exponents only.

   a. $x^3 \bullet x^2 = x^6$

   b. $\frac{1}{6x^{-3}} = 6x^3$

2. Simplify each expression. Write the expression with positive exponents only.

   a. $\left(5x^2\right)^3$

   b. $\left(-6x^3\right)^2$

   c. $\frac{9x^5}{3x^2}$

   d. $4x^{-5}$

   e. $\left(\frac{3x^3y}{5xy^3}\right)^2$

   f. $\frac{1}{\left(3x^2\right)^{-4}}$

HOMEWORK EXERCISES

Study Tips: 1. Review your exponent note cards.
2. Work for a half hour and take a break.

Skill Building Exercises

1. Simplify.

a. $-3 + 5$ b. $-7 - (-2)$ c. $5(-2)$

Practice Exercises

2. Simplify each expression. Write the expression with positive exponents only.

a. $8x^5x^3$ b. $2x^3x^{-2}$ c. $\left(x^2y^5\right)^3$ d. $\left(5x^{-3}\right)^4$

e. $6x^{-1}$ f. $\frac{5}{2x^{-3}}$ g. $\frac{9x^5}{18x^2}$ h. $\frac{x^4y^3}{9x^6y}$

i. 9^0 j. $\left(\frac{6}{x^2}\right)^3$ k. $\left(\frac{x^4}{2y^5}\right)^{-3}$ l. $\left(7x^5\right)^{-2}$

3. Many MAT 011 students take AST 120, Introduction to Astronomy, to satisfy their science requirement at MCCC. The following problem comes from AST 120 and is a follow up to Practice Exercise 4 from Introduction to Positive Exponents on page 243.

The life expectancy of a star, T, is proportional to its mass divided by its luminosity, L, or

$$T = \frac{M}{L} \bullet 10^{10} \text{ years.}$$

a. Review problem 4 page 243, and the formula $L = M^{3.5}$. Substitute this formula into the equation above for L and use properties of exponents to simplify the formula for T.

b. How long can a 4 solar mass star live? (This is a star whose mass is 4 times that of the sun's. M = 4.)

c. How long can a 0.5 solar mass star live? (This is a star whose mass is half of the sun's. M = 0.5.)

Reading and Writing Mathematics

4. State the eight properties of exponents.

5. Find the **mistake**. Write a sentence describing what the student did wrong.

Simplify each expression. Write the expression with positive exponents only.

a. $\left(3x^2\right)^4 = 81x^6$ b. $\left(3x^2\right)\left(4x\right) = 12x^2$ c. $-7x^{-2} = 7x^2$

SECTION 3.4 INTRODUCTION TO ALGEBRAIC FRACTIONS PREVIEW

Objectives: This section will introduce fractions with a simple application and then explain reducing, multiplying, and dividing algebraic fractions.

Example 1. Suppose the cost of removing p percent of the particle pollution from the water of a polluted lake is indicated by the equation:

$$C = \frac{4,300p}{100 - p}$$

a. Find the cost for p = 70.

$C = \frac{4,300 \bullet 70}{100 - 70}$ Substituted 70 for p.

$C = \frac{301,000}{30}$ Multiplied in the numerator and subtracted in the denominator.

$C = 10,033.33$ Divided.

The cost of removing 70% of the pollution from the lake is $10,033.33.

b. Find the cost for p = 80.

$C = \frac{4,300 \bullet 80}{100 - 80}$ Substituted 80 for p.

$C = \frac{344,000}{20}$ Multiplied in the numerator and subtracted in the denominator.

$C = 17,200$ Divided.

The cost of removing 80% of the pollution from the lake is $17,200.

c. Find the cost for p = 90.

$$C = \frac{4,300 \bullet 90}{100 - 90}$$
$$C = 38,700$$

The cost of removing 90% of the pollution from the lake is $38,700.
The cost does not increase at a constant rate. The cost went up approximately $7,000 when p increased from 70 to 80 percent while the cost went up approximately $21,000 when p increased from 80 to 90 percent. If you compute the cost for 95% and 99%, you will see that the cost increases dramatically.

d. Find the cost for p = 100.

$$C = \frac{4,300 \bullet 100}{100 - 100}$$
$$C = \frac{430,000}{0}$$

Division by zero is undefined, so we cannot calculate the cost of removing all of the pollution.

Study Tip: You should write on a note card that a numerator divided by zero is undefined and review it at least twice a week.

Reducing Algebraic Fractions: The basic idea behind reducing fractions is $\frac{8}{8}=1$ and $\frac{x}{x}=1$ when x is not zero.

Example 2. Reduce $\frac{24x}{9x}$ to lowest terms.

$\frac{24x}{9x}=\frac{8\bullet 3x}{3\bullet 3x}$ Write 24 as $8\bullet 3$ and 9x as $3\bullet 3x$. Writing a term as a product is called **factoring**. 8 and 3 are **factors** of 24 and 3 and 3 are factors of 9. We must choose factors which have a common number. Other factors of 24, such as 4 and 6 or 2 and 12, are not as desirable.

$=\frac{8\bullet \mathbf{3x}}{3\bullet \mathbf{3x}}$ Identify the like factors.

$=\frac{8}{3}$ Cancel the 3x because $\frac{3x}{3x}=1$.

Rule: **Multiplying and Dividing Fractions:** The rules for multiplying and dividing fractions are:

$\frac{a}{b}\bullet\frac{c}{d}=\frac{ac}{bd}$, multiply the numerators and denominators then reduce.

$\frac{a}{b}\div\frac{c}{d}=\frac{ad}{bc}$, use the reciprocal of the second fraction (invert the divisor) then multiply.

Example 3. Multiply $\frac{30x^3}{14}\bullet\frac{7}{6x^2}$ and reduce to the lowest terms.

$\frac{30x^3}{14}\bullet\frac{7}{6x^2}=\frac{210x^3}{84x^2}$ Multiplied 30 times 7 in the numerator and 14 times 6 in the denominator.

$=\frac{210x}{84}$ Subtracted the exponents.

$=\frac{30x}{12}$ 7 is a common factor for both 210 and 84, $210 = 7\bullet 30$. And $84 = 7\bullet 12$

$=\frac{5x}{2}$ 6 is a common factor for both 30 and 12, $30 = 6\bullet 5$. And $12 = 6\bullet 2$

Study Tip:
1. Write the formulas for multiplying and dividing fractions on a note card and review them at least twice a week.
2. Students must know the multiplcation facts in order to successfully manipulate fractions. If you had problems with fractions in the past, take time to practice the multiplication facts, the Learning Assistence Lab should be able to help.

Example 4. Divide $\frac{18}{15x^2} \div \frac{12}{25x^4}$ and reduce to lowest terms.

$$\frac{18}{15x^2} \div \frac{12}{25x^4} = \frac{18}{15x^2} \bullet \frac{25x^4}{12}$$

Took the reciprocal of $\frac{12}{25x^2}$.

$$= \frac{450x^4}{180x^2}.$$

Multiplied 18 times 25 in the numerator and 15 times 12 in the denominator.

$$= \frac{450x^2}{180}$$

Subtracted the exponents.

$$= \frac{45x^2}{18}$$

10 is a common factor of 450 and 180, $450 = 10 \bullet 45$ and $180 = 10 \bullet 18$

$$= \frac{5x^2}{2}$$

9 is a common factor of 45 and 18, $45 = 9 \bullet 5$ and $18 = 9 \bullet 2$

Common Errors: The following problems are **NOT** correct.

1. $\frac{x-2}{x} = -2.$ 2. $\frac{4x-5}{4} = x-5.$ 3. $\frac{9}{3-x} = \frac{3}{-x}$

In each problem above, **terms** (what are being added or subtracted) are cancelled. Only **factors** (what are being multiplied) can be cancelled. In problem 1, the x is incorrectly cancelled. In problem 2, the fours are incorrectly cancelled. In problem 3, the 9 and the 3 are reduced incorrectly.

Using the Concept of Reducing Fractions to Change Units.

The method of converting units is sometimes called the "Conversion Factor Method of Unit Conversion", an important concept in science classes. Most MCCC students are required to take a science course in order to graduate.

Example 5. Convert 90 feet per second to miles per hour.

To begin, write 90 feet per minute as a fraction, $\frac{90 \text{ feet}}{1 \text{ minute}}$.

Write 1 minute = 60 seconds as a fraction (or ratio),

$$\frac{60 \text{ seconds}}{1 \text{ minute}}.$$

Multiply the two fractions together,

$$\frac{90 \text{ feet}}{1 \text{ second}} \times \frac{60 \text{ seconds}}{1 \text{ minute}}.$$

Cancel the seconds and multiply 90 and 60. This is shown below:

$$\frac{90\text{ feet}}{1\text{ second}} \times \frac{60\text{ seconds}}{1\text{ minute}} = \frac{5{,}400\text{ feet}}{1\text{ minute}}$$

So, 90 feet per second is the same as 5,400 feet per minute.
The entire process of converting 90 feet per second to miles per hour is explained below. The conversion, 1 mile = 5,280 feet is needed.

$$\frac{90\text{ feet}}{1\text{ second}} \times \frac{60\text{ seconds}}{1\text{ minute}} \times \frac{60\text{ minutes}}{1\text{ hour}} \times \frac{1\text{ mile}}{5{,}280\text{ feet}}$$

$$\frac{90\text{ feet}}{1\text{ second}} \times \frac{60\text{ seconds}}{1\text{ minute}} \times \frac{60\text{ minutes}}{1\text{ hour}} \times \frac{1\text{ mile}}{5{,}280\text{ feet}} = \frac{61.36\text{ miles}}{\text{hour}}$$

90 feet per second is the same as 61.36 miles per hour.

Example 5. Humans have been shown to have accumulated as much as 4 $\mu g/g$ of body weight of DDT in their tissues. If a woman weighs 156 pounds, how much DDT is in her body?

Explanation: 4 $\mu g/g$ means that there are 4 μg of DDT per gram of body weight. 1 μg is 10^{-6} grams, or a very small weight.

$$156\text{ pounds} \times \frac{454\text{ grams}}{1\text{ pounds}} \times \frac{4\mu g}{\text{grams}} \times \frac{1\text{ gram}}{10^6 \mu g} =$$

$$156\text{ pounds} \times \frac{454\text{ grams}}{1\text{ pounds}} \times \frac{4\mu g}{\text{grams}} \times \frac{1\text{ gram}}{10^6 \mu g} = 0.2833\text{ grams}$$

Conversions:
454 grams = 1 pound

$10^6\ \mu g = 1\text{ gram}$.

The woman has 0.2833 grams of DDT in her body.

Summary: This section should help you better understand the arithmetic of fractions. For students who are planning on taking MAT 100, Intermediate Algebra, you will see this topic again.

- You cannot divide by zero. (The answer is undefined.)

- The **factors** of a quantity are any two expressions that when multiplied together result in that quantity.

- To **reduce a fraction**, factor the numerator and denominator and then cancel all the factors that are in both the numerator and denominator.

- To **multiply two fractions**, multiply the numerators and denominators and then reduce.

$$\frac{a}{b} \bullet \frac{c}{d} = \frac{ac}{bd}$$

- To **divide two fractions**, use the reciprocal of the second fraction and then multiply.

$$\frac{a}{b} \div \frac{c}{d} = \frac{a}{b} * \frac{d}{c} = \frac{ad}{bc}$$

CLASS WORK

1. Suppose the cost of removing p percent of the particulate pollution from the exhaust gases at an industrial site is indicated by

$$C = \frac{6800p}{100 - p}$$

Find the cost for

a. $p = 75$

b. $p = 85$

c. $p = 95$

d. $p = 100$

e. Use the results from parts a through d along with the points given in the table below to graph $C = \dfrac{6800p}{100 - p}$.

P	C	Point
0	0	(0, 0)
25	2,267	(25, 2267)
50	6800	(50, 6800)
75		
85		
95		

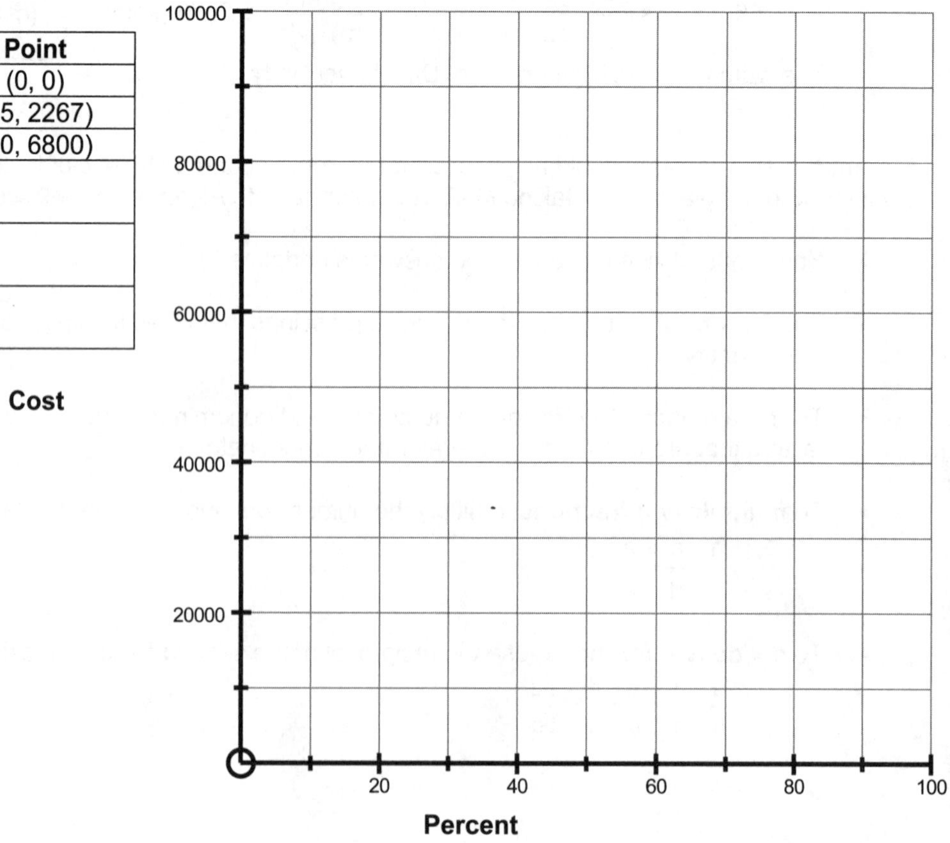

Cost

100000
80000
60000
40000
20000
20
40
60
80
100

Percent

2. Reduce to lowest terms.

a. $\dfrac{24x^3}{32x}$

b. $\dfrac{-5x}{15x^2}$

3. Multiply or divide as indicated and reduce to lowest terms.

a. $\dfrac{8x}{5} \bullet \dfrac{15}{16x}$

b. $\dfrac{21x^2}{10} \div \dfrac{7x^3}{15}$

c. $\dfrac{-24x^3}{8} \div \dfrac{3}{5x^3}$

4. A printer cartridge costs $24.99 and contains 13 milliliters of ink. Use the concept of reducing fractions to find the cost per gallon.

   Conversion: 1 ml = 2.642×10^{-4}

5. Using the concept of reducing fractions to change units.

   A faucet drips one drop of water every two seconds, how much water drips in one week.

Conversions:
20 drops = 1 teaspoon
96 teaspoons = 1 pint
8 pints = 1 gallon

GROUP EXERCISE

1. Suppose the cost of removing p percent of the particulate pollution from the exhaust gases at an industrial site is indicated by

$$C = \frac{7200p}{100 - p}$$

Find the cost for

a. $p = 85$ b. $p = 95$ c. $p = 99$

d. $p = 100$ (What does this say about removing all of the exhaust gases at the industrial site?)

e. Use the results from parts a through d along with the points given in the table below to graph $C = \frac{7200p}{100 - p}$.

P	C	Point
0	0	(0, 0)
25	2,400	(25, 2400)
50	7200	(50, 7200)
65	13,371	(65, 13371)
75	21,600	(75, 21600)

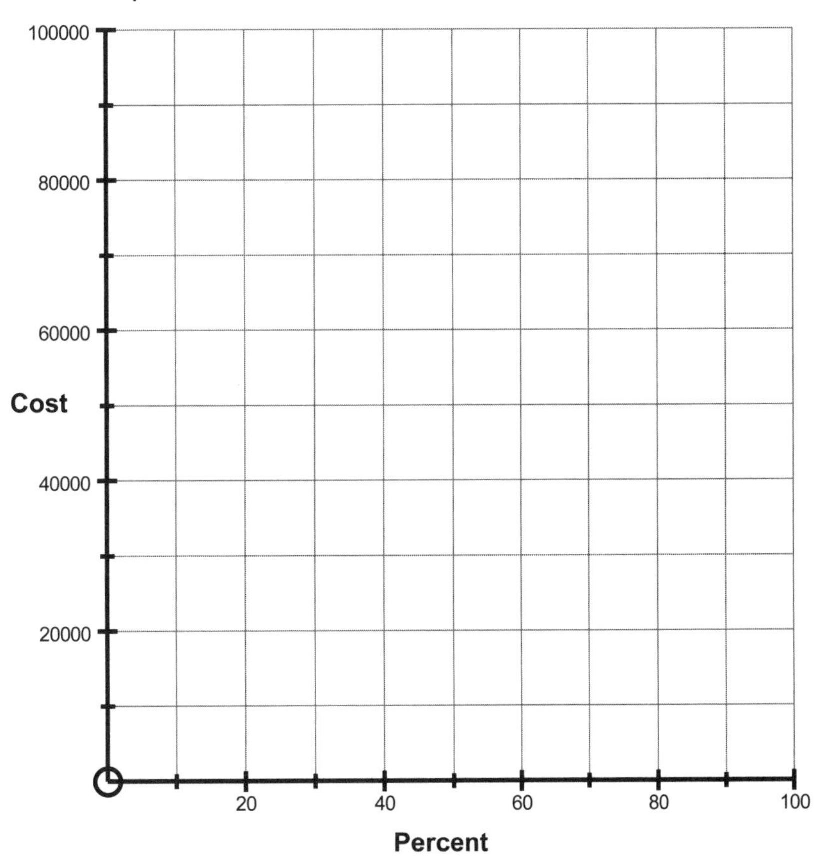

2. Reduce to lowest terms.

$$\frac{9x^3}{27x}$$

3. Multiply or divide as indicated and reduce to lowest terms.

a. $\frac{16x}{20} \bullet \frac{8x^2}{3}$

b. $\frac{-81x}{10} \div \frac{9x^3}{5}$

HOMEWORK EXERCISES

Study Tips: 1. Review your note cards.
2. Use your loose leaf notebook.
3. Take difficult problems to the Learning Assistance Lab.

Skill Building Exercises

1. Reduce the fraction $\frac{24}{32}$.

2. Multiply or divide as indicated and reduce to lowest terms.

a. $\frac{8}{9} \bullet \frac{15}{28}$

b. $\frac{7}{16} \div \frac{4}{14}$

Practice Exercises

3. Suppose for a certain city the cost C of obtaining drinking water with p percent impurities is indicated by

$$C = \frac{120{,}000}{p} - 1{,}200$$

Find the cost for

a. $p = 15$

b. $p = 5$

c. $p = 1$

d. $p = 0$ (What does this say about the drinking water in this town?)

4. Suppose the cost C of removing p percent of the particulate pollution from the exhaust gases at an industrial site is indicated by

$$C = \frac{8{,}300p}{100 - p}$$

Find the cost for

a. $p = 80$

b. $p = 90$

c. $p = 95$

d. $p = 100$ (What does this say about removing all of the exhaust gases at the industrial site?)

5. Reduce to lowest terms.

a. $\frac{9x}{6x}$

b. $\frac{27y}{15y}$

c. $\frac{2x^2}{8x^3}$

d. $\frac{6y^3}{15x}$

e. $\frac{-30x^2}{48x^5}$

f. $\frac{16x^3}{-32x}$

6. Multiply or divide as indicated and reduce to lowest terms.

a. $\frac{2x}{3} \bullet \frac{6}{3x}$ b. $\frac{6x}{5} \div \frac{3x}{10}$ c. $\frac{7}{3y} \div 3y$

d. $\frac{2x^2}{9} \bullet \frac{18}{4x}$ e. $\frac{3x^2}{4} \bullet \frac{16}{12x^3}$ f. $\frac{-6x^3}{5} \div \frac{18x}{10}$

7. a. Convert 90 miles per hour to feet per second.

Go Back: See example 5 on page 270.

b. The pitcher's mound is 60.5 feet from home plate. If the pitcher throws a 90 mile per hour fastball how long will it take the baseball to reach home plate? (Distance = Rate • Time)

8. A student is 6 feet tall. How tall is he in centimeters? The conversions needed for this problem are: 1 inch = 2.54 centimeters, 1 foot = 12 inches.

Reading and Writing Mathematics

9. Explain why the fours in the expression to the right cannot be cancelled: $\frac{3x+4}{4}$.

10. In the problem, find the **mistake** and write a sentence describing the error. Also, write a suggestion so that any student who makes this type of mistake will have a way to remember not to make the error again.

$$\frac{-3x^2}{5} \div \frac{25}{6x} = \frac{-3x^2}{5} \div \frac{25}{6x}$$
$$= \frac{-3 \bullet x \bullet x}{5} \div \frac{5 \bullet 5}{3 \bullet 2 \bullet x}$$
$$= \frac{-x}{1} \div \frac{5}{2}$$
$$= \frac{-x}{1} \bullet \frac{2}{5}$$
$$= \frac{-2x}{5}$$

Study Tip: Detailed solutions to problems 1, 2, 3, 5a, c, e, 6a, c, e, and 7 can be found on the MAT 011 Electronic Resource page. See page vii.

SECTION 3.5 ADDING AND SUBTRACTING ALGEBRAIC FRACTIONS PREVIEW

Objectives: This section will explain how to add and subtract fractions.

Procedure:

1. Find the least common denominator, LCD.
   a. For numbers, the least common denominator is the smallest number into which all of the denominators divide evenly.
   b. For variables, the least common denominator is the variable with the highest exponent.
2. Convert each fraction to a fraction with the least common denominator.
   a. Decide what you need to multiply each denominator by to get the LCD.
   b. Multiply the numerator and denominator by this quantity.
3. Combine the numerators and write as a single fraction.

Example 1. Add $\frac{7}{4x}-\frac{3}{10}$.

The LCD is 20x

$\frac{7}{4x}-\frac{3}{10}=$. The smallest number into which 4 and 10 divide without a remainder is 20. The variable with the highest exponent is x.

$\frac{7}{4x}\left(\frac{5}{5}\right)-\frac{3}{10}\left(\frac{2x}{2x}\right)=$ You needed to multiply 4x by 5 to get 20x. You needed to multiply 10 by 2x to get 20x.

$\frac{35}{20x}-\frac{6x}{20x}=$ Multiplied each fraction

$\frac{35-6x}{20x}$ Wrote as a single fraction. Note that 35 and 6x are unlike terms and can't be combined.

Example 2. Add $\frac{5}{6x^2}+\frac{8}{15x^3}$.

The LCD is $30x^3$.

$\frac{5}{6x^2}+\frac{8}{15x^3}=$ The smallest number into which both 6 and 15 divide without a remainder is 30. The variable with the highest exponent is x^3.

$\frac{5}{6x^2}\left(\frac{5x}{5x}\right)+\frac{8}{15x^3}\left(\frac{2}{2}\right)=$ You needed to multiply $6x^2$ by 5x to get $30x^3$. You needed to multiply $15x^3$ by 2 to get $30x^3$.

$\frac{25x}{30x^3}+\frac{16}{30x^3}=$ Multiplied each fraction.

$\frac{25x+16}{30x^3}=$ Wrote as a single fraction.

Study Tip: You should write the steps to add algebraic fractions on a note card, along with an example, so you can understand what they mean.

Summary: This section should help you better understand how to add and subtract numerical fractions. Learning to find the least common denominator (LCD) is imperative when working with fractions. For students planning on taking MAT 100, Intermediate Algebra, you will see these again.

CLASS WORK

1. There is a big difference in how fractions are multiplied and how they are added.

Compute $\frac{1}{2}\bullet\frac{1}{3}$.

Compute $\frac{1}{2}+\frac{1}{3}$.

Combine into single fractions and reduce to lowest terms.

1. $\frac{9x}{10}+\frac{3x}{5}$ STEP

2. $\frac{9y}{8}+3y$ STEP

3. $\dfrac{7}{8x}-\dfrac{5}{6x}$

STEP

4. $\dfrac{3}{2x}-\dfrac{7}{5}$

STEP

5. $\frac{2}{9x}+\frac{5}{6x^2}$ STEP

6. $\frac{9}{5x}-\frac{1}{15x^3}$ STEP

GROUP EXERCISE

Describe the **mistake**:

1. $\frac{6x}{5}+\frac{3x}{2}=\frac{9x}{7}$

2. $\frac{3x}{8}+\frac{5}{2x}=$

$$\left(\frac{3x}{8}\right)\left(\frac{x}{x}\right)+\left(\frac{5}{2x}\right)\left(\frac{4x}{4x}\right)=$$

$$\frac{3x^2}{8x}+\frac{20x}{8x}=$$

$$\frac{3x^2+20x}{8x}$$

Describe each step.

3. $\frac{3}{4y^2}-\frac{5}{6y^3}=$

$$\left(\frac{3}{4y^2}\right)\left(\frac{3y}{3y}\right)-\left(\frac{5}{6y^3}\right)\left(\frac{2}{2}\right)=$$ ____________________________

$$\frac{9y}{12y^3}-\frac{10}{12y^3}=$$ ____________________________

$$\frac{9y-10}{12y^3}$$ ____________________________

Combine into single fractions and reduce to lowest terms.

4. $6x+\frac{3x}{5}$

5. $\frac{7}{4x^3}-\frac{9}{10x}$

HOMEWORK EXERCISES

Study Tip: Review your fraction note cards.

Skill Building Exercises

1. Combine $\frac{7}{9}+\frac{6}{15}$ into a single fraction and reduce to lowest terms.

Practice Exercises

Combine into single fractions and reduce to lowest terms.

2. $\frac{3}{5x}-\frac{2}{5x}$

3. $\frac{3}{5x}-\frac{2}{3}$

4. $\frac{4m}{3}+\frac{m}{7}$

5. $\frac{2}{3}-\frac{3}{4y}$

6. $\frac{5}{8m^3}-\frac{1}{12m}$

7. $\frac{5}{3y}+\frac{3}{4y^2}$

8. $\frac{2}{9n^2}-\frac{5}{12n^4}$

9. $\frac{3}{2x^2}+\frac{4}{3x}$

10. $\frac{x^2}{4}-\frac{x}{3}$

11. $\frac{1}{5x^3}+7$

Reading and Writing Mathematics

12. In each problem, find the **mistake** and write a sentence describing the error. Also, write a suggestion so that any student who makes this type of mistake will have a way to remember not to make the error again.

Combine into single fractions and reduce to lowest terms.

a. $\frac{2x}{9}+\frac{5}{6x}$

$$=\left(\frac{2x}{9}\right)\left(\frac{2x}{2x}\right)+\left(\frac{5}{6x}\right)\left(\frac{3}{3}\right)$$

$$=\frac{4x^2}{18x}+\frac{15}{18x}$$

$$=\frac{19x^2}{18x}$$

$$=\frac{19x}{18}$$

b. $\frac{7x}{5}+\frac{2x}{3}$

$$\frac{7x}{5}+\frac{2x}{3}=\frac{9x}{8}$$

13. Describe each step.

$$\frac{11}{2y}+\frac{8}{3y^2}=$$

$$\left(\frac{11}{2y}\right)\left(\frac{3y}{3y}\right)+\left(\frac{8}{3y^2}\right)\left(\frac{2}{2}\right)=$$ ______________________________

$$\frac{33y}{6y^2}+\frac{16}{6y^2}=$$ ______________________________

$$\frac{33y+16}{6y^2}$$ ______________________________

14. A classmate asks you to look over his work. The mathematics is correct. Make four suggestions that would improve the presentation of the problem. Review the problem the way a teacher might look at it.

Combine into a single fraction and reduce to lowest terms.

$$\frac{\cancel{5}\ 25x}{3x^3}-\frac{\cancel{2}\ 2x^2}{15x} \qquad 15x^3$$

$$25x-2x^2$$

$$\frac{25x-2x^2}{15x^3}$$

Study Tips: 1. If any of the problems is not clear to you, ask questions in the next class session, see your instructor during office hours, or go to the Learning Assistance Lab.

2. Do not proceed until you have mastered this section.

3. Students must know the multiplication facts in order to successfully manipulate fractions. If you had problems with fractions in the past, take time to practice the multiplication facts, the Learning Assistance Lab should be able to help.

4. Multimedia resources are available at the MAT 011 web site, AV Library, and Learning Lab.

5. Detailed solutions to problems 1, 3, 5, 7, 9, 11, 12 and 14 can be found on the MAT 011 Electronic Resource page. See page vii.

SECTION 3.6 SOLVING EQUATIONS WITH FRACTIONS PREVIEW

Objective: This section will demonstrate how to solve equations with fractions.

Procedure: To solve an equation with fractions, multiply all the terms by the least common denominator, LCD, and reduce the fractions. This will eliminate them. Then use your skills from Chapter 1 to solve the equation.

Example 1. Solve

$\frac{5}{6x} - \frac{2}{9x} = \frac{7}{3}$	The LCD is 18x.
$(18x)\frac{5}{6x} - (18x)\frac{2}{9x} = (18x)\frac{7}{3}$	Multiplied all the terms by 18x.
$(3)\frac{5}{1} - (2)\frac{2}{1} = (6x)\frac{7}{1}$	Reduced. $18x \div 6x = 3$, $18x \div 9x = 2$, $18x \div 3 = 6x$. Note that all of the denominators are one. You don't need to write the one.
$15 - 4 = 42x$	Multiplied.
$11 = 42x$	Combined like terms.
$\frac{11}{42} = x$	Divided both sides by 42.

The traditional answer to fractional equations is a fraction. However, dividing and writing the answer as a decimal is also correct.

Example 2. Solve

$\frac{x-5}{10} - \frac{x+2}{5} = 6$	The LCD is 10.
$(10)\frac{x-5}{10} - (10)\frac{x+2}{5} = (10)6$	Multiplied all the terms by 10.
$(x-5) - 2(x+2) = (10)6$	Reduced the fractions.
$x - 5 - 2x - 4 = 60$	Used the distributive property.
$-x - 9 = 60$	Combined like terms.
$-x = 69$	Added nine to both sides.
$x = -69$	Divided both sides by negative one.

Study Tip: You should write the procedure on a note card, along with an example, so you can understand how to solve equations involving fractions.

Summary: The new concept in this section: When solving equations with fractions, multiply all of the terms by the LCD and then reduce.

Students often confuse the procedures for adding or subtracting fractions (simplifying expressions) with solving equations with fractions. When adding fractions, you want the LCD in your answer. When solving equations, you use the LCD to eliminate the fractions.

CLASS WORK

Solve each equation and describe each step.

1. $\frac{3x}{5}+\frac{7}{2}=\frac{x}{10}$ STEP

NOTES

2. $\frac{4}{x} - \frac{4}{3} = \frac{8}{5x}$

STEP

3. Solve each equation.

$$\frac{y-4}{2} - \frac{y-3}{9} = \frac{5}{18}$$

4. Solve the inequality.

$$\frac{3}{4} - \frac{5}{3} > \frac{5}{6}$$

5. The formula $A = \frac{1}{2}h(b_1 + b_2)$ represents the area of a trapezoid. h is the height and, b_1 and b_2 represents the length of the two bases.

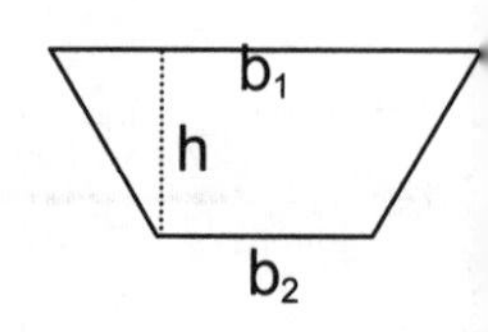

a. If h = 5 inches and b_1 equals 9 inches, find b_2 so that the area is **between** 27 and 38 square inches.

b. Solve the equation for b_2.

Study Tip: New students must learn to budget their time in order to be successful in college. It is especially important when you have a test. See page iv and complete a weekly planner for the week of your third MAT 011 test. Make sure you include three one hour blocks to study for your upcoming MAT 011 exam.

GROUP EXERCISE

1. Describe each step.

$$\frac{5x}{8}-\frac{3}{16}=\frac{7x}{24}$$

Step

$$\left(\frac{5x}{8}\right)\left(\frac{48}{1}\right)-\left(\frac{3}{16}\right)\left(\frac{48}{1}\right)=\left(\frac{7x}{24}\right)\left(\frac{48}{1}\right)$$ ____________________

$$(5x)(6)-(3)(3)=(7x)(2)$$ ____________________

$$30x-9=14x$$ ____________________

$$-9=-16x$$ ____________________

$$\frac{9}{16}=x$$ ____________________

2. Find the mistake.

$$\frac{x+5}{4}-\frac{x-3}{6}=\frac{7}{12}$$

$$\left(\frac{12}{1}\right)\left(\frac{x+5}{4}\right)-\left(\frac{12}{1}\right)\left(\frac{x-3}{6}\right)=\left(\frac{12}{1}\right)\left(\frac{7}{12}\right)$$

$$3(x+5)-2(x-3)=7$$

$$3x+15-2x-6=7$$

$$x+9=7$$

$$x=-2$$

Solve each equation.

3. $\frac{6}{5}+\frac{8x}{15}=\frac{7x}{3}$

4. $\frac{x-2}{2}-\frac{3x+5}{4}=\frac{3}{8}$

HOMEWORK EXERCISES

Study Tip: Make sure your homework problems are well organized. Don't be afraid to re-do problems.

Skill Building Exercises

1. Solve each problem.

   a. $3x - 4 = 12 - x$ b. $7 - 3(2x + 6) = 2x - 12$

Practice Exercises

Solve each equation.

Study Tip: Do not confuse the procedure for adding and subtracting fractions (simplifying expressions) with solving equations involving fractions.

2. $\frac{5}{18} - \frac{4x}{3} = \frac{11}{6}$

3. $\frac{2x}{21} + \frac{4}{7} = \frac{5x}{3}$

4. $\frac{8}{5x} + \frac{4}{3} = \frac{1}{15}$

5. $\frac{5}{12} - \frac{1}{3x} = \frac{7}{6}$

6. $2x - \frac{7}{5} = \frac{3x}{10}$

7. $\frac{9}{8} + 3x = \frac{5x}{12}$

8. $\frac{x+1}{3} - \frac{3x+2}{2} = \frac{7}{6}$

9. $\frac{3x+5}{4} - \frac{x-2}{20} = \frac{9}{5}$

10. Solve the following inequalities. Recall that when you multiply or divide by a negative number you must change the direction of the inequality.

    a. $\frac{2x}{5} + \frac{1}{3} > \frac{4x}{15}$ b. $\frac{1}{3} - \frac{5x}{2} \le \frac{7}{12}$

11. The equation $C = \frac{5}{9}(F - 32)$ converts temperature in Fahrenheit, F, to Celsius, C. For each problem set up an equation and solve it.

Go Back: See Classwork problem 5 on page 290.

    a. If the temperature is **above** 8° Celsius, what must the corresponding temperature in Fahrenheit be?

    b. If the temperature is **between** –2° Celsius and 12° Celsius, what is the corresponding temperature in Fahrenheit?

    c. Solve the equation for F.

Reading and Writing Mathematics

Describe each step.

12. $$\frac{5x}{9}-\frac{7}{36}=\frac{11x}{6}$$ Step

$$\left(\frac{5x}{9}\right)\left(\frac{36}{1}\right)-\left(\frac{7}{36}\right)\left(\frac{36}{1}\right)=\left(\frac{11x}{6}\right)\left(\frac{36}{1}\right)$$ ______________________

$$(5x)(4) - 7 = (11x)(6)$$ ______________________

$$20x - 7 = 66x$$ ______________________

$$-7 = 46x$$ ______________________

$$\frac{-7}{46}=x$$ ______________________

13. $$\frac{2x+5}{8}-\frac{x-3}{2}=\frac{7}{4}$$ Step

$$\left(\frac{2x+5}{8}\right)\left(\frac{8}{1}\right)-\left(\frac{x-3}{2}\right)\left(\frac{8}{1}\right)=\left(\frac{7}{4}\right)\left(\frac{8}{1}\right)$$ ______________________

$$2x + 5 - 4(x - 3) = (7)(2)$$ ______________________

$$2x + 5 - 4x + 12 = 14$$ ______________________

$$-2x + 17 = 14$$ ______________________

$$-2x = -3$$ ______________________

$$x=\frac{3}{2}$$ ______________________

14. In each problem, find the **mistake** and write a sentence describing the error. Also, write a suggestion so that any student who makes this type of mistake will have a way to remember not to make the error again.

Solve.

a. $$\frac{2}{x}-\frac{7}{5}=\frac{6}{15}$$

$$\left(\frac{2}{x}\right)\left(\frac{15x}{1}\right)-\left(\frac{7}{5}\right)\left(\frac{15x}{1}\right)=\frac{6}{15}\left(\frac{15x}{1}\right)$$

$$30x - 21x = 6$$

$$-5x = 6$$

$$x=\frac{-6}{5}$$

b. $$\frac{3x-2}{2}-\frac{x-5}{4}=\frac{7}{12}$$

$$\left(\frac{12}{1}\right)\left(\frac{3x-2}{2}\right)-\frac{12}{1}\left(\frac{x-5}{4}\right)=\left(\frac{12}{1}\right)\left(\frac{7}{12}\right)$$

$$6(3x-2)-3(x-5)=7$$

$$18x-12-3x-15=7$$

$$15x-27=7$$

$$15x=34$$

$$x=\frac{34}{15}$$

15. A classmate asks you to look over his work. The mathematics is correct. Make four suggestions that would improve the presentation of the problem. Review the problem the way a teacher might look at it.

Solve the equation $$\overset{\overset{3}{\cancel{12}}}{\frac{2x+1}{\cancel{4}}}-\overset{\overset{4}{\cancel{12}}}{\frac{x+7}{\cancel{3}}}=\overset{\overset{1}{\cancel{12}}}{\frac{7}{\cancel{12}}}$$

$6x+3-4x-28 \quad 7$

$2x+3 \quad 35$

$2x \quad 32$

$x=32/2$

Study Tips: 1. If any of the problems is not clear to you, ask questions in the next class session, see your instructor during office hours, or go to the Learning Assistance Lab.

2. Review the MAT 011 web site for help.

3. Detailed solutions to problems 3, 5, 7, 9, 10, and 11 can be found on the MAT 011 Electronic Resource page. See page vii.

SECTION 3.7 RATIO AND PROPORTION PROBLEMS PREVIEW

Objective: This section will cover applications involving fractions.

Vocabulary: A **ratio** is the comparison of two quantities that have the same units. A ratio is usually expressed as a fraction.

A **rate** is the comparison of two quantities that have different units. A rate is usually expressed as a fraction.

Example 1. Which is the better buy? 10 ounces of peanut butter for $1.24 or 16 ounces of peanut butter for $1.89?

To answer the question, form the ratio, $\frac{\text{cost}}{\text{ounces}}$.

$\frac{1.24}{10} = .124$ For 10 ounces, the cost is 12.4 cents per ounce.

$\frac{1.89}{16} = .1181$ For 16 ounces, the cost is 11.81 cents per ounce.

The 16 ounce jar of peanut butter is the better buy because it is cheaper per ounce.

The two rates in the problem are $\frac{1.24}{10}$ and $\frac{1.89}{16}$.

Vocabulary: A **proportion** is a statement which indicates two ratios or rates are equal. (or two equal fractions.)

Example 2. Solve the proportion problem. $\frac{8}{x} = \frac{12}{17}$

Rule: The basic procedure for solving a proportion problem is to cross multiply.

$$\frac{8}{x} \times \frac{12}{17}$$

Cross multiplying means to multiply the denominator of one fraction with the numerator of the other fraction. This can only be done when solving a proportion problem.

$\frac{8}{x} \times \frac{12}{17}$	
$17 \bullet 8 = 12x$	Crossed multiplied.
$136 = 12x$	Multiplied.
$11.33 = x$	Divided both sides by 12.

Study Tip: You should write the procedure on a note card, along with an example, so you can understand how to solve proportion problems. Review the card frequently.

Example 3. Two people pooled their money to buy lottery tickets. Darrel contributed $25 while Selena put in $20. If they won 8.2 million dollars, how much should each person receive?

Organize the information in a table for each person.

Darrel

	Tickets	**Winnings**
Share	25	?
Total	25 + 20	8.2 million

The ratio will be $\frac{\text{Share}}{\text{Total}}$. There are two ratios, one for tickets and one for winnings. These two ratios should be equal.

$$\frac{25}{45}=\frac{W}{8.2}$$

$25 \bullet 8.2 = 45W$ Crossed multiplied.

$205 = 45W$ Multiplied.

$4.556 = W$ Divided both sides by 45.

Darrel should win 4.556 million dollars.

Explanation: The answer above is actually $W = 4.\overline{5}$, or in practical terms, W = 4.55555556. So Darrel should win $4,555,555.56.

Selena

	Tickets	**Winnings**
Share	20	?
Total	25 + 20	8.2 million

The ratio will be $\frac{\text{Share}}{\text{Total}}$. There are two ratios, one for tickets and one for their winnings. These two ratios should be equal.

$$\frac{20}{45}=\frac{W}{8.2}$$

$20 \bullet 8.2 = 45W$ Crossed multiplied.

$164 = 45W$ Multiplied.

$3.644 = W$ Divided both sides by 45.

Selena should win 3.644 million dollars.

Explanation: Using the same reasoning as in computing Darrel's answer, the answer above is actually $W = 3.6\overline{4}$, or in practical terms, W = 3.644444444. So Selena should win $3,644,444.44.

Example 4. In order to estimate the number of fish in a lake, 85 fish are caught, tagged, and released. Later, 64 fish are caught, and 23 have been tagged. Estimate the total number of fish in the lake.

Let T represent the total number of fish in the lake. For the second catch, 23 fish were tagged out of a total of 64. When the information is organized in a table, the rows should be labeled **Tagged** and **Total**. Since fish are caught twice, the columns should be labeled **First Catch** and **Second Catch**.

	First Catch	**Second Catch**
Tagged	85	23
Total	T	64

Explanation: The first catch, 85 fish are tagged out of the lake's total fish population.

The ratio is $\frac{\text{tagged}}{\text{total}}$. The first catch's ratio should equal the second catch's ratio.

$\frac{85}{T} = \frac{23}{64}$

$85 \bullet 64 = 23T$ Cross Multiply.

$5,440 = 23T$ Multiply.

$237 = T$ Divide both sides by 23.

We estimate that there are 237 fish in the lake.

Summary: Ratio and proportion problems can occur in everyday life. Maybe you don't divide lottery winnings or count fish in a lake every day, but this application can be used to fairly divide something based on each person's input, estimate something based on a sample, determine dosage of medicine based on weight, convert recipes, and determine cost per unit.

Definitions:

Ratio: A ratio is the comparison of two quantities that have the same units. A ratio is usually expressed as a fraction.

Rate: A rate is the comparison of two quantities that have different units. A rate is usually expressed as a fraction.

Proportions: A proportion is a statement which indicates two ratios or rates are equal. (or two equal fractions.)

To solve proportion problems, cross multiply.

To solve applications:

- Create a table that organizes the information in the problem.
- Decide what units make up the ratio.
- Set up the proportion and solve.

CLASS WORK

Ratios and Rates:

1. Bob earns $250 each week, but $15 is withheld for medical insurance. Find the ratio of medical insurance to total pay.

2. Which is the better buy?

   8 oz. of jelly for $1.59 or 12 oz. of jelly for $1.80?

3. If a line rises 8 units for every 2 horizontal units, what is the slope of the line?

4. A ratio is:

   A rate is:

Proportions:

5. A proportion is:

Solve:

6. $\frac{x}{5} = \frac{7}{15}$

7. $\frac{6}{x} = \frac{5}{7}$

8. In order to establish the number of fish in a lake, 30 fish are caught, tagged, and released. Later 70 fish are caught, and 14 are found to have been tagged. Estimate the number of fish in the lake.

9. Two people put their money together to buy lottery tickets. The first person contributed \$15, and the second person put in \$25. If they won 2.4 million dollars, how much does each person win?

10. Many successful MAT 011 students take CHE 121 General Inorganic Chemistry to fulfill their science requirement at MCCC. The following problem comes from CHE 121.

Charles' Law: The volume of gas is directly proportional to its Kelvin temperature for a fixed amount of gas at a constant pressure. That is, V (volume) divided by T (temperature) is constant. Charles' Law can be stated as a proportion problem

$$\frac{V_1}{T_1} = \frac{V_2}{T_2}$$

Where V_1 is the volume of the gas at temperature T_1 and V_2 is the volume of the gas at temperature T_2.

Note: Kelvin is a temperature scale similar to Celsius. Kelvin = C^{o} + 273.15. The temperature of 0 Kelvin or -273.15^{o} Celsius is considered the coldest possible temperature.

An average adult inhales a volume of 0.50 liters of air with each breath. If the air is warmed from room temperature (20° C = 293 K) to body temperature (37° C = 310 K) while in the lungs, what is the volume of the air when exhaled?

GROUP EXERCISE

1. Three people pooled their money to buy lottery tickets. The first person contributed $20, the second put in $30 and the third gave $35. If they won 7.8 million dollars, how much did each person win?

Go Back: Review Example 3 on page 297 or Problem 9 on page 300. Also, make sure you practice good group work habits. Make sure everyone is involved in solving the problems.

2. To determine the number of people who voted for Al Gore in Florida during the 2000 presidential election, CBS polled 160 people when they exited their polling place. Of 160 people, 82 said that they voted for Gore. If there are 5,816,000 registered voters in Florida and assuming they all vote, use a proportion to predict the total number of people who voted for Gore in Florida.

HOMEWORK EXERCISES

Study Tips: 1. Do your homework with a friend.
2. Review your note cards.

Skill Building Exercises

1. Solve each proportion problem:

   a. $\frac{6}{x} = \frac{9}{4}$

   b. $\frac{7x}{2} = \frac{6}{5}$

Practice Exercises

2. Which is the better buy?

   75 ounces of laundry detergent for $2.10 or
   90 ounces of laundry detergent for $2.70

Go Back: Review example 1 on page 296 or problem 2 on page 299.

3. Which is the better buy?

   10 ounces of tuna for $1.09 or
   15 ounces of tuna for $1.61

4. To estimate the number of bears in a forest, 8 are caught, tagged, and released. Later 9 bears are caught, and 2 are found to have been tagged. Estimate the number of bears in the forest.

Go Back: Review example 4 on page 298 or problem 8 on page 300.

5. If a car can go 110 miles on 5 gallons of gas, how far can it go on 12 gallons of gas?

6. To estimate the number of people in Reading, population 27,000, who have no health insurance, 160 people were polled, and 18 said they had no health insurance. Estimate the number of people in Reading who don't have any health insurance.

7. A laser printer can print 7 pages every 2 minutes. How long will it take to print 81 pages?

8. Three people pooled their money to buy lottery tickets. The first person contributed \$20; the second put in \$24, and the third gave \$31. If they won 12.6 million dollars, how much did each person win?

Go Back: Review example 3 on page 297 or problem 9 on page 300.

9. The area of a circle is indicated by the formula

$$A = \pi r^2$$

(π is approximatly 3.14 or use the pi key on your calculator; the radius, r is one half the diameter.)

   a. One pizza has a diameter of 10 inches. Another has a diameter of 14 inches. How much larger is the 14 inch pizza than the 10 inch one?

   b. If the 10 inch pizza costs \$5.95, and the 14 inch pizza costs \$6.95, which size pizza is the better buy? Write a sentence explaining why.

   c. If a 12 inch (diameter) pizza costs \$7.99, what is a fair price for a 6 inch diameter pizza?

Reading and Writing Mathematics

10. Ratio and proportion problems occur frequently in daily life. Write down a situation where you had to solve a ratio or proportion problem.

Study Tip: Detailed solutions to problems 1a, b, 3, 4, 5, 6, 7, 8, 9a, b, and c can be found on the MAT 011 Electronic Resource page. See page vii.

CHAPTER 3 REVIEW

This unit introduces exponents and algebraic fractions. Many of these skills are needed in MAT 100, Intermediate Algebra. Since the content is so important and can be confusing, plan to spend extra time in test preparation.

Section 3.1: Introduction to Positive Exponents:

Definition: a^n means a times itself n times.

Example 1. Compute -5.8^6 using your calculator.
$-5.8^6 = -38{,}068.69254$

Example 2. Compute $(-5.8)^6$ using your calculator.
$(-5.8)^6 = 38{,}068.69254$

Example 3. There are 1,000 bacteria initially present in a culture. The culture grows at a rate of 4% an hour. Complete the table below to find an equation that models the number of bacteria.

Hours	**Calculation**	**Number of Bacteria**
initially		1,000
1	$1{,}000 \bullet 1.04$	1,040
2	$1{,}000 \bullet 1.04^2$	1,082
3	$1{,}000 \bullet 1.04^3$	1,125
4	$1{,}000 \bullet 1.04^4$	1,170
h	$1{,}000 \bullet 1.04^h$	B

The equation is $B = 1{,}000 \bullet 1.04^h$.

Section 3.2: Negative Exponents and Scientific Notation:

Definition: A negative exponent requires the use of the reciprocal to make the exponent positive..

Example 4. $\left(\frac{2}{3}\right)^{-5} = \left(\frac{3}{2}\right)^5$

Example 5. Compute -3.5^{-4} using your calculator.
$-3.5^{-4} = -0.006664$

Example 6. Use the formula $P = A\left[\frac{i}{1-(1+i)^{-n}}\right]$ to find the monthly payments on a 60 month car loan of $22,000 at an annual interest rate of 4%.

P is what we want to find.
A = 22,000
i = 0.003333 (.04/12)
n = 60

$$P = 22{,}000\left[\frac{0.003333}{1-(1+0.003333)^{-60}}\right]$$
$$P = 22{,}000\left[\frac{0.003333}{1-(1.003333)^{-60}}\right]$$
$$P = 22{,}000\left[\frac{0.003333}{1-0.8190}\right]$$
$$P = 22{,}000\left[\frac{0.003333}{0.181}\right]$$
$$P = 22{,}000[0.01841]$$
$$P = 405.02$$

The monthly payment for the car loan is \$405.02.

Definition: A number in scientific notation has the form $P \bullet 10^n$ where $1 \leq P < 10$.

Example 7. Write 2,450,000,000,000 in scientific notation.

$$2{,}450{,}000{,}000{,}000 = 2.45 \bullet 10^{12}$$

Explanation: The 2 is in the 10^{12} place.

Example 8. Write $5.38 \bullet 10^{-7}$ in decimal notation.

$$5.38 \bullet 10^{-7} = 0.000000538$$

Example 9. Use your calculator to compute $\dfrac{4.89 \bullet 10^{12}}{1.56 \bullet 10^{-7}}$.

$$\frac{4.89 \bullet 10^{12}}{1.56 \bullet 10^{-7}} = 3.135 \bullet 10^{19}$$

Section 3.3: Properties of Exponents:

The properties of exponents are:

Property 1. $a^n \bullet a^m = a^{n+m}$

Property 2. $(a^n)^m = a^{nm}$

Property 3. $(ab)^n = a^n b^n$

Property 4. $a^{-n} = \dfrac{1}{a^n}$

Property 5. $\dfrac{1}{a^{-n}} = a^n$

Property 6. $\dfrac{a^n}{a^m} = a^{n-m}$

Property 7. $a^0 = 1$

Property 8. $\left(\dfrac{a}{b}\right)^n = \dfrac{a^n}{b^n}$

Example 10. Simplify $(4x^5)^3$. Write with positive exponents.

$$(4x^5)^3 = 4^3(x^5)^3 = 64x^{15}$$

Example 11. Simplify $\frac{6x}{2x^{-4}}$. Write with positive exponents.

$$\frac{6x}{2x^{-4}} = \frac{6xx^4}{2} = 3x^5$$

Section 3.4: Introduction to Algebraic Fractions:

To reduce fractions: Factor the numerator and denominator and then cancel like factors.

Example 12. Reduce $\frac{18x^3}{10x^5}$.

$$\frac{18x^3}{10x^5} = \frac{2 \bullet 9 \bullet x \bullet x \bullet x}{2 \bullet 5 \bullet x \bullet x \bullet x \bullet x \bullet x} = \frac{9}{5x^2}$$

To multiply fractions: $\frac{a}{b} \bullet \frac{c}{d} = \frac{ac}{bd}$ multiply the numerators and denominators and then reduce.

Example 13. Multiply $\frac{15x^2}{6} \bullet \frac{8}{5x^4}$.

$$\frac{15x^2}{6} \bullet \frac{8}{5x^4} = \frac{5 \bullet 3 \bullet x \bullet x}{3 \bullet 2} \bullet \frac{4 \bullet 2}{5 \bullet x \bullet x \bullet x \bullet x} = \frac{4}{x^2}$$

To divide fractions: $\frac{a}{b} \div \frac{c}{d} = \frac{ad}{bc}$, take the reciprocal of the divisor then multiply. Then reduce.

Example 14. Divide $\frac{12}{27x^2} \div \frac{4x}{9}$.

$$\frac{12}{27x^2} \div \frac{4x}{9} = \frac{4 \bullet 3}{9 \bullet 3 \bullet x \bullet x} \bullet \frac{9}{4x} = \frac{1}{x^3}$$

Section 3.5: Adding and Subtracting Fractions:

To add and subtract fractions:

4. Find the least common denominator, LCD.
   a. For numbers, the least common denominator is the smallest number into which all of the denominators divide evenly.
   b. For variables, the least common denominator is the variable with the highest exponent.
5. Convert each fraction to a fraction with the least common denominator.
   a. Decide what you need to multiply each denominator by to get the LCD.
   b. Multiply the numerator and denominator by this quantity.
6. Combine the numerators and write as a single fraction.

Example 15. Add $\frac{5}{4x^2}+\frac{7}{6x}$.

$$\frac{5}{4x^2}+\frac{7}{6x}= \qquad \text{LCD } 12x^2.$$

$$\frac{5}{4x^2}\left(\frac{3}{3}\right)+\frac{7}{6x}\left(\frac{2x}{2x}\right)=$$

$$\frac{15}{12x^2}+\frac{14x}{12x^2}=$$

$$\frac{15+14x}{12x^2}$$

Section 3.6: Solving Equations with Fractions:

To solve an equation involving fractions, multiply all the terms by the LCD and then reduce.

Example 16. Solve $\frac{2x}{9}-\frac{4x-5}{6}=2$.

$\frac{2x}{9}-\frac{4x-5}{6}=2$	The LCD is 18
$\left(\frac{18}{1}\right)\frac{2x}{9}-\left(\frac{18}{1}\right)\frac{4x-5}{6}=(18)2$	Multiplied all the terms by 18.
$(2)2x-3(4x-5)=(18)2$	Reduced.
$4x-12x+15=36$	Used distributive property.
$-8x+15=36$	Combined like terms.
$-8x=21$	Subtracted 15 from both sides.
$x=\frac{-21}{8}$	Divided both sides by –8.

Section 3.7: Ratio and Proportion Problems:

Definitions:

Ratio: A ratio is a fraction that compares two different quantities.

Proportions: A proportion is two equal ratios.

To solve proportion problems, cross multiply.

Example 17. Two school clubs have a car washing fundraiser. Eight members from the Math Club and five members from the Astronomy Club participate. If they raise $462, how much should the Math Club receive?

- Organize the information into a table.

Math Club

	Money	**Participants**
Share	?	8
Total	462	8 + 5

- Set up the proportion problem.

$$\frac{M}{462} = \frac{8}{13}$$

$13M = 3{,}696$ Cross Multiply.

$M = 284.31$ Divide both sides by 13.

The Math Club should receive $284.31.

Study Tips:
1. Practice the review test starting on the next page by placing yourself under realistic exam conditions
2. Find a quiet place and use a timer to simulate test conditions.
3. Write your answers in your homework notebook or make copies of the exam. You may then re-take the exam for extra practice.
4. Check your answers. The answers to the review test are on page 459.
5. There is an additional exam available on the MAT 011 web page, **www.mc3.edu/aa/career/MATHSCI/mathprog/mat011/mat011.htm**
6. Do NOT wait until the night before to study. Practice.

CHAPTER 3 REVIEW TEST

1. Simplify. Write with positive exponents.

a. $x^5 \cdot x^2$

b. $\frac{x^3}{x^5}$

c. y^0

d. $\left(x^5\right)^2$

e. $\left(2x^2\right)^3$

f. $x^{-7}x^2$

g. $\frac{x^2}{x^{-5}}$

h. $\frac{9x^{-2}}{x^3}$

2. Compute using a calculator.

a. 2.5^{-3}

b. -3.6^4

c. $(-3.6)^4$

3. Compute using a calculator.

a. $\left(2.5\text{x}10^5\right)\left(8.6\text{x}10^7\right)$

b. $\left(8.1\text{x}10^{-3}\right)\left(6.2\text{x}10^{-11}\right)$

4. Write in scientific notation.

a. 8,300,000

b. 0.000614

5. Write in decimal notation.

a. $4.2\text{x}10^5$

b. $3.1\text{x}10^{-3}$

6. Perform the indicated operation.

a. $\frac{4x^5}{3y^2} \cdot \frac{9x}{2y^3}$

b. $\frac{4x^2}{7} \div 14x^5$

c. $\frac{5}{2x} - \frac{7}{3x^2}$

d. $\frac{11}{5x} + \frac{1}{3}$

7. Steve and Sarah pool their money and buy $25 worth of lottery tickets. Steve puts in $10 and Sarah puts in $15. They won 1.75 million dollars. How should they split their winnings?

Study Tip: If you don't remember how to do a problem, look through the unit until you find an example similar to the one giving you difficulty.

8. There are 500 bacteria in a culture. The culture grows at 7% a day.

a. Complete the table.

DAY	CALCULATION	POPULATION
Initial Day		500
1 Day later		
2 Days later		
3 Days later		
n Days later		

b. What is the equation that relates population to number of days?

c. How many bacteria are there after 30 days?

d. How many bacteria are there after 60 days?

9. Use the formula:

Payment of Debts $$P = A\left[\frac{i}{1-(1+i)^{-n}}\right]$$

P is the monthly payment

A is the amount of the loan

n is the number of payments

i is the interest rate per month

a. Find the monthly payments of a 30 year mortgage at 9% annual interest on a \$200,000 home. (Hints: $i=\frac{0.09}{12}$ and $n = 12 \bullet 30$.)

b. If you can afford a \$300 car payment for 36 months at 4.5% annual interest what is the cost of the car? (Hint: $i=\frac{0.045}{12}$.)

10. Convert 10 miles to millimeters.
Conversions needed: 1 mile = 5,280 feet, 1 inch = 25.6 millimeters.

11. Solve.

a. $\frac{x}{3}+9=\frac{3x-3}{2}$

b. $\frac{x}{4}-\frac{x-3}{2}=2$

Study Tip: Detailed solutions to all the problems can be found on the MAT 011 Electronic Resource page. See page vii.

CHAPTER 4

QUADRATICS

SECTION 4.1 INTRODUCTION TO QUADRATICS
PREVIEW

Objectives: In this section, you will add, subtract, multiply, and graph quadratics.

Vocabulary: The standard format of a **quadratic equation** is $\mathbf{y = ax^2 + bx + c}$; a, b, c are constants; x is the independent variable, and y is the dependent variable. Quadratics are also called **second degree polynomials** because the highest exponent is 2. The slope-intercept equation from the second chapter, $y = mx + b$, is called a **first degree polynomial** because the highest exponent is one.

Why study quadratics? The graphs of quadratic equations result in parabolas (U shaped graphs that open up or down). This feature of quadratics makes them good models for describing the path of a ball thrown in the air or describing the profit of a company (examples of which you may see in Finite Mathematics, or Microeconomics.)

Example 1. A boy lying on his back uses a sling shot to fire a rock straight up in the air with an initial velocity (the force the boy uses to fire the rock) of 64 feet per second. The quadratic equation that models the height of the rock is

$$h = -16t^2 + 64t.$$

a. Find the height of the rock when t = 0.

In the formula, $h = -16t^2 + 64t$, replace t with 0.

$h = -16(0)^2 + 64(0)$
$h = 0$

The rock is zero feet in the air at zero seconds.
(This is the point right before he shoots the rock in the air.)

b. Find the height of the rock when t = 1.

In the formula, $h = -16t^2 + 64t$, replace t with 1.

$h = -16(1)^2 + 64(1)$
$h = -16(1) + 64(1)$
$h = 48$

Explanation: Only the "1" is being squared; the –16 is multiplied by 1^2.

The rock is 48 feet in the air at one second.

c. Find the height of the rock when t = 2.

In the formula, $h = -16t^2 + 64t$, replace t with 2.

$h = -16(2)^2 + 64(2)$
$h = -16(4) + 64(2)$
$h = -64 + 128$
$h = 64$

Explanation: Order of operations requires that you apply exponents before multiplying.

The rock is 64 feet in the air at 2 seconds.

d. Find the height of the rock when t = 3.
In the formula, $h = -16t^2 + 64t$, replace t with 3.

$$h = -16(3)^2 + 64(3)$$
$$h = -16(9) + 64(3)$$
$$h = -144 + 192$$
$$h = 48$$

The rock is 48 feet in the air at 3 seconds.

e. Find the height of the rock when t = 4.
In the formula, $h = -16t^2 + 64t$, replace t with 4.

$$h = -16(4)^2 + 64(4)$$
$$h = -16(16) + 64(4)$$
$$h = -256 + 256$$
$$h = 0$$

The rock is zero feet in the air at 4 seconds; that is, the rock has hit the ground.

f. Graph the points obtained in parts a through e.

The height of the rock depends on the time, so h is the dependent variable, and t is the independent variable. The points have the form (t, h).

Organize the results from parts a through e into a table:

t	h	(t, h)
0	0	(0, 0)
1	48	(1, 48)
2	64	(2, 64)
3	48	(3, 48)
4	0	(4, 0)

The points to graph are (0, 0), (1, 48), (2, 64), (3, 48), (4, 0).

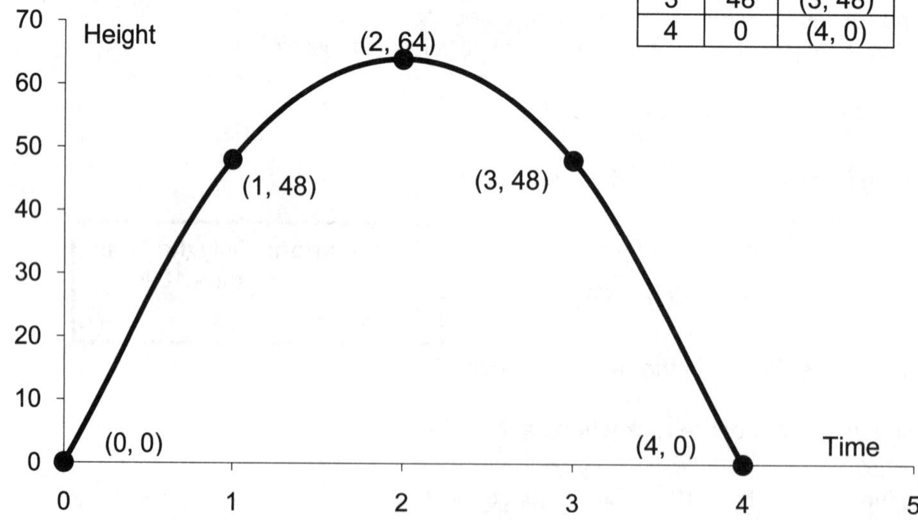

From the graph, the rock reaches its greatest height at 2 seconds. The maximum height is 64 feet. The maximum or minimum point of a quadratic is called the **vertex**. You will learn how to find the vertex in Section 4.3, "Quadratic Applications and Graphs."

From the graph, the rock is on the ground at zero seconds (right before the boy shoots it) and at 4 seconds (when the rock lands). These points are the **time intercepts**. You will learn how to find them in the next Section 4.2, "Applications of the Quadratic Formula."

Adding and Subtracting Quadratics:

Vocabulary: To add or subtract quadratics, combine like terms. **Like terms,** originally presented in the Section 1.3, "Simplifying Algebraic Expressions," have the same variable and the same exponent. For example $2x^2$ and $5x^2$ are like terms while $3x^2$ and $7x$ are not.

. A **coefficient,** originally presented in Section 1.3, "Simplifying Algebraic Expressions," is the number multiplying the variable. For example, the coefficient of $2x$ is 2, and the coefficient of $-x^2$ is -1.

Rule: To combine like terms, add their coefficients

Example 2. Simplify $4x + 7x^2 - 3x + 4x^2$.

The like terms are $4x$, $-3x$ and $7x^2$, $4x^2$.

To simplify, add the coefficients of the like terms, $4 - 3$ and $7 + 4$.

$$4x + 7x^2 - 3x + 4x^2 = x + 11x^2$$

Recall the **distributive property**: Definition $a(b + c) = ab + ac$.

Example 3. Simplify $3(6x - 5)$

$3(6x-5) =$	Can't combine the unlike terms inside the parentheses.
$3 \bullet 6x - 3 \bullet 5 =$	Used the distributive property; multiplied 6x by 3 and then –5 by 3.
$18x - 15$	

Example 4. Simplify $2(4x^2+3x)-5(2x^2-3)$.

$2(4x^2+3x)-5(2x^2-3)=$	
$8x^2+6x-10x^2+15=$	Used the distributive property.
$-2x^2+6x+15$	Combined like terms.

Example 5. The equation for profit is: Profit = Revenue – Cost

If the revenue equation for a company is:

$$R=-2x^2+45x$$

and the cost equation is:

$$C=2x^2-23x+56.$$

Find the profit equation for the company.

$P = \quad R \quad - \quad C$ $P=(-2x^2+45x)-(2x^2-23x+56)$	Substituted the revenue and cost equations into the formula for profit. Must use parentheses.
$=1(-2x^2+45x)-1(2x^2-23x+56)$ $=-2x^2+45x-2x^2+23x-56$	Used the distributive property. Multiplied the revenue equation by 1 and the cost equation by –1.
$=-4x^2+68x-56$	Combined like terms.

Multiplying Two Binomials.

Vocabulary: A **bi**nomial has two terms (just as a **bi**cycle has two wheels).

Rule: To multiply two binomials, multiply each term of the first by each term of the second.

Example 7. Multiply $(x+2)(5x+3)$.

$$(x+2)(5x+3) =$$
$$x \bullet 5x + x \bullet 3 + 2 \bullet 5x + 2 \bullet 3 = \quad \text{Multiplied x by 5x and 3 and multiply 2 by 5x and 3.}$$
$$5x^2 + 3x + 10x + 6 =$$
$$5x^2 + 13x + 6 \quad \text{Combined like terms.}$$

FOIL is a simple mnemonic to remember how to multiply two binomials.

Example 8. Multiply $(8x+6)(x+7)$.

F indicates the product of the **F**irst terms, $8x \bullet x = 8x^2$.
O indicates the product of the **O**uter terms, $8x \bullet 7 = 56x$.
I indicates the product of the **I**nner terms, $6 \bullet x = 6x$.
L indicates the product of the **L**ast terms, $6 \bullet 7 = 42$.

F O I L

$$(8x+6)(x+7) = 8x \bullet x + 8x \bullet 7 + 6 \bullet x + 6 \bullet 7$$
$$= 8x^2 + 56x + 6x + 42$$
$$= 8x^2 + 62x + 42$$

Example 9. Multiply $(2x-5)^2$.

$$(2x-5)^2 = (2x-5)(2x-5)$$

F O I L

$$= 2x \bullet 2x - 2x \bullet 5 - 5 \bullet 2x - 5 \bullet (-5)$$
$$= 4x^2 - 10x - 10x + 25$$
$$= 4x^2 - 20x + 25$$

Study Tip: Write a note card explaining the mnemonic FOIL. Review the card frequently.

Summary: Quadratics are important equations in physics and microeconomics. The technique for adding and subtracting quadratics is the same as we have been practicing all semester; that is, add or subtract the like terms. To multiply, use the distributive property or **FOIL**. The vertex of the quadratic will be explained in more detail in the section on "Graphing Quadratics and Applications." The vertex is the maximum or minimum point on the graph of the quadratic.

CLASS WORK

Evaluating quadratics:

1. William Tell shoots an arrow straight up into the air with an initial velocity of 160 feet per second. The height (in feet) of the arrow is indicated by the equation

$$h = -16t^2 + 160t + 6,$$

where t is the number of seconds the arrow is in the air.
Find the height of the arrow for:

a. $t = 0$

b. $t = 2$

c. $t = 5$

d. $t = 8$

e. $t = 10$

f. According to the calculations above, when will the arrow reach its maximum height (vertex)?

g. According to the calculations above, when will the arrow hit the ground?

h. Graph the points obtained in a through e.

t	h	Ordered Pair (t, h)
0	6	(0, 6)
2	262	(2, 262)
5	406	(5, 406)
8	262	(8, 262),
10	6	(10, 6)

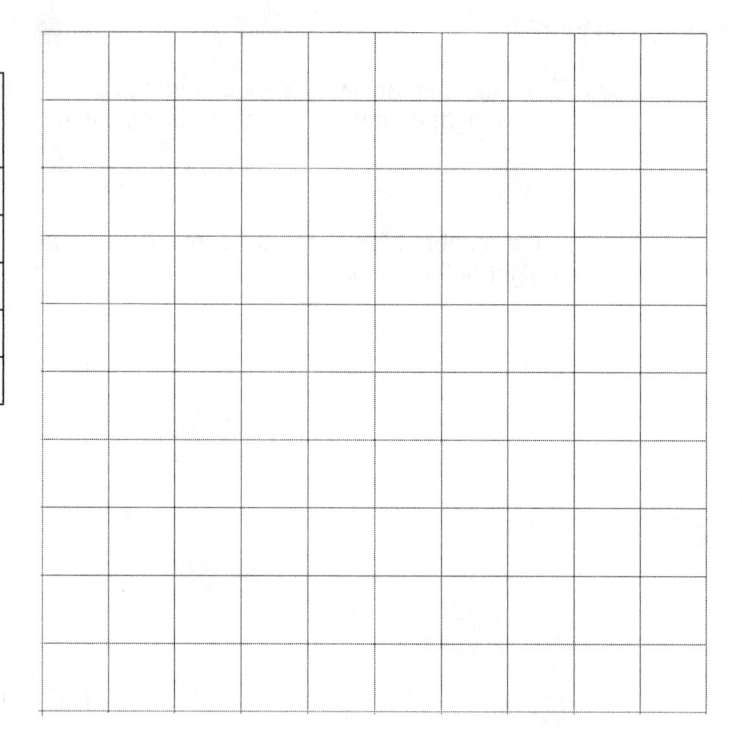

Combining like terms

2. What are like terms?

3. How do we combine like terms?

4. Simplify.

a. $-8x^2 + 2x - 8 - 6x^2 + 10x + 2$

b. $2(3x^2 + 5x - 10) - 4(x^2 - 6x + 3)$

c. $5(2x^2 + 5) - (8x^2 + 2x - 4)$

d. The equation for profit is Profit = Revenue – Cost. If the revenue equation for a company is

$$R = -5x^2 + 17x$$

and the cost equation for a company is

$$C = 3x^2 - 27x + 40.$$

Find the equation for profit.

Multiplying two binomials (FOIL)

5. What is a binomial?

6. Multiply.

a. $(x + 5)(x + 3)$

b. $(x - 6)(x + 2)$

c. $(x - 7)(x - 5)$

d. $(2x + 5)(3x - 8)$

e. $(3x + 4)^2$

GROUP EXERCISE

Study Tips: 1. Review pertinent note cards first.

2. Have one person record the problem as the group solves it.
3. Have another person do the graphing as the group explains it.

For Triple Bubble Gum Company, the cost of making x thousand pieces of gum a day is $C = x^2 - 19x + 48$, and the revenue from selling x thousand pieces of gum a day is $R = -x^2 + 9x$.

1. Find the profit equation for Triple Bubble Gum Co.
   (Profit = Revenue – Cost)

2. Find the profit for

   a. $x = 0$ b. $x = 2$ c. $x = 3$

   d. $x = 7$ e. $x = 10$ f. $x = 12$

3. Graph the points obtained in Parts a through f.

x	p	Ordered Pair (x, p)

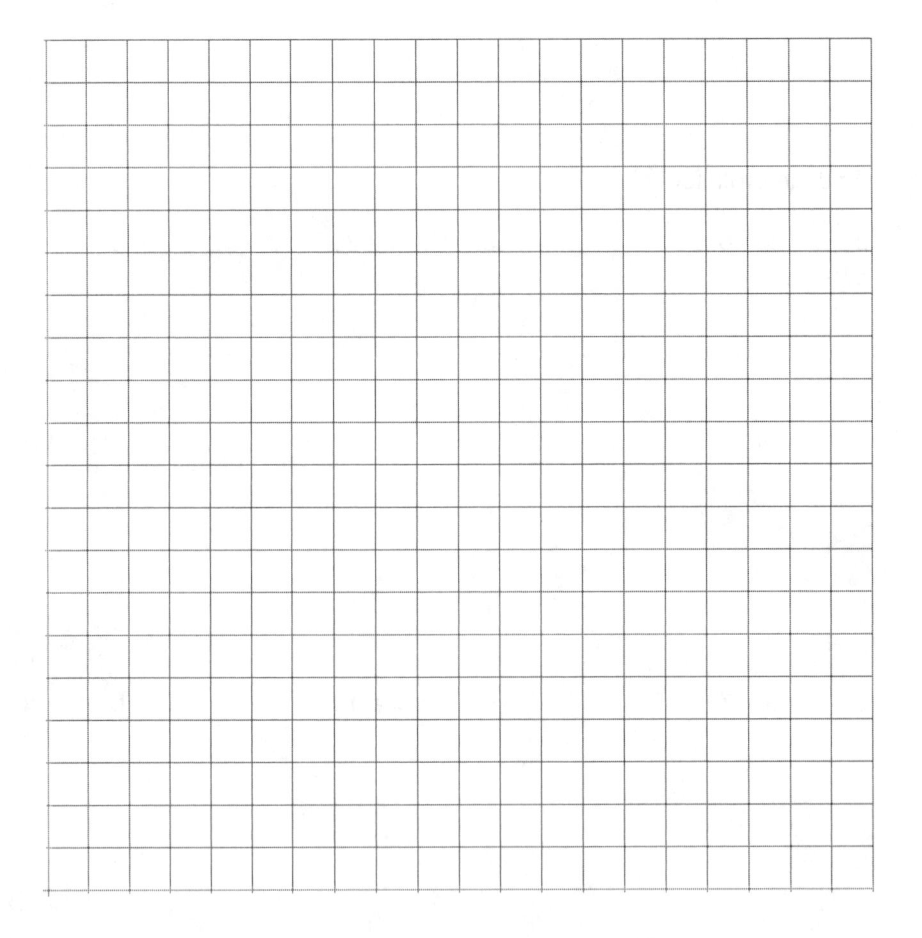

4. When will the company make no profit or x intercepts?
(These points are called the **break even** points)

5. When will the company make the most profit?
(this point is called the **vertex**.)

HOMEWORK EXERCISES

Study Tips: 1. Remember to use your loose leaf notebook.
2. Have all of your graphing materials at hand.
3. Review problems from Preview, Class Work, and Group Exercise.

Skill Building Exercises

1. Perform the indicated operation.

   a. 3^2 b. $-16(3)^2$ c. $-16(3)^2 + 256(3) + 80$

2. Simplify

   a. $4x + 5 - 3x - 6$ b. $5 - (3x - 2)$

Practice Exercises

3. A rocket is launched from the top of a cliff with an initial velocity of 256 feet per second. The height (in feet) of the rocket is indicated by the equation:

$$h = -16t^2 + 256t + 80,$$

where t is the number of seconds the rocket is in the air.
Find the height of the rocket for

   a. $t = 0$ b. $t = 3$ c. $t = 8$

   d. $t = 10$ e. $t = 16$ f. $t = 17$

   g. According to the calculations above, when will the rocket reach its maximum height?

   h. According to the calculations above, estimate when the rocket hits the ground.

   i. Graph the points a through f.

4. Simplify

   a. $-2x^2 + 8x - 10 - 2x^2 + 4x + 7$ b. $3(2x^2 + 5x - 8) - 2(5x^2 + 6x - 2)$

   c. $(-16x^2 + 8x - 5) - (3x^2 - 5x + 2)$ d. $3(-2x^2 + 6) + 2(3x^2 - 9x)$

   e. $2(3x^2 - 8x - 5) + 3(-4x^2 - 3x + 8)$ f. $(-3x^2 + 4x - 10) - (8x^2 - 2x + 5)$

5. The equation for profit is Profit = Revenue – Cost. If the revenue equation for a company is

$$R = -3x^2 + 8x$$

and the cost equation for a company is

$$C = x^2 - 9x + 72.$$

Find the equation for profit.

6. Multiply.

a. $(x + 2)(x + 3)$

b. $(x + 4)(x - 3)$

c. $(x - 7)(x - 4)$

d. $(x + 8)(x - 8)$

e. $(x + 9)(x - 9)$

f. $(3x - 1)(2x + 3)$

g. $(x + 3)^2$

h. $(x - 5)^2$

Reading and Writing Mathematics

7. What are like terms?

8. How do you combine like terms?

9. In each problem, find the **mistake** and write a sentence describing it. Also, write a suggestion so that any student who makes this type of error will have a way to remember not to make the mistake again.

a. $3(3x^2 + 4x - 7) - (2x^2 - 5x + 4) = 9x^2 + 12x - 21 - 2x^2 - 5x + 4$
$= 7x^2 + 7x - 17$

b. $(x + 6)^2 = x^2 + 36$

c. $2(5x^2 + x - 4) - 3(2x + 6) = 10x^2 + 2x - 8 - 6x - 18$
$= 12x^2 - 6x - 26$

10. In the problem below, describe each step in simplifying the quadratic.

$2(x^2 - 3x + 5) - (4x^2 + 6x - 1)$

$= 2x^2 - 6x + 10 - 4x^2 - 6x + 1$ ______________________________

$= -2x^2 - 12x + 11$ ______________________________

SECTION 4.2 APPLICATIONS OF THE QUADRATIC FORMULA PREVIEW

Objective: This section will show you how to solve quadratic equations.

Vocabulary: The **quadratic equation** is $ax^2 + bx + c = 0$. a, b and c are constants, and x is the variable.

The **quadratic formula**, $x = \frac{-b \pm \sqrt{b^2 - 4ac}}{2a}$, is used to solve a quadratic equation.

Analyzing $x = \frac{-b \pm \sqrt{b^2 - 4ac}}{2a}$.

- a, b, and c are numbers that will be substituted into the formula.

  a is the coefficient of the squared variable.

  b is the coefficient of the variable to the first power.

  c is the constant.

- The symbol $\pm$ gives two solutions to the equation.
  One solution is with the + sign, $x = \frac{-b + \sqrt{b^2 - 4ac}}{2a}$ and the other solution is with the – sign, $x = \frac{-b - \sqrt{b^2 - 4ac}}{2a}$.

- $\sqrt{}$ is the square root symbol.

  1. The $\sqrt{16} = 4$ because $4^2 = 16$.
  2. The $\sqrt{35} \approx 5.916$ because $5.916^2 \approx 35$.
  3. Your calculator is essential for this section. Make sure you can find the $\sqrt{}$ button on your calculator.
  4. You can only compute the square root of nonnegative numbers.
  5. If you try to compute $\sqrt{-5}$ your calculator will give an error message.
     If you take Intermediate Algebra, you will learn about square roots of negative numbers.

Study Tip: Write the quadratic equation and quadratic formula on notecards, so you can reference them when you do your homework.

Example 1. Suppose you are standing on top of a cliff 375 feet above the canyon floor, and you throw a rock up in the air with an initial velocity of 82 feet per second. The equation that models the height of the rock above the canyon floor is:

$$h = -16t^2 + 82t + 375.$$

Find how long it takes the rock to hit the canyon floor.

Find t when h = 0.
Solve $0 = -16t^2 + 82t + 375$.

Explanation: One side of the quadratic equation must be zero.

Indentify the constants a, b, and c.

$a = -16$, $b = 82$, $c = 375$

Explanation:
a is the coefficient of the variable that is squared.

b is the coefficient of the variable to the first power.

c is the constant.

Use the quadratic formula

$$t = \frac{-b \pm \sqrt{b^2 - 4ac}}{2a}$$

with $a = -16$, $b = 82$, and $c = 375$.

$$t = \frac{-82 \pm \sqrt{82^2 - 4(-16)(375)}}{2(-16)}$$

Substituted a, b, and c into the quadratic formula.

$$t = \frac{-82 \pm 175.3}{2(-16)}$$

Used calculator to simplify the square root. You should see $\sqrt{(}$ when you use the square root key.
Then type $82^2 + 4 \bullet 16 \bullet 375)$ and =.
It is + because $-4(-16)(375) = 4(16)(375)$.
These directions are for the TI-30X IIS calculator.

$$t = \frac{-82 + 175.3}{2(-16)} \text{ or } t = \frac{-82 - 175.3}{2(-16)}$$

Separated the formula into the + and – parts.

$$t = \frac{93.3}{-32} \text{ or } t = \frac{-257.3}{-32}$$

Combined the numerators.

$$t = -2.916 \text{ or } t = 8.041$$

Divided.

$T = -2.916$ is a meaningless answer since t is how long it takes the rock to hit the canyon floor, and you can't have negative time.

$T = 8.041$ seconds is how long it takes the rock to hit canyon floor.

The rock will hit the canyon floor in 8.041 seconds.

Example 2. A rancher has 500 yards of fencing to enclose two adjacent pig pens that rest against the barn. If the area of the two pens must total 20,700 square yards, what should the dimensions of the pens be?

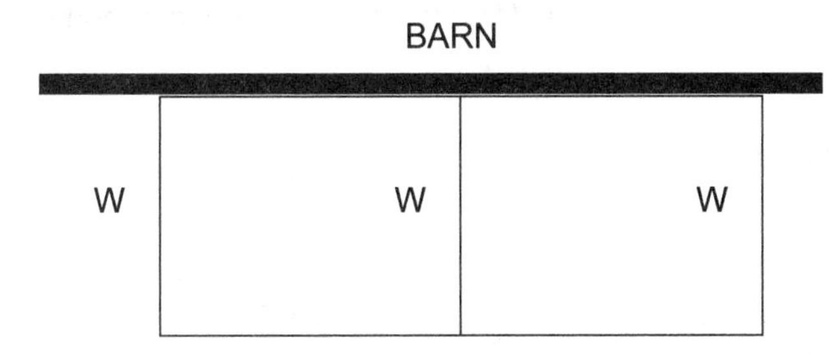

L represents the length of both pens.

a. Use the table to find the equation for the area of the pens.

Width	Length	Area
50	$500 - 3 \bullet 50 = 350$	$50 \bullet 350 = 17{,}500$
75	$500 - 3 \bullet 75 = 275$	$75 \bullet 275 = 20{,}625$
85	$500 - 3 \bullet 85 = 245$	$85 \bullet 245 = 20{,}825$
W	$500 - 3 \bullet W = L$	$W(500 - 3W)$

Explanation: Since there are 3 widths, we multiply 50 times 3. The rancher has 500 yards of fencing, so subtract $3 \bullet 50$ from 500 to find the length.

b. Simplify the equation for area.

$A = W(500 - 3W)$

$= 500W - 3W^2$ Used the distributive property.

$= -3W^2 + 500W$ Wrote the equation with the squared term first.

c. Find W when A = 20,700.

$20{,}700 = -3W^2 + 500W$ Substituted 20,700 for A.

$0 = -3W^2 + 500W - 20{,}700$ Subtracted 20,700 from both sides. The quadratic equation MUST have one side equal to zero.

$a = -3,\ b = 500,\ c = -20{,}700$ **a** is the coefficient of W^2. **b** is the coefficient of W. **c** is the constant.

$$W = \frac{-b \pm \sqrt{b^2 - 4ac}}{2a}$$ The quadratic formula.

$$W = \frac{-500 \pm \sqrt{500^2 - 4(-3)(-20{,}700)}}{2(-3)}$$ Substituted the values of a, b, and c into the quadratic formula.

$$W = \frac{-500 \pm 40}{2(-3)}$$ Used calculator to simplify the square root. You should see $\sqrt{(}$ when you use the square root key. Type $500^2 - 4 \bullet 3 \bullet 20700)$ and =. The directions are for the TI-30X IIS.

$W = \dfrac{-500+40}{2(-3)}$ or $W = \dfrac{-500-40}{2(-3)}$ Separated the formula into the + and – parts.

$W = \dfrac{-460}{-6}$ or $W = \dfrac{-540}{-6}$ Simplified the numerator and denominator.

$W = 76.67$ or $W = 90$ Divided.

The width is 76.67 or 90 yards.

d. Find the length of the pens.

From the table in Part a, $L = 500 - 3W$. Substitute W = 76.67 and W = 90 into the equation for length, L = 500 – 3w,

Substitute $W = 76.67$	Substitute $W=90$
$L = 500 - 3 \bullet 76.67$	$L = 500 - 3 \bullet 90$
$L = 270$	$L = 230$

The dimensions of the pig pens that yield an area of 20,700 square yards are 76.67 by 270 yards and 90 by 230 yards.

Example 3. During the course of an experiment, it is important to monitor the temperature of oxygen. Using the data from the experiment, the following quadratic can model the temperature of the oxygen,

$$T = 0.26m^2 - 4.1m + 7.9$$

where T is measured in Celsius, and m represents the minutes that the experiment has run. Determine when the temperature of the oxygen is 0 degree Celsius.

The question asks you to find m when T = 0.

$0 = 0.26m^2 - 4.1m + 7.9$ Substituted T = 0 into the equation.

$a = 0.26,\ b = -4.1,\ c = 7.9$ Identified the coefficients in the quadratic equation.

$m = \dfrac{-(-4.1) \pm \sqrt{(-4.1)^2 - 4(0.26)(7.9)}}{2(0.26)}$ Substituted the values of a, b, and c into the quadratic formula. **Note that –b is** –(–4.1) **and simplifies to 4.1 in the line below.**

$m = \dfrac{4.1 \pm 2.932}{0.52}$ Computed the square root portion of the quadratic formula.

$m = \dfrac{4.1+2.932}{0.52},\ m = \dfrac{4.1-2.932}{0.52}$ Separated the formula into the + and – parts.

$m = \dfrac{7.032}{0.52},\ m = \dfrac{1.168}{0.52}$ Simplified the numerator and denominator.

m = 13.52, 2.246 Divided.

The temperature of the oxygen will be 0 degrees Celsius in 2.246 minutes and 13.52 minutes.

Study Tip: The key idea demonstrated in example 3 is how to handle a negative b in the quadratic equation.

Summary: This section shows us how to solve a new type of equations, the quadratics. These have important applications in many fields, such as business, physics, and engineering. Learn the difference between the quadratic equation and the quadratic formula.

The quadratic equation is $ax^2 + bx + c = 0$.

- One side of the equation must be zero.
- a is the coefficient of x^2.
- b is the coefficient of x.
- c is the constant term.

The quadratic formula, $x = \frac{-b \pm \sqrt{b^2 - 4ac}}{2a}$ solves the quadratic equation.

- The formula yields two solutions.
- The calculator is used to find the answers.
- The first step in evaluating the formula is to simplify the square root.

NOTES

CLASS WORK

1. The revenue generated by selling *x* items is indicated by

$$R = 280x - 0.4x^2,$$

and the cost of making *x* items is indicated by

$$C = 5000 + 0.6x^2.$$

a. Find the profit function.

b. Find the number of items the company needs to sell in order to break even.

c. How many items must be sold (and made) if a profit of $439 is to be generated?

2. During the course of an experiment it is important to monitor the temperature of oxygen. Using the data from the experiment, the following quadratic can model the temperature of the oxygen,

$$T = 0.2m^2 - 1.3m + 3.0$$

where T is measured in Celsius, and m represents the minutes that the experiment has run. Determine when the temperature of the oxygen is 1 degree Celsius.

3. Suppose you want to enclose a rectangle with a 40 inch string, and you use a wall of the room for one side of the rectangle.

a. Make a table and find the formula for the area of the rectangle.

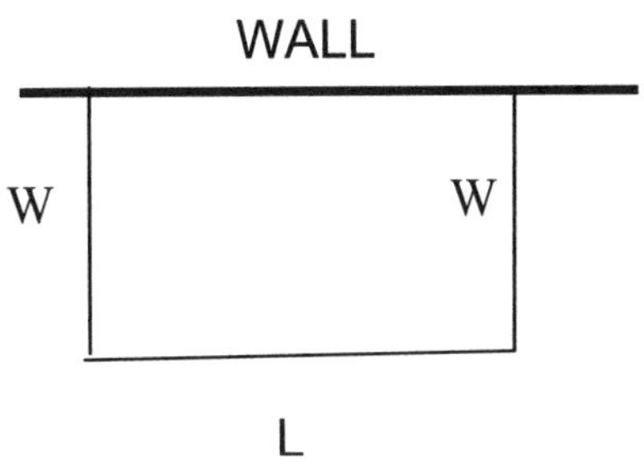

WALL

W W

L

WIDTH	LENGTH	AREA

b. Find the dimensions of the rectangle if the area is 65 square inches.

4. A 10 cm stick is broken into two pieces. One is placed at a right angle to form an upside down "T" shape. By attaching wires from the ends of the base to the end of the upright piece, a framework for a sail is formed.

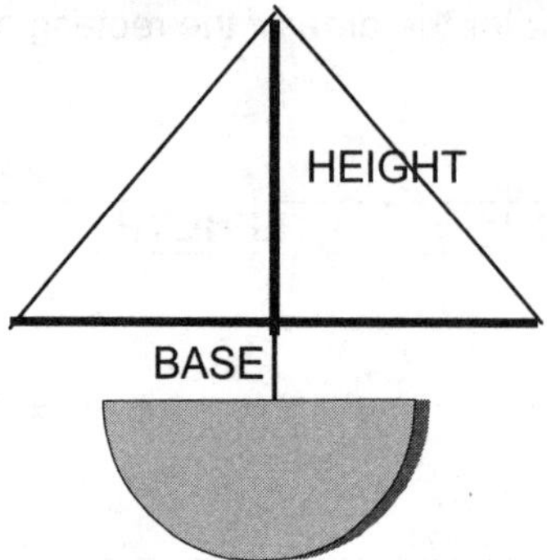

a. Complete the table below.

BASE	HEIGHT	AREA $\left(A = \frac{1}{2}bh\right)$
0	10-0 = 10	$\frac{1}{2}(0 \cdot 10) = 0$ sq cm
2	10-2 = 8	$\frac{1}{2}(2 \cdot 8) = 8$ sq cm
4		
6		
8		
10		
b		

b. Simplify the formula for area.

c. What should the base of the sail be if the area must be 10 sq. cm?

GROUP EXERCISE

Study Tip: This section is the foundation for the next part of your work in this chapter. Make sure everyone in your group understands the quadratic formula and the quadratic equation.

1. King Company computes the revenue for making x refrigerators per month by:

$$R = -0.7x^2 + 800x \text{ dollars.}$$

The cost of manufacturing x refrigerators per month is:

$$C = 0.3x^2 - 100x + 5250.$$

Go Back: Review Problem 2 on page 335.

a. Find the equation for profit. ($P = R - C$)

b. Find how many refrigerators King Co. would have to manufacture and sell if they want to have a profit of $100,000.

HOMEWORK EXERCISES

Study Tips:

1. Review pertinent note cards.
2. Review class notes from this section.
3. Some of the problems are long. Have plenty of paper ready in your loose leaf notebook.
4. Refer to Appendix C and the CD that accompanies the textbook to learn how to use the TI-30X IIS calculator.

Skill Building Exercises

1. Use your calculator to compute each of the following.

   a. $\sqrt{42}$ b. $\sqrt{38-5}$ c. $\sqrt{15^2-4(3)(7)}$

2. Define the quadratic equation.

3. For each quadratic equation below identify a, b, and c.

   a. $0=4x^2-6x+7$ b. $0=-2x^2+5x-12$ c. $2x^2-5=0$

Practice Exercises

4. A rancher has 360 yards of fence to enclose a rectangular pasture. If the pasture should be 8,000 square yards in area, what should the dimensions of the pasture be? (Hint: You may need a table to find the equation.)

Go Back: Review Example 2 on page 331 or Problem 3 on page 337. Note in this problem there are two lengths needed for the fence, not just one length.

L

W PASTURE W

L

WIDTH	LENGTH	AREA

5. A flare is fired from the bridge of the Titanic. The height in feet of the flare is indicated by the equation where t is measured in seconds

$$h=-16t^2+140t+40.$$

How long is the flare in the air?

Go Back: Review Example 1 on page 330.

6. The total cost (in dollars) for a company to manufacture and sell x items per week is:

$$C = 0.6x^2 - 140x + 6200$$

and the revenue (in dollars) by selling all x items is:

$$R = -0.4x^2 + 130x$$

How many items must be sold to obtain a weekly profit of $10,000?

Go Back: Review Problem 1 on page 335.

7. The quadratic equation $P = 0.10t^2 - 2.93t + 31.2$ (Source: Digest of Educational Statistics) can be used to approximate the percentage of young adults who reported using marijuana. P is the percentage, and t is the number of years since 1980. Use the equation to:

   a. Find the percentage of teenagers who used marijuana in the year 2001.

   b. According to the formula, when will the percentage of teenagers who used marijuana be 16 percent?

8. The total cost (in dollars) for a company to manufacture and sell x items per week is:

$$C = 60x + 300,$$

while the revenue (in dollars) from selling all x items is:

$$R = 100x - 0.5x^2.$$

How many items must be sold to obtain a weekly profit of $300?
(Hint: $P = R - C$.)

9. During the course of an experiment, the temperature of hydrogen must be monitored. Using the data from the experiment, the following quadratic can model the temperature of the oxygen,

$$T = 0.45m^2 - 3.6m + 11.2$$

where T is measured in Celsius, and m represents the minutes that the experiment has run. Find when the temperature of the oxygen is 7 degree Celsius.

Reading and Writing Mathematics

10. a. State the quadratic formula.

    b. Write a sentence describing when the formula is used.

11. Describe the steps in solving the following problem.

$2x^2 - 4x + 5 = 8$

$2x^2 - 4x - 3 = 0$ ______________________________

a = 2 b = –4, c = –3 ______________________________

$x = \frac{-(-4) \pm \sqrt{(-4)^2 - 4(2)(-3)}}{2(2)}$ ______________________________

$x = \frac{-(-4) \pm 6.325}{2(2)}$ ______________________________

$x = \frac{4 \pm 6.325}{4}$ ______________________________

$x = \frac{4 + 6.325}{4}, \; x = \frac{4 - 6.325}{4}$ ______________________________

x =2.581, x = -0.5813 ______________________________

12. Find the **mistake** in the problem below.

The revenue generated by selling *x* items is indicated by

$$R = 6.2x - 0.6x^2,$$

and the cost of making *x* items is indicated by

$$C = 0.7x^2 + 1.8x + 1.$$

R and C are in millions of dollars and x is in thousands.

a. Find the profit function.

$$P = (6.2x - 0.6x^2) - (0.7x^2 + 1.8x + 1)$$
$$P = 6.2x - 0.6x^2 - 0.7x^2 - 1.8x - 1$$
$$P = -1.3x^2 + 4.4x - 1$$

b. How many items must be made (and sold) if a profit of 1.5 million dollars is to be generated?

$$-1.3x^2 + 4.4x - 1 = 15$$
$$-1.3x^2 + 4.4x - 2.5 = 0$$
$$a = -1.3, b = 4.4, c = -2.5$$

$$x = \frac{-4.4 \pm \sqrt{4.4^2 - 4(-1.3)(-2.5)}}{2(-1.3)}$$

$$x = \frac{-4.4 \pm 5.689}{2(-1.3)}$$

$$x = \frac{-4.4 + 5.689}{2(-1.3)}, \; x = \frac{-4.4 - 5.689}{2(-1.3)}$$

$$x = -0.4958, x = 3.880$$

The company will earn 1.5 million dollars if they sell 3.880 items.

13. This exercise requires you to review a fellow student's work. Read her work carefully. Then make suggestions to your classmate. Try to evaluate the problem from the instructor's point of view. There is nothing wrong with the numbers in her work; however it isn't ready to be submitted. List 5 improvements she should make in order to get a good grade on the assignment.

A rancher has 1,000 yards of fencing to enclose three adjacent pig pens that rest against the barn. If the area of the three pens must total 60,000 square yards, what should the dimensions of the pens be?

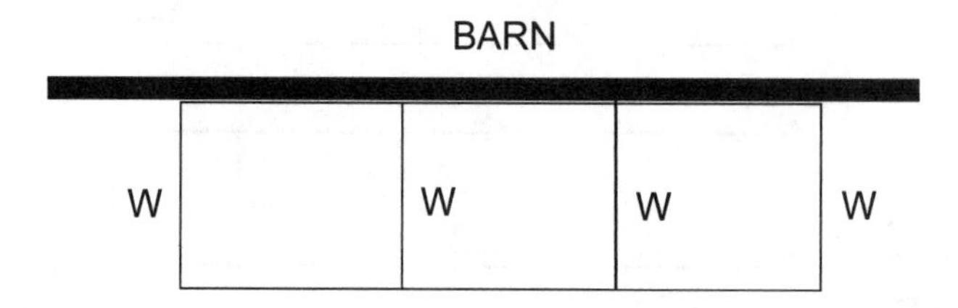

a. Use the table to find the equation for the area of the pens.

Width	Length	Area
50	800	40000
75	$1,000-4(75)=700$	$75(700)=52,500$
85	$1,000-4(85)=660$	$85(660)=56,100$
W	$1,000-4W$	$W(1,000-4W)$

b. Simplify the equation for area.

$$W(1,000-4W)$$
$$1,000W-4W^2$$

c. Find the dimensions.

$$60,000=1,000W-4W^2$$
$$0=1,000W-4W^2-60,000$$

$$a=-4,\ b=1,000,\ c=-60,000$$
$$\sqrt{1,000^2-4(-4)(-60,000)}$$
$$\frac{-1,000\pm 200}{2(-4)}$$
$$W=100,\ 150$$

SECTION 4.3 QUADRATIC APPLICATIONS AND GRAPHS PREVIEW

Objectives: This section explores further key points in the graph of a quadratic, the vertex and the intercepts. These points will be interpreted in applications.

Example 1. A boy lying on his back uses a sling shot to fire a rock straight up in the air with an initial velocity (the force the boy uses to shoot the rock) of 64 feet per second. The quadratic equation that models the height of the rock is

$$h = -16t^2 + 64t.$$

(This example comes from Section 4.1 "Introduction to Quadratics", pg 317.)

On Page 318, we generated the following values:

Time	Height	Point on Graph
0	0	(0, 0)
1	48	(1, 48)
2	64	(2, 64)
3	48	(3, 48)
4	0	(4, 0)

We used the points to obtain the graph below. The vertex and intercepts are also labeled on the graph.

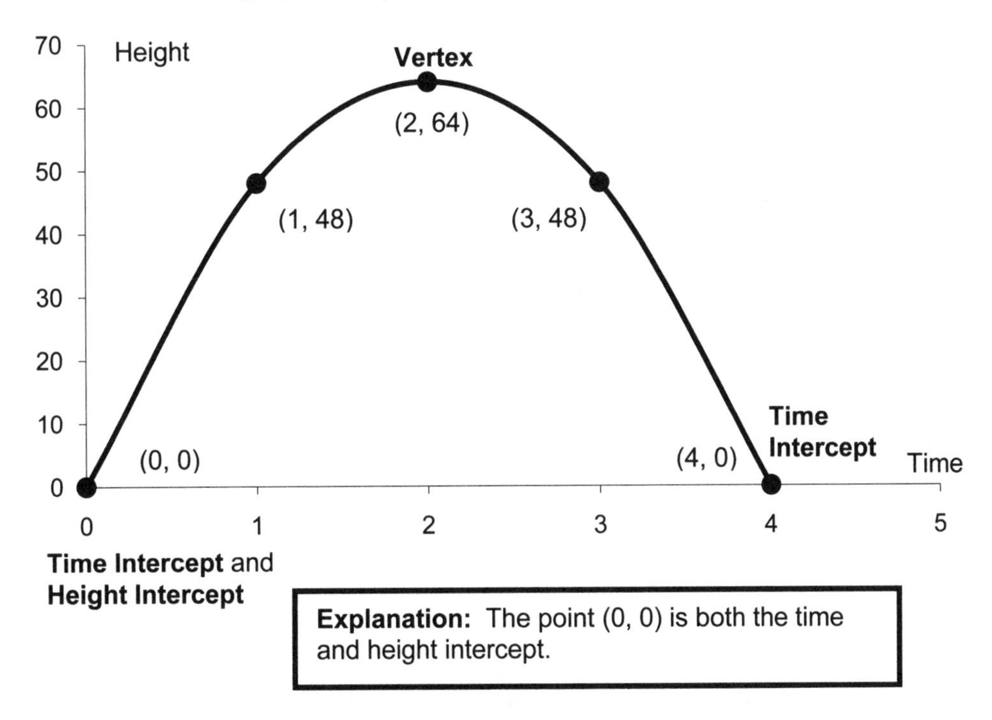

Explanation: The point (0, 0) is both the time and height intercept.

The **vertex**, (2,64) represents the maximum height of the rock. The rock reaches a maximum height of 64 feet in 2 seconds.

The **Time Intercepts,** (0, 0) and (4, 0) represent when the rock is on the ground. The rock is on the ground at zero seconds, before it is shot, (which is the **Height Intercept**) and at 4 seconds, it hits the ground.

To graph a quadratic indicated by the equation, $y = ax^2 + bx + c$, master the following terms:

Vocabulary: **Vertex:** The vertex is the maximum or minimum point on the graph.

To find the vertex :

a. Find the x coordinate: $x = \frac{-b}{2a}$.

b. Find the y coordinate: Substitute the value for x obtained in Part a into the formula $y = ax^2 + bx + c$.

x intercept: Set y = 0 and solve $0 = ax^2 + bx + c$ using the quadratic formula,

$$x = \frac{-b \pm \sqrt{b^2 - 4ac}}{2a}.$$

y intercept: Set x = 0 and find y. y will always be c, the constant.

Study Tip: Write the procedure and definitions on three note cards for easy reference.

Example 2. The company D+++ makes computer games. The cost of making g games per month is $C = 0.4g^2 - 32g + 625$. The revenue from selling g games per month is $R = -0.6g^2 + 52g$. The units for g are in hundreds, and C and R are in thousands of dollars.

a. Find the profit equation.

Profit = Revenue - Cost	Profit formula.
$P = (-0.6g^2 + 52g) - (0.4g^2 - 32g + 625)$	Substituted equations for revenue and cost. Must use parentheses around the revenue and cost equations.
$P = -0.6g^2 + 52g - 0.4g^2 + 32g - 625$	Used the distributive property. Multiplied the revenue equation by one, and the cost equation by negative one.
$P = -g^2 + 84g - 625$	Combined like terms.

b. Find the **vertex** and explain what the vertex means in terms of making computer games.

The formula for the g coordinate is $g = \frac{-b}{2a}$.

From the equation for profit, a = –1, b = 84.

$$g = \frac{-84}{2(-1)} = 42$$

Find the P coordinate:

$P = -g^2 + 84g - 625$	Equation for profit.
$P = -(42)^2 + 84(42) - 625$	Substituted 84 for g.
$P = -1{,}764 + 84(42) - 625$	Squared 42, not –42.
$P = 1{,}139$	Simplified.

The vertex is (42, 1139). If D+++ sells 4,200 games, then they will earn a maximum profit of $1,139,000.

c. Find the **g intercepts** and explain what they mean in terms of making computer games.

To find the g intercept, set P = 0.

Solve $0 = -g^2 + 84g - 625$.

Use the quadratic formula, a = –1, b = 84, c = –625.

$$g = \frac{-b \pm \sqrt{b^2 - 4ac}}{2a}$$ The quadratic formula.

$$g = \frac{-84 \pm \sqrt{84^2 - 4(-1)(-625)}}{2(-1)}$$ Substituted the values for a, b, and c.

$$g = \frac{-84 \pm 67.498}{2(-1)}$$ Simplified the square root. Enter $\sqrt{(84^2 - 4 * 625)}$ into the calculator.

$$g = \frac{-84 + 67.498}{-2} \text{ or } \frac{-84 - 67.498}{-2}$$ Separated formula into + and – parts.

g = 8.251 or 75.75. Simplified.

The g intercepts are (8.251, 0) and (75.75, 0).
If they sell 825 or 7,575 games, then they will break even.

d. Find the **g intercepts** and explain what they mean in terms of making computer games.

To find the P intercept, set g = 0.

$P = -0^2 + 84 \bullet 0 - 625$

$P = -625$

The P intercept is (0, –625).
The company's start up costs are $625,000.

Explanation: One explanation for the profit having two break even points is how efficient a company is at making a product. Making very few items is usually inefficient. At some point, the factory becomes very efficient at manufacturing the product, but if the factory tries to make too many items the company becomes inefficient at producing its product.

e. Graph the function.

Plot the points:

Vertex. (42, 1139).
The **g intercepts**. (8.251, 0) and (75.75, 0).
The **P intercept**. (0, –625).

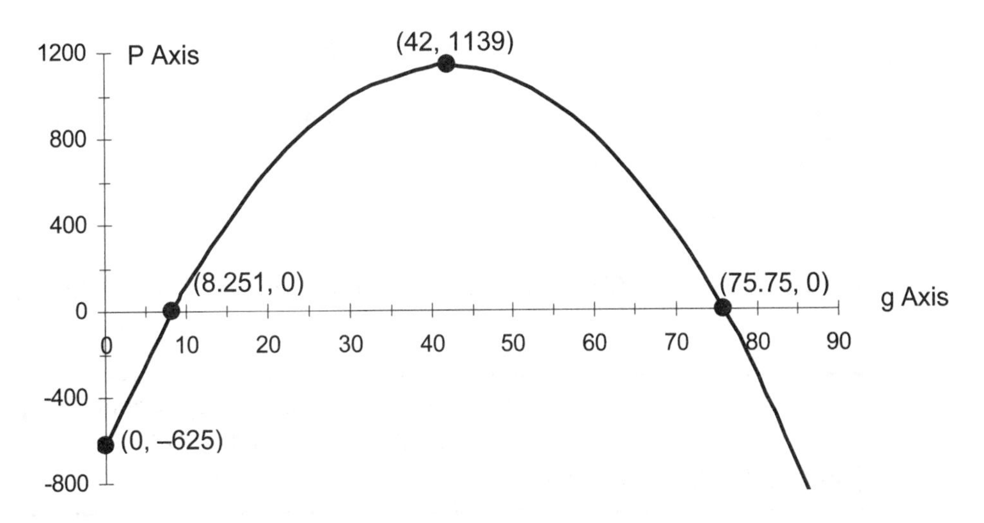

Remember that the units for g are in hundreds, and the units for P are thousands.

f. Suppose D+++ needs to make a profit of $500,000 (P = 500) a month. Sketch this line on the graph obtained in Part b and find where the line intersects the graph of the quadratic. Write a sentence explaining what the answers mean.

Sketch P = 500 on the graph from the previous page.

P = 500 is a horizontal line.

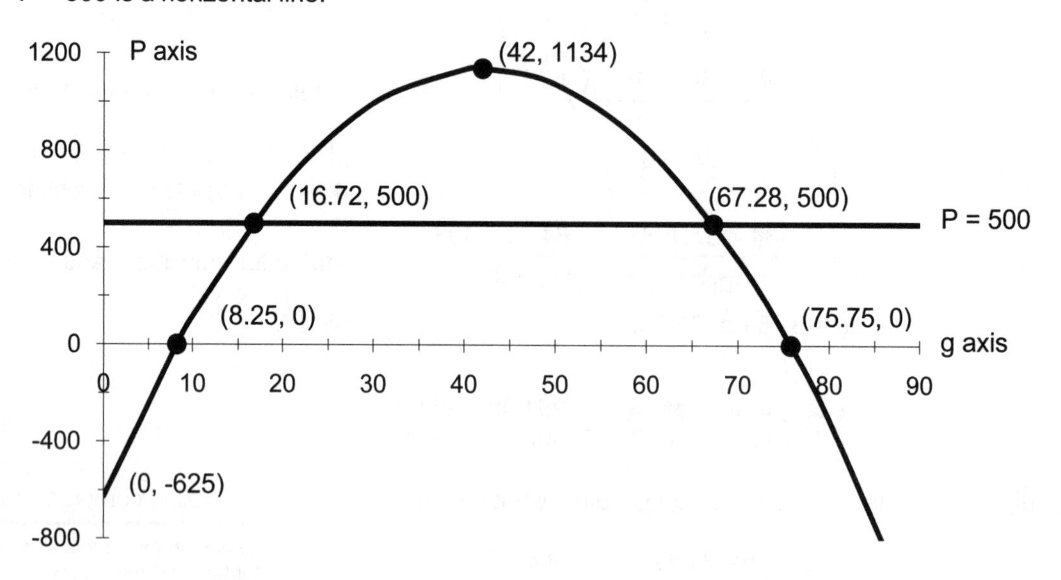

$500 = -g^2 + 84g - 625$ Substituted 500 for P.

$0 = -g^2 + 84g - 1{,}125$ Subtracted 500 from both sides.

$a = -1,\ b = 84,\ c = -1{,}125$ Identified a, b and c.

$g = \frac{-b \pm \sqrt{b^2 - 4ac}}{2a}$ Used the quadratic formula.

$g = \frac{-84 \pm \sqrt{84^2 - 4(-1)(-1{,}125)}}{2(-1)}$ Substituted the values for a, b, c.

$g = \frac{-84 \pm 50.56}{2(-1)}$ Simplified the square root.

$g = \frac{-84 + 50.56}{2(-1)}$ or $g = \frac{-84 - 50.56}{2(-1)}$ Separated formula into + and – parts.

g = 16.72 or 67.28. Simplified.

If D+++ wants a profit of $500,000, then they need to make and sell 1,672 or 6,728 games.

> **Explanation:** The graph gives an estimate of where the horizontal line, P = 500, and the equation for profit, $P = -g^2 + 84g - 625$ intersect. Algebra gives the exact point where they intersect.

c. Using the graph and the answers to Part c, determine how many computer games must be made and sold to guarantee a profit greater than $500,000.

The company will earn a profit of more than $500,000 when the profit graph is above the horizontal line P = 500. This problem is similar to the example on page 197 in Section 2.9 "Applications of Graphs".

This occurs between the points g = 16.72 and g = 67.28 or

$$16.72 < g < 67.28.$$

The company will earn more than $500,000 when they make and sell between 1,672 and 6,728 computer games.

Example 3. A kennel operator wants to enclose three adjacent dog pens of equal size against a wall. He has 96 meters of fence.

a. Find the formula for area.

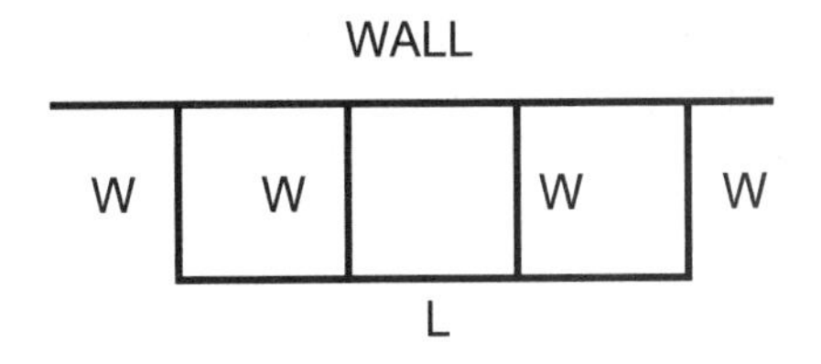

Width	Length	Area $A = L \bullet W$
10	$96 - 4 \bullet 10 = 56$	$56 \bullet 10 = 560$ sq. meters
15	$96 - 4 \bullet 15 = 36$	$36 \bullet 15 = 540$ sq. meters
20	$96 - 4 \bullet 20 = 16$	$16 \bullet 20 = 320$ sq. meters
W	$96 - 4 \bullet W$	$W(96 - 4 \bullet W)$

Explanation: The most difficult part of the table is finding the value for length. If the farmer uses 10 meters for the width of the pens, and there are 4 widths, then he has used $4 \bullet 10$, or 40 meters of fencing. To find how much fencing he has left for the length, subtract 40 from 96, the total amount of fencing available to the farmer.

The formula for the area of the dog pens is

$A = W(96 - 4 \bullet W)$

$A = 96W - 4 \bullet W^2$ Use the distributive property.

$A = -4W^2 + 96W$ Write the squared term first.

b. Find the **vertex** and explain what it means in terms of the dog pens.

The formula for the W coordinate is $W = \frac{-b}{2a}$.

From the equation for profit, a = –4, b = 96.

$$W = \frac{-96}{2(-4)} = 12$$

Find the A coordinate:

$A = -4W^2 + 96W$	Equation for area.
$A = -4(12^2) + 96 \bullet 12$	Substituted 12 for W.
$A = -4(144) + 96 \bullet 12$	Squared 12.
$A = 576$	Simplified.

The vertex is (12, 576).

The **vertex**, (12, 576) represents the maximum area of the three dog pens. When W = 12, the maximum area will be 576. (The length of all three pens will be 48 or the length of one dog pen will be 16.) There will be three dog pens each 12 by 16 meters.

c. Find the **W intercepts** and explain what they mean in term of the dog pens

To find the W intercept, set A = 0.

Solve $0 = -4W^2 + 96W$.

Use the quadratic formula, a = –4, b = 96, c = 0.

$W = \frac{-b \pm \sqrt{b^2 - 4ac}}{2a}$	The quadratic formula.
$W = \frac{-96 \pm \sqrt{96^2 - 4(-4)(0)}}{2(-4)}$	Substituted the values for a, b, and c.
$W = \frac{-96 \pm 96}{2(-4)}$	Simplified the square root. 96 is the "obvious" answer because $\sqrt{96^2} = 96$.
$W = \frac{-96 + 96}{-8}$ or $W = \frac{-96 - 96}{-8}$	Separated formula into + and – parts.
W = 0 or 24	Simplified.

The W intercepts are (0, 0) and (24, 0).

The **W intercepts**, (0, 0) and (24, 0) represent the widths of the dog pens that will yield zero area.

d. Find the **A intercept** and explain what it means in term of the dog pens

To find the A intercept, set W = 0.

$A = -4(0)^2 + 96 \bullet 0$

$A = 0$

Explanation: If the width of a rectangle is zero, then the area has to be zero.

The A intercept is (0, 0).

The **A intercept**, (0, 0) is the area when W = 0.

e. Graph the function

Plot the points:

Vertex. (12, 576).

The **W intercepts**. (0, 0) and (24, 0).

The **A intercept**. (0, 0).

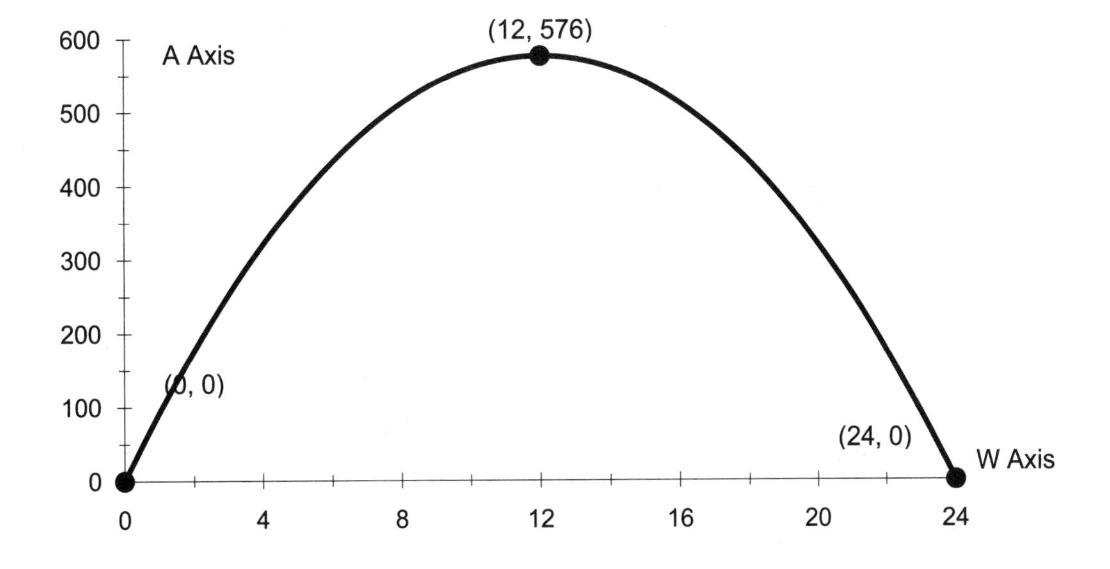

f. Suppose the total area has to be 400 square meters. Graph A = 400 and find the dimensions of the dog pens.

Sketch A = 400 on the graph from the previous page.

A = 400 is a horizontal line.

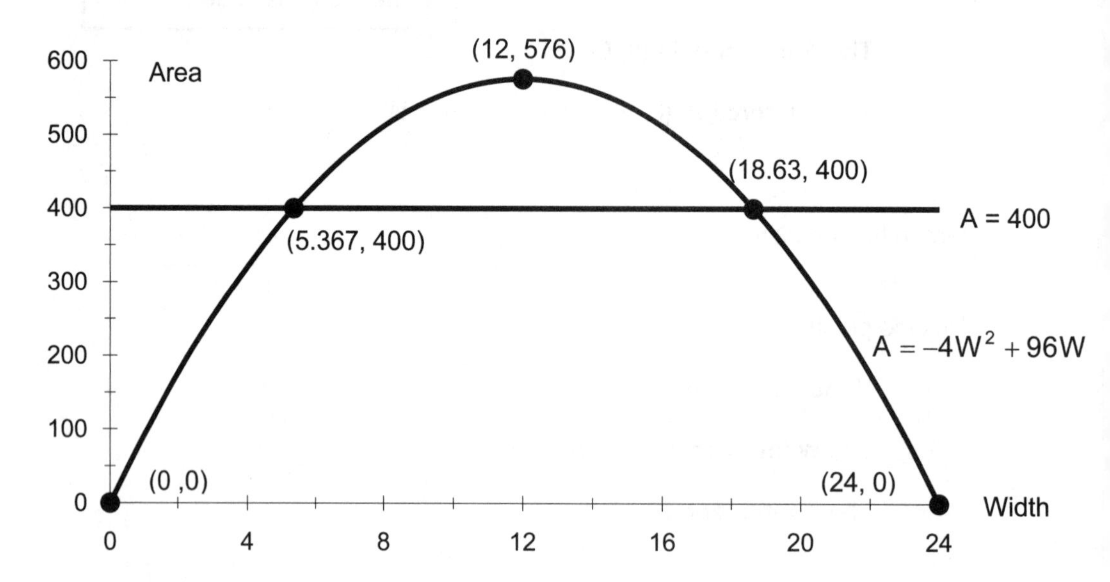

$400 = -4W^2 + 96W$	Substituted 400 for A.
$0 = -4W^2 + 96W - 400$	Subtracted 400 from both sides.
$a = -4,\ b = 96,\ c = -400$	Identified a, b and c.
$W = \dfrac{-b \pm \sqrt{b^2 - 4ac}}{2a}$	Use the quadratic formula.
$W = \dfrac{-96 \pm \sqrt{96^2 - 4(-4)(-400)}}{2(-4)}$	Substituted the values for a, b and c.
$W = \dfrac{-96 \pm 53.07}{2(-4)}$	Simplified the square root.
$W = \dfrac{-96 + 53.07}{2(-4)}$ or $W = \dfrac{-96 - 53.07}{2(-4)}$	Separated formula into + and – parts.
$W = 5.367$ or 18.63	Simplified.

Since W, the width, is know, the length L can be found by using the formula A = LW.
Solve for L by dividing both sides by W.

$$L = \frac{A}{W}$$

Substitute 400 for A and 5.367 for W.

$$L = \frac{400}{5.367} = 74.53$$

Substitute 400 for A and 18.63 for W.

$$L = \frac{400}{18.63} = 21.47$$

The dimensions of the dog pens that will give an area of 400 square meters are 5.367 by 74.53 and 18.63 by 21.47.

Example 4. During the course of an experiment, the temperature of oxygen must be monitored. Using the data from the experiment, the following quadratic can model the temperature of the oxygen,

$$T = 0.26m^2 - 4.1m + 7.9$$

where T is measured in Celsius, and m represents the minutes that the experiment has run. Graph the equation by finding the vertex and the intercepts. Label these points on the graph and explain what the vertex and intercepts mean in terms of the model.

Go Back: This is the same model that was used in Example 3 on page 332. That example found when the temperature was zero.

- Find the **vertex** of $T = 0.26m^2 - 4.1m + 7.9$.

  The formula for the m coordinate of the vertex is $m = \frac{-b}{2a}$.

  From the equation for temperature, a = 0.26, b = –4.1

  $$m = \frac{-(-4.1)}{2(0.26)} = 7.885.$$

  Find the T coordinate:

$T = 0.26m^2 - 4.1m + 7.9$	Equation for temperature.
$T = 0.26(7.885)^2 - 4.1(7.885) + 7.9$	Substituted 7.885 for m.
$T = -8.263$	Simplified.

  The vertex is (7.885, –8.263).

- Find the m intercepts of $T = 0.26m^2 - 4.1m + 7.9$

  To find the m intercepts, set T = 0.

  Solve $0 = 0.26m^2 - 4.1m + 7.9$.

  Use the quadratic formula, a = 0.26, b = –4.1, c = 7.9.

$m = \frac{-b \pm \sqrt{b^2 - 4ac}}{2a}$	The quadratic formula.
$m = \frac{-(-4.1) \pm \sqrt{(-4.1)^2 - 4(0.26)(7.9)}}{2(0.26)}$	Substituted the values of a, b, and c.
$m = \frac{4.1 \pm 2.932}{0.52}$	Simplified the square root. Entered $\sqrt{((-4.1)^2 - 4 \bullet 0.26 \bullet 7.9)}$ into the calculator.
$m = \frac{4.1 + 2.932}{0.52}$, $m = \frac{4.1 - 2.932}{0.52}$	Separated formula into + and – parts.
m = 13.52, 2.246	Simplified.

  The m intercepts are (13.52, 0) and (2.246, 0).

- Find the T intercepts of $T = 0.26m^2 - 4.1m + 7.9$

  To find the T intercept, set m = 0.
  $T = 0.26(0)^2 - 4.1(0) + 7.9$
  $T = 7.9$

  The T intercept is (0, 7.9).

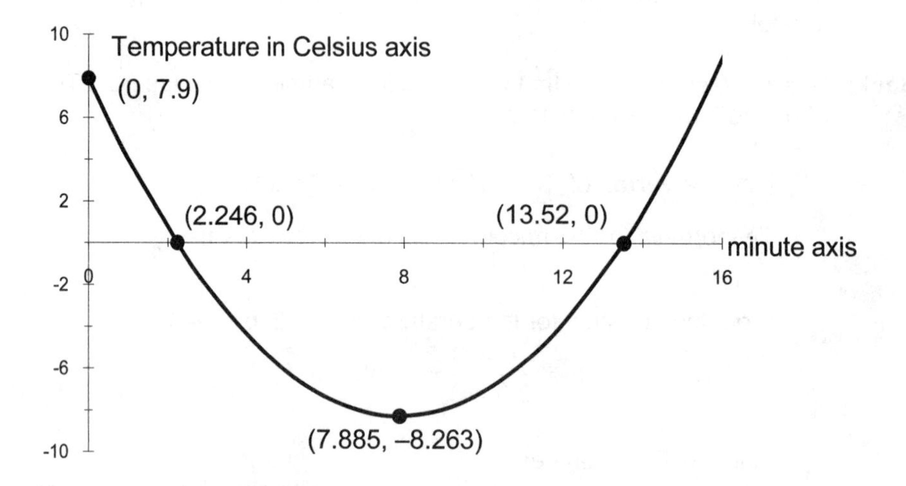

Vertex: The temperature will be a minimum at 7.885 minutes. The minimum temperature will be –8.263 degrees Celsius.

m intercepts: The temperature will be zero degrees Celsius at 2.246 and 13.52 minutes.

T intercept: The temperature was 7.9 degrees Celsius at the start of the experiment.

Study Tips: Quadratics are U shaped. In some cases, they are U shaped as in the example above or ∩ shaped as in examples 1 through 3. If a in the equation, $y = ax^2 + bx + c$, is positive, then the graph is U shaped, that is, opens up. If a is negative, the graph is ∩ shaped, that is, opens down. This fact should be written on a note card.

Summary: Graphs of quadratics appear in subjects as diverse as microeconomics and physics. This section summarizes the major ideas of the unit.

To graph a quadratic, $y = ax^2 + bx + c$, you should find:

- The **vertex.**
  The formula for the x coordinate is
  $$x = \frac{-b}{2a}.$$
  To find the y coordinate, substitute your answer for the x coordinate in the equation $y = ax^2 + bx + c$.

- The **x intercepts.**
  Set y = 0 and solve the equation, $0 = ax^2 + bx + c$, using the quadratic formula
  $$y = \frac{-b \pm \sqrt{b^2 - 4ac}}{2a}.$$

- The **y intercept.**
  Set x = 0 in the equation, $y = ax^2 + bx + c$, and find y. Note, when x = 0, y = c.

If **a is negative,** generally the graph looks like this:

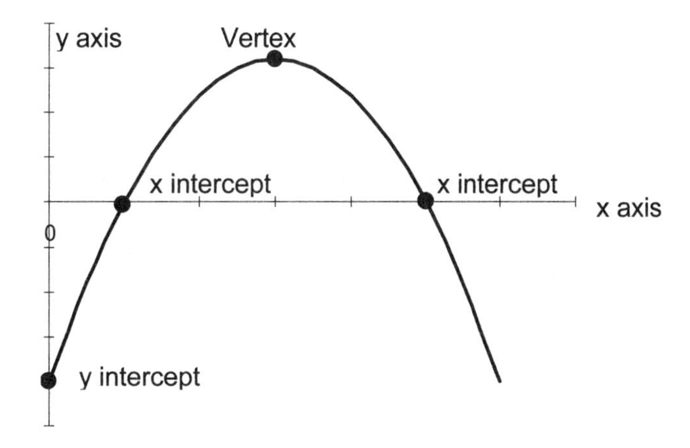

If **a is positive,** generally the graph looks like this:

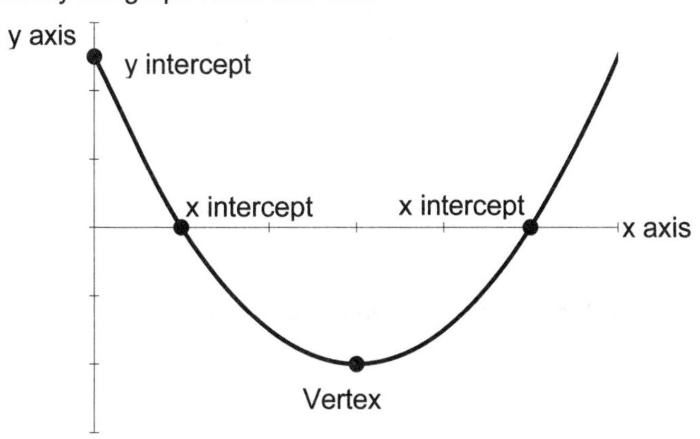

CLASS WORK

1. Earl Black makes tea bags. The cost of making x million tea bags per month is

$$C = x^2 - 38x + 400.$$

The revenue from selling x million tea bags per month is

$$R = -x^2 + 78x.$$

C and R are in thousands of dollars.

a. Find the equation for profit.

b. Find the **vertex** and explain what it means in terms of making tea bags.

c. Find the **x intercepts** and explain what they mean in terms of making tea bags.

d. Find the **P intercept** and explain what it means in terms of making tea bags.

e. Graph the profit equation.

Vertex	
x intercepts	
P intercept	

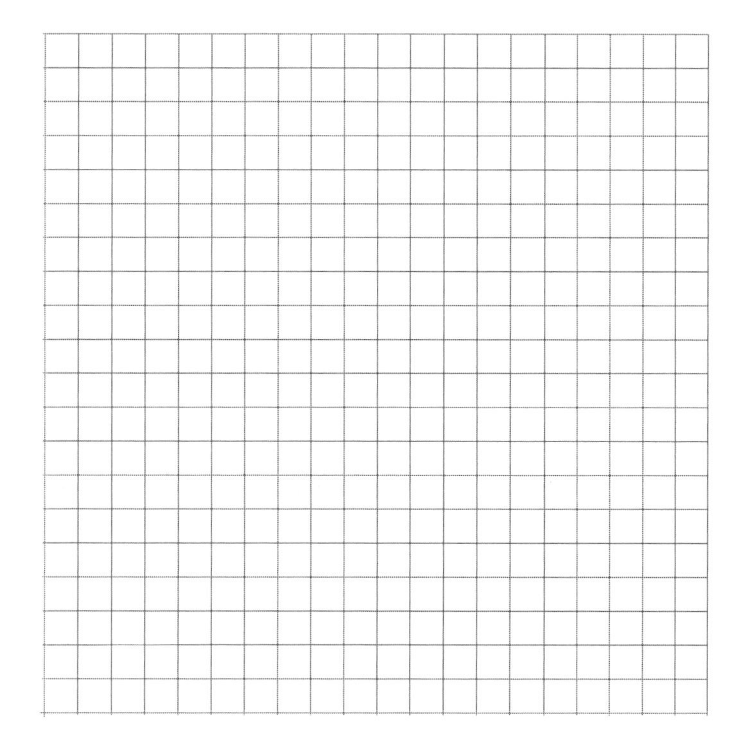

f. Suppose Earl Black needs to make $500,000 in profit (P = 500). Graph this line on the graph above and find where the line intersects the graph of the quadratic. Explain what the answers mean.

g. Using the graph and the answers to Part d, determine how many tea bags must be made and sold that will guarantee a profit of greater than $500,000.

2. An angry algebra student stands at the top of a 250 foot cliff and throws his algebra book upward with a velocity of 64 feet per second. The height of the book above the floor of the canyon t seconds after the book is thrown is indicated by

$$h = -16t^2 + 64t + 250 \text{ feet.}$$

a. Find the **vertex** and explain what it means in terms of the book being thrown off the cliff.

b. Find the **t intercepts** and explain what they mean in terms of the book being thrown off the cliff. Why should there be only one reasonable t intercept?

c. Find the **h intercept** and explain what it means in terms of the book being thrown off the cliff.

d. Graph $h = -16t^2 + 64t + 250$

Vertex	
t intercept	
h intercept	

3. Ms. Farmer wants to enclose two adjacent chicken coops of equal size against the hen house wall. She has 66 feet of chicken-wire fencing and would like the chicken coop to be as large as possible.

a. Find the formula for the area of the chicken coops.

Hen House Wall

W W W

L

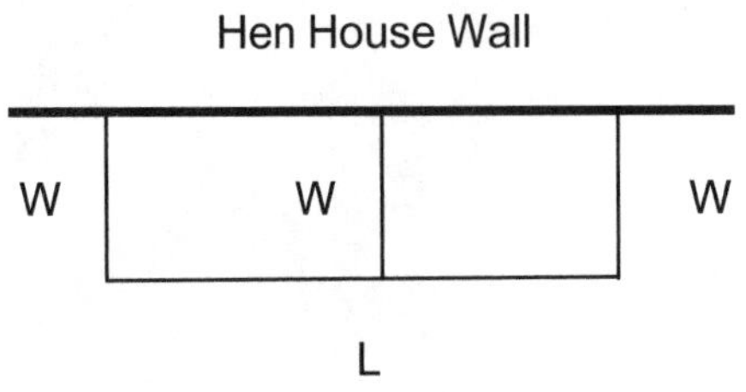

WIDTH	LENGTH	AREA

b. Find the **vertex** and explain what it means in terms of the area of the chicken coops.

c. Find the **W intercepts** and explain what they mean in terms of the area of the chicken coops.

d. Find the **A intercept** and explain what it means in terms of the area of the chicken coops.

e. Graph the equation for the Area of the chicken coops.

Vertex	
W intercept	
A intercept	

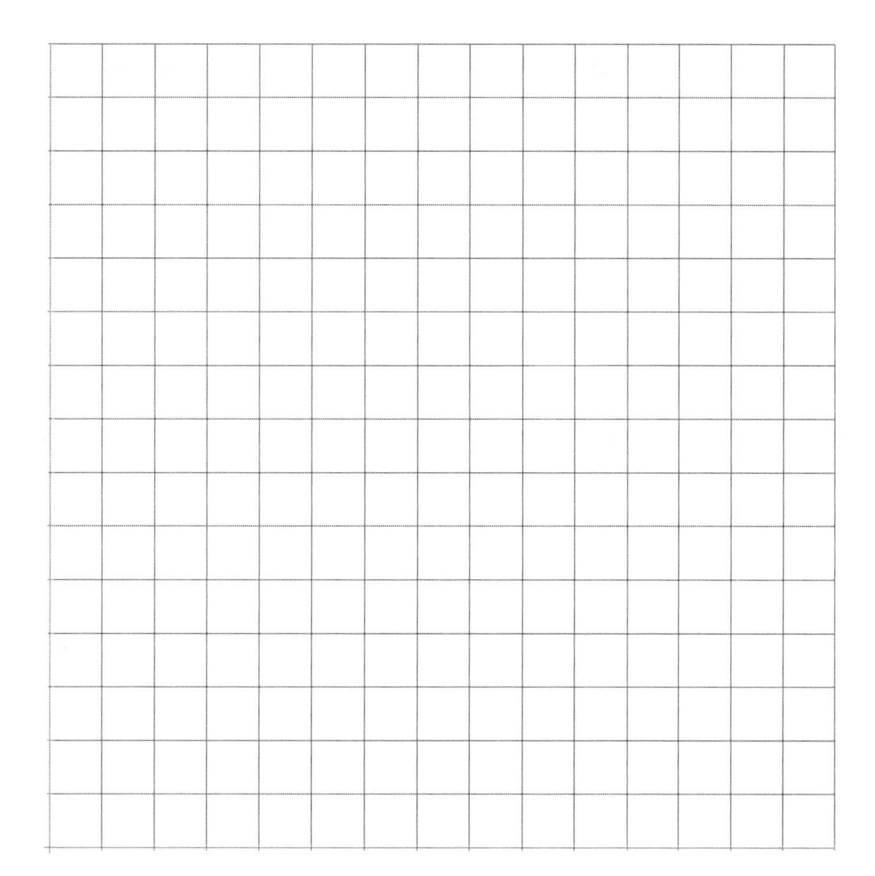

f. Mr. Urban comes along and tells Ms. Farmer that the chicken coops should only have an area of 360 square feet. Represent this idea in the graph of Part b by graphing the line $A = 360$ and find the dimensions of the chicken coop.

4. The following quadratic equation can be used to model the daily high temperature of the science station at Rothera Point, Adelaide Island, Antarctica, for the year 2005,

$$T = 0.00042d^2 - 0.146d + 1.9$$

Source: British Antarctica Survey, National Environmental Research Council

where T is the temperature in Celsius, and d is the number of days of the year (for January 1, d = 1).

a. Find the **vertex** and explain what it means in terms of the daily high temperature of the science station.

b. Find the **d intercepts** and explain what they mean in terms of the daily high temperature of the science station.

c. Find the **T intercept** and explain what it means in terms of the daily high temperature of the science station.

d. Graph the equation $T = 0.00042d^2 - 0.146d + 1.9$

Vertex	
d intercepts	
T intercept	

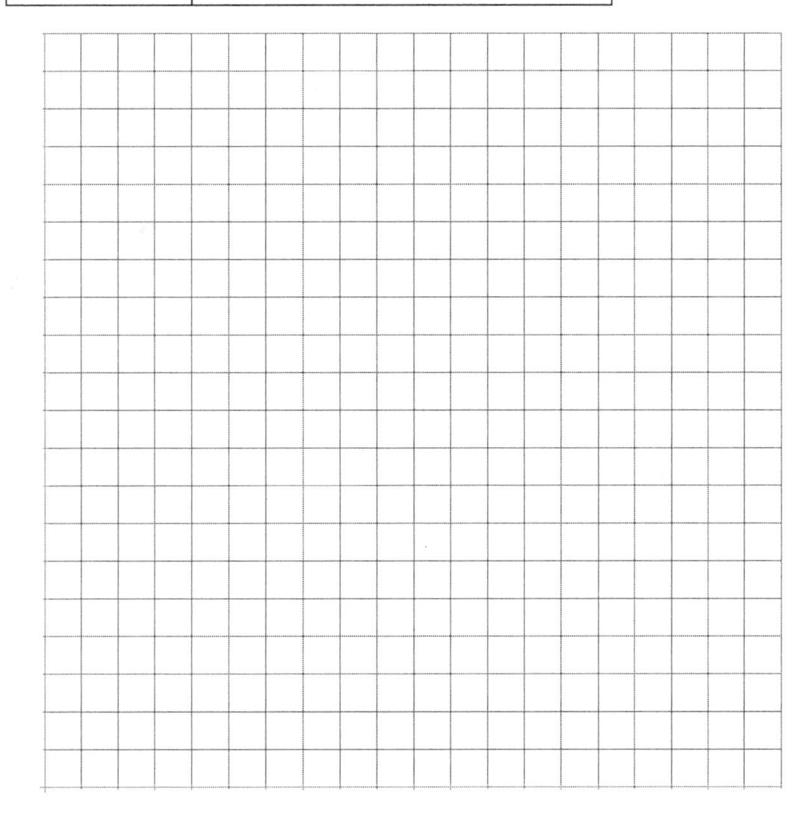

GROUP EXERCISE

Go Back: 1. Review Example 2 on page 346 or Problem 1 on page 356.

2. Take your time and make sure everyone in your group understands how to do each part.

1. Soul Shoe Company makes x thousand shoes per week. The cost of making x thousand shoes per week is

$$C = 0.3x^2 - 11x + 13$$

and the revenue from selling x thousand shoes per week is

$$R = -0.7x^2 + 7x.$$

C and R are in thousand dollar units.

a. Find the equation for profit. ($P = R - C$)

b. Find the **vertex** and explain what it means in terms of making shoes.

c. Find the **x intercepts** and explain what they mean in terms of making shoes.

d. Find the **P intercept** and explain what it means in terms of making shoes.

e. Graph the profit equation.

Vertex	
x intercepts	
P intercept	

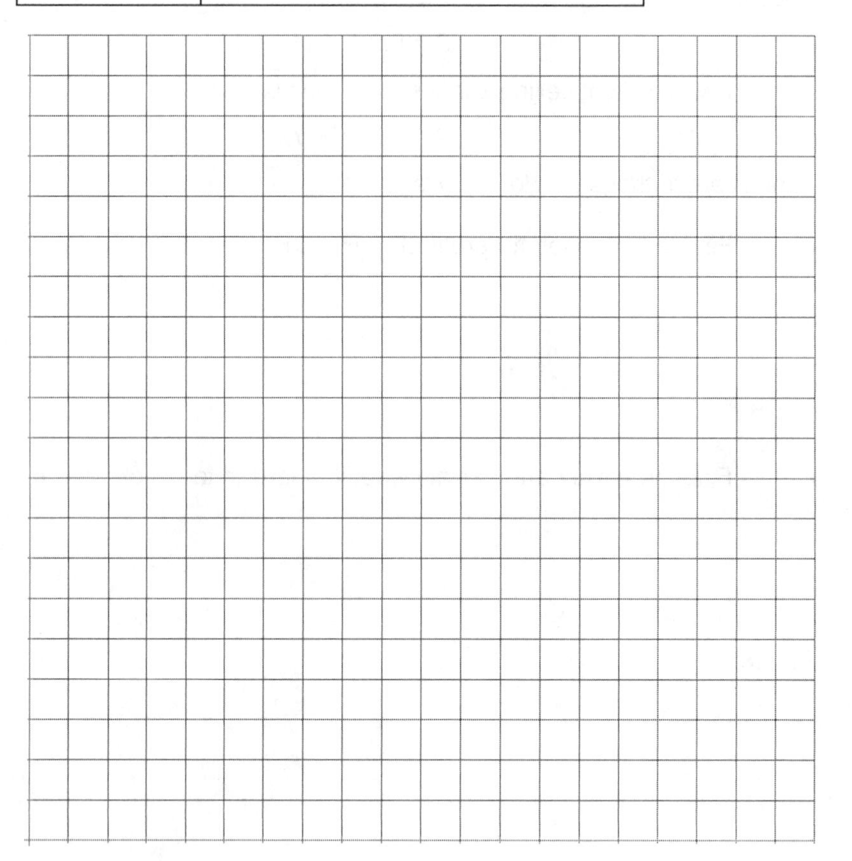

f. Suppose Soul Shoe Company needs to make $50,000 in profit for the week (P = 50). Graph this line on the graph above and find where the line intersects the graph of the quadratic. Explain what the answers mean in terms of making shoes.

g. Using the graph and the answers to Part c, determine how many shoes must be made and sold that will guarantee a profit of greater than $50,000.

HOMEWORK EXERCISES

Study Tips: 1. Make sure you have all of the materials needed to create a graph: graph paper, colored pencils, and a ruler.
2. Have your note cards handy for easy reference.

Skill Building Exercises

1. Solve: $-x^2 + 36x - 87 = 0$.

2. Evaluate: $P = -x^2 + 36x - 87$ when x = 18.

3. What is the P intercept of $P = -x^2 + 36x - 87$?

Practice Exercises

4. Mr. Twisted makes pretzels. The cost of making x thousands of pretzels per week is

$$C = 0.4x^2 - 28x + 87.$$

The revenue from selling x thousands of pretzels per week is

$$R = -0.6x^2 + 8x.$$

C and R are in thousands of dollars.

Go Back: Review Example 2 on page 346 or Problem 1 on page 356 or the group work problem, page 365.

a. Find the equation for profit. (Profit = Revenue - Cost)

b. Find the **vertex** and explain what it means in terms of making pretzels.

c. Find the **x intercepts** and explain what they mean in terms of making pretzels.

d. Find the **P intercept** and explain what it means in terms of making pretzels.

e. Graph the profit equation. Make sure you label the axes and use an appropriate scale.

f. Suppose Mr. Twisted needs to make $40,000 in profits (P = 40). Graph this line on the graph created in part b and find out where the line intersects the graph of the quadratic. Explain what the answers mean.

5. Dr. Torus makes doughnuts. The cost of making x thousands of doughnuts a month is

$$C = 4x^2 - 62x + 35$$

and the revenue from selling x thousand doughnuts a month is

$$R = -3x^2 + 15x.$$

C and R are in hundreds of dollars.

a. Find the equation for profit. (Profit = Revenue - Cost).

b. Find the **vertex** and explain what it means in terms of making doughnuts.

c. Find the **x intercepts** and explain what they mean in terms of making doughnuts.

d. Find the **P intercept** and explain what it means in terms of making doughnuts.

e. Graph the profit equation. Make sure you label the axes and use an appropriate scale.

f. Suppose Dr. Torus needs to make $8,000 a day in profit (P = 80). Graph this line on the graph created in part e and determine where the line intersects the graph of the quadratic. Explain what the answers mean.

6. The Star Spangle Banner Fireworks Company launches its Liberty Bell rocket every Labor Day (the company is a little confused). The height, in feet, of the rocket is indicated by the equation

$$h = -16t^2 + 200t \text{ where t is in seconds.}$$

Go Back: Review Example 2 on page 358.

a. Graph the equation. Explain what the vertex, t-intercepts, and h-intercept mean in terms of the Liberty Bell rocket. Make sure you label the axes and choose an appropriate scale.

b. Find the **vertex** and explain what it means in terms of the Liberty Bell Rocket.

c. Find the **t intercepts** and explain what they mean in terms of the Liberty Bell rocket.

d. Find the **h intercept** and explain what it means in terms of the Liberty Bell rocket.

e. Graph the profit equation. Make sure you label the axes and use an appropriate scale.

d. Suppose the Liberty Bell rocket must be ignited 300 feet above the ground. Graph this requirement on the graph above. Find where the line intersects the graph of the quadratic and explain what the answers mean.

7. A farmer has 1800 feet of fencing. She wants to fence in a rectangular organic garden. The garden borders on a river.

Go Back: Review Example 3 on page 360.

a. Find an equation for the area of the pasture.

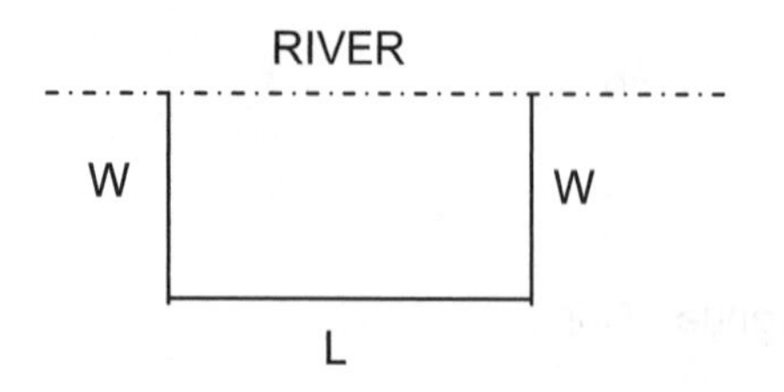

WIDTH	LENGTH	AREA

b. Find the **vertex** and explain what it means in terms of the area of the garden.

c. Find the **w intercepts** and explain what they mean in terms of the area of the garden.

d. Find the **A intercept** and explain what it means in terms of the area of the garden.

e. Graph the area equation. Make sure you label the axes and use an appropriate scale.

8. The following quadratic equation can be used to model the daily high temperature of the science station at Byrd Island, South Georgia, Antarctica, for the year 2005,

$$T = 0.00013d^2 - 0.056d + 4.1$$

Source: Weather Underground

where T is the temperature in Celsius and d is the number of days of the year (for January 1, d = 1).

Go Back: Review Example 4 on page 362.

a. Find the **vertex** and explain what it means in terms of the high temperature of the science station.

b. Find the **d intercepts** and explain what they mean in terms of the high temperature of the science station.

c. Find the **T intercept** and explain what it means in terms of the high temperature of the science station.

d. Graph the profit equation. Make sure you label the axes and use an appropriate scale.

9. During the course of an experiment, the temperature of hydrogen must be monitored. Using the data from the experiment, the following quadratic can model the temperature of the oxygen,

$$T = 0.05m^2 - 3.6m + 46$$

where T is measured in Celsius and m represents the minutes that the experiment has run.

Go Back: Review Example 4 on page 362.

a. Find the **vertex** and explain what it means in terms of the temperature of hydrogen.

b. Find the **m intercepts** and explain what they mean in terms of the high temperature of hydrogen.

c. Find the **T intercept** and explain what it means in terms of hydrogen.

d. Graph the temperature equation. Make sure you label the axes and use an appropriate scale.

Reading and Writing Mathematics

10. Write a sentence describing the vertex of a graph of the quadratic.

11. What is the formula for finding the x coordinate of the vertex?

12. Write a sentence describing how to find the y coordinate of the vertex.

13. List the important points you need to find to graph a quadratic.

14. How can you tell if the graph will be ∪ shaped or ∩ shaped?

15. A student in your class created the following graph of a quadratic equation. Which point, A, B, C, or D, do you think is incorrect?

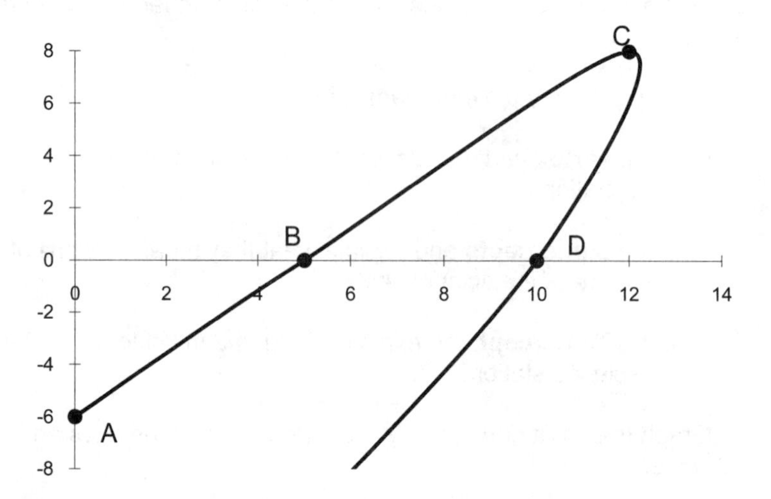

16. This exercise requires you to review a fellow student's work. Read her work carefully. Then make suggestions to your classmate. Try to evaluate the problem from the instructor's point of view. There is nothing wrong with the mathematics in her work; however it isn't ready to be submitted. List at least five improvements she should make in order to get a good grade on the assignment.

    The company Well makes computer games. The cost of making g games per month is $C = 0.6g^2 - 28g + 425$. The revenue from selling g games per month is $R = -1.4g^2 + 64g$. The units for g are hundreds, and C and R are in thousands of dollars.

    a. Find the profit equation.

    $-1.4g^2 + 64g - 0.6g^2 + 28g - 425$
    $-2g^2 + 92g - 425$

b. Graph the equation. Explain what the vertex and the g and p intercepts mean in terms of making computer games. Label the axes and use an appropriate scale.

$$\frac{-92}{-4} = 23$$

$$-2\ 23^2 + 92\ 23 - 425$$

$$633$$

$$.\ -2g^2 + 92g - 425 = 0$$

$$\frac{-92 \pm \sqrt{92^2 - 4(-2)(-425)}}{2(-2)}$$

$$\frac{-92 \pm 71.16}{2(-2)}$$

$$5.21,\ 40.79$$

$$-425$$

If the company sells 23 thousand games, then they will earn a maximum profit of \$633,000.

If the company sells 521 or 4,079 games, then they will break even.

The company's loses \$425,000 if they sell nothing.

c. Suppose Well needs to make a profit of \$400,000 (P = 400) a month. Sketch this line on the graph obtained in Part b and find where the line intersects the graph of the quadratic. Write a sentence explaining what the answers mean.

$$-2g^2 + 92g - 425 = 400$$

$$-2g^2 + 92g - 825 = 0$$

$$\frac{-92 \pm \sqrt{92^2 - 4(-2)(-825)}}{2(-2)}$$

$$\frac{-92 \pm 43.17}{2(-2)}$$

$$33.79,\ 12.21$$

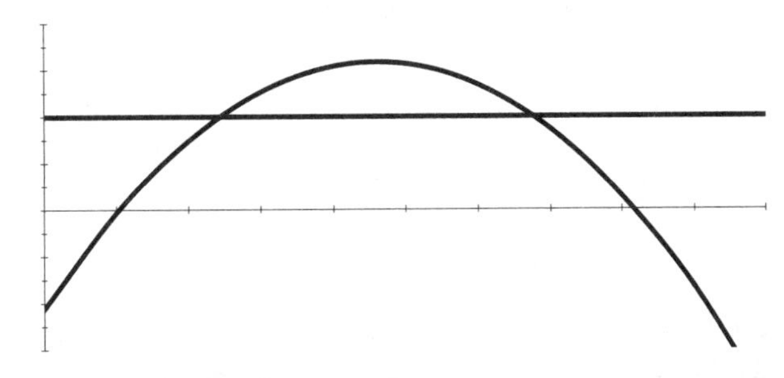

Well will make \$400,000 if they sell 3,379 or 1221 games.

d. Using the graph and the answers to Part c, determine how many computer games must be made and sold to guarantee a profit greater than \$400,000.

Well will make more than \$400,000 if they sell between 1221 and 3,379 games.

SECTION 4.4 FACTORING
PREVIEW

Objectives: Factoring is an algebraic technique used to separate an expression into its component parts. When the component parts are multiplied together, the result is the original expression. This can sometimes be used to solve quadratic equations. Factoring is an important skill in MAT 100, Intermediate Algebra.

Vocabulary: An algebraic expression is **factored** if the last operation in evaluating the expression is multiplication.

Example 1. Which expression is factored, $x^2 - 5x - 24$ or $(x-8)(x+3)$?
Pick a value for x and substitute it into the expression.

Let x = 3.

For $x^2 - 5x - 24$	For $(x-8)(x+3)$
$= 3^2 - 5(3) - 24$	$= (3-8)(3+3)$
$= 9 - 5(3) - 24$	$= (-5)(6)$
$= 9 - 15 - 24$	$= -30$
$= -30$	Last operation was multiplication.
Last operation was subtraction.	

Since the last operation for $(x-8)(x+3)$ was multiplication, then $(x-8)(x+3)$ is factored.

> **Explanation:** Less formally, an algebraic expression is factored when it has parentheses.

Vocabulary: The distributive property is a(b + c) = ab + ac. The left hand side is factored and a is the **common factor.**

Example 2. Factor $6x^2 + 12x$.

$6x^2 + 12x = 6 \bullet x \bullet x + 6 \bullet 2 \bullet x$ Find factors of $6x^2$ and $12x$.

$= \mathbf{6} \bullet \mathbf{x} \bullet x + \mathbf{6} \bullet 2 \bullet \mathbf{x}$ Identify the common factors, 6 and x.

$= 6x(x+2)$ Factor out 6x.

You should be able to check by using the distributive property.

Example 3. Factor $8x^3 + 4x$.

$8x^3 + 4x = 2 \bullet 4 \bullet x \bullet x \bullet x + 4 \bullet 1 \bullet x$ Find factors of $8x^3$ and $4x$.

$= 2 \bullet \mathbf{4} \bullet \mathbf{x} \bullet x \bullet x + \mathbf{4} \bullet 1 \bullet \mathbf{x}$ Identify the common factors, 4, x.

$= 4x(2x^2 + 1)$ Factor out 4x.

> **Explanation:** Although $8x^3 + 4x$ is equal to both $2x(4x^2 + 2)$ and $4(2x^3 + x)$ neither are considered completely factored because in both cases a common multiple, 2 in $2x(4x^2 + 2)$ and x in $4(2x^3 + x)$ can still be factored from the terms in the parenthesis.

Factoring Trinomials: (A trinomial has three terms.) To factor a trinomial, recall the acronym FOIL.

Study Tip: Check your note cards for the definition of FOIL.

Example 4. Multiply $(x+3)(x+5)$.

$$(x+3)(x+5) = x^2 + 5x + 3x + 15$$
$$= x^2 + 8x + 15$$

$(x+3)(x+5)$ is factored while $x^2 + 8x + 15$ is not. To factor trinomials, you need to know how the 8x and the 15 were computed. The 8x came from adding 5x and 3x while 15 came from multiplying 5 and 3.

Example 5. Factor $x^2 + 8x + 15$. (This is from Example 4.)

We need two numbers that when added equal 8 and when multiplied equal 15.

3 and 5 add up to 8 and when multiplied are15.

So $x^2 + 8x + 15 = (x+3)(x+5)$.

Example 6. Factor $x^2 - 4x - 12$.

We need two numbers that when added equal –4 and when multiplied equal –12.

–6 and 2 add up to –4 and when multiplied are –12.

So $x^2 - 4x - 12 = (x-6)(x+2)$.

Example 7. Factor $x^2 - 64$.

This is not a trinomial, but it can become one by adding 0x.

$x^2 - 64 = x^2 + 0x - 64$

We need two numbers that when added equal 0 and when multiplied equal –64.

–8 and 8 add to 0 and when multiplied are –64.

So $x^2 - 64 = (x-8)(x+8)$.

This example is called factoring the difference of perfect squares, and you will see this again if you take MAT 100, Intermediate Algebra.

Vocabulary: $a^2 - b^2$ is the **difference of perfect squares**.

The difference of perfect squares have a special factoring formula:

$$a^2 - b^2 = (a-b)(a+b)$$

Solving Quadratic Equations by Factoring:
If you multiply two quantities and the result is zero, then you know that one of the quantities must be zero. In mathematical notation

$$\text{if } a \bullet b = 0 \text{ then } a = 0 \text{ or } b = 0.$$

Example 8. Solve $x^2-11x+30=0$.

$x^2-11x+30=0$	
$(x-5)(x-6)=0$	Factored $x^2-11x+30$.
$(x-5)=0$ or $(x-6)=0$	Set each factor equal to zero.
$x=5$ or $x=6$	Solved each equation.

Example 9. Solve $9x^2+15x=0$.

$9x^2+15x=0$	
$3 \bullet 3 \bullet x \bullet x + 5 \bullet 3x = 0$	Factored $9x^2$ and $15x$.
$3x(3x+5)=0$	Factored out the common factor of $3x$.
$3x=0$ or $3x+5=0$	Set each factor equal to zero.
$x=0$ or $x=\frac{-5}{3}$	Solved each equation.

Before you think that factoring to solve quadratics is a lot easier than using the quadratic formula, you need to know that factoring doesn't always work. Consider changing Example 8 by just one to $x^2-11x+31=0$. You cannot find two numbers that when added equal –11 and when multiplied equal 31. In fact, to factor $x^2-11x+31$ you must use the quadratic formula. You will learn how to factor any quadratic equation in Precalculus I, MAT 161.

Summary: Two techniques for factoring are presented in this unit. The first is common factors which use the distributive property, ab + ac = a(b + c). The other one is factoring trinomials. To factor trinomials, you need to know how FOIL works. If you take MAT 100, Intermediate Algebra, you will see more factoring.

CLASS WORK

1. When is an algebraic expression in factored form?

2. Which expression is factored?

   a. $x^2 + 7x - 30$ or $(x + 10)(x - 3)$

   b. $6x^2 + 3x$ or $3x(2x + 1)$

3. Identify the common factors and factor the expression.

   a. $2x + 8$

   b. $8x + 4$

   c. $16x^2 - 24x$

4. Factor these trinomials.

a. $x^2 + 7x + 12$

b. $x^2 + 11x + 28$

c. $x^2 - 5x + 6$

d. $x^2 - 36$

5. Solve by factoring.

a. $x^2 - 6x - 16 = 0$

b. $20x^2 + 10x = 0$

Study Tip: New students must learn to budget their time in order to be successful in college. It is especially important when you have a test. See page iv and complete a weekly planner for the week of your last MAT 011 test. Make sure you include three one hour blocks to study for your upcoming MAT 011 exam. Also, make a weekly planner for the week of final exams. Make sure you include 5 one hour blocks to study for your MAT 011 final.

GROUP EXERCISES

Factor.

1. $8x^2 + 20x$

2. $x^2 - 5x - 14$

3. $x^2 - 121$

Solve.

4. $x^2 + 11x + 30 = 0$

5. $6x^2 - 3x = 0$

HOMEWORK EXERCISES

Study Tips: 1. Review Class Work, Overview, and Group Exercises.
2. Have your note cards ready for important definitions.

Skill Building Exercises

1. Find the greatest common factor.

   a. 18, 36 b. 20, –36 c. $2x,\ 6x^2$

2. Find two numbers when multiplied equal 36 and when added equal 13.

3. Find two numbers when multiplied equal –30 and when added equal 1.

Practice Exercises

4. Factor.

   a. $6x + 9$ b. $14x - 7$ c. $-10x + 50$

   d. $8x^2 - 6x$ e. $27x^2 - 18x$ f. $15x^3 - 5x^2$

   g. $x^2 + 7x + 6$ h. $x^2 - 8x + 15$ i. $x^2 - 6x + 9$

   j. $x^2 - 3x - 18$ k. $x^2 + 13x + 30$ l. $x^2 - 15x + 50$

   m. $x^2 - 100$ n. $x^2 - 36$ o. $x^2 - 81$

5. Solve by factoring.

   a. $x^2 + 7x + 6 = 0$ b. $x^2 - 5x - 50 = 0$ c. $12x^2 + 20x = 0$

Reading and Writing Exercises

6. What does it mean for an algebraic expression to be factored?

7. Which expression is factored?

   a. $2x^2 + 8x$ or $2x\,(x + 4)$

   b. $(x - 3)\,(x + 1)$ or $x^2 - 2x - 3$

8. Describe the **mistake**.

   a. $6x^2 + 3x = 3x\,(2x)$ b. $x^2 - 9 = x - 3$

CHAPTER 4 REVIEW

This chapter introduced you to quadratics. The two major topics are the quadratic formula and graphs of quadratics. These topics have many applications in business, physics, and geometry. Factoring is an important topic in MAT 100, Intermediate Algebra.

Section 4.1: Introduction to Quadratics:

Example 1. Simplify: $3(2x^2-5x+7)-5(6x^2-4)$

$3(2x^2-5x+7)-5(6x^2-4)$

$=6x^2-15x+21-30x^2+20$ Used the distributive property.

$=-24x^2-15x+41$ Combined like terms.

Example 2. Multiply: $(2x-5)(3x+7)$.

$(2x-5)(3x+7)=6x^2+14x-15x-35$ Multiplied using FOIL.

$=6x^2-1x-35$ Combined like terms.

Example 3. Multiply: $(x-6)^2$.

$(x-6)^2=(x-6)(x-6)$ Wrote the square as a product.

$=x^2-6x-6x+36$ Multiplied using FOIL.

$=x^2-12x+36$ Combined like terms.

Section 4.2: Applications of the Quadratic Formula:

Definition: $ax^2+bx+c=0$ is the quadratic equation.

Definition: $x=\dfrac{-b\pm\sqrt{b^2-4ac}}{2a}$ is the quadratic formula.

Example 4. A farmer wants to enclose two adjacent chicken coops against a barn. He has 125 feet of fence. What should the dimensions be if he wants the total area to be 700 square feet.

a. Complete the table to find the equation for area.

Barn

W W W

L

WIDTH	LENGTH	AREA
10	$125-3\bullet10=95$	$10\bullet95=950$
15	$125-3\bullet15=80$	$15\bullet80=1{,}200$
30	$125-3\bullet30=35$	$30\bullet35=1{,}050$
W	$125-3\bullet W$	$W(125-3\bullet W)$

$A=W(125-3W)$

$=125W-3W^2$ Used the distributive property.

$=-3W^2+125W$ Wrote the squared term first.

b. Find W when A = 700.

$700 = -3W^2 + 125W$	Substituted 700 for A.
$0 = -3W^2 + 125W - 700$	Subtracted 700 from both sides.
a = –3, b = 125, c = –700	Identified a, b, and c.
$W = \dfrac{-b \pm \sqrt{b^2 - 4ac}}{2a}$	The quadratic formula.
$W = \dfrac{-125 \pm \sqrt{125^2 - 4(-3)(-700)}}{2(-3)}$	Substituted the values of a, b, and c into the quadratic formula.
$W = \dfrac{-125 \pm 85}{2(-3)}$	Simplified the square root.
$W = \dfrac{-125 + 85}{2(-3)}$ or $W = \dfrac{-125 - 85}{2(-3)}$	Wrote as two solutions.
$W = 6.667$ or $W = 35$	Simplified.

The dimensions of the chicken coop that will yield an area of 700 square feet are 35 by 20 feet and 6.667 by 105 feet. (To get the length divide 700 by 6.667 and 35.)

Section 4.3: Quadratic Applications and Graphs:

To graph a quadratic, $y = ax^2 + bx + c$ you must find:

1. The vertex:

   The x coordinate is computed with the formula $x = \dfrac{-b}{2a}$.

   The y coordinate is computed by substituting the x coordinate into $y = ax^2 + bx + c$.

2. The x intercept:

   Set y = 0 and solve $0 = ax^2 + bx + c$ using the quadratic formula.

3. The y intercept:

   Substitute x = 0 into $y = ax^2 + bx + c$. Note that when x = 0, y = c.

Example 5. The cost equation for making juice boxes is $C = 0.6B^2 - 24B + 36$, and the revenue equation is $R = -0.4B^2 + 18B$. B is in millions, and C and R are in thousands of dollars.

a. Find the profit equation.

Profit = Revenue - Cost	Formula for profit.
$P = (-0.4B^2 + 18B) - (0.6B^2 - 24B + 36)$	Substituted the equations for revenue and cost. (Note the need for parentheses).
$P = -0.4B^2 + 18B - 0.6B^2 + 24B - 36$	Used the distributive property.
$P = -B^2 + 42B - 36$	Combined like terms.

b. Graph the profit equation and explain what the vertex, B, and P intercepts mean in terms of the problem.

- Find the vertex of $P = -B^2 + 42B - 36$.

The formula for the B coordinate is $B = \frac{-b}{2a}$.

a = –1, b = 42.

$$B = \frac{-42}{2(-1)}$$

B = 21

Find the P coordinate. Substitute B = 21 into $P = -B^2 + 42B - 36$.

$$P = -21^2 + 42 \bullet 21 - 36$$
$$P = 405$$

The vertex is (21, 405).

- Find the B intercept. Set P = 0.

Solve $0 = -B^2 + 42B - 36$.

a = –1, b = 42, c = –36.

$$B = \frac{-42 \pm \sqrt{42^2 - 4(-1)(-36)}}{2(-1)}$$

$$B = \frac{-42 \pm 40.25}{2(-1)}$$

$$B = \frac{-42 + 40.25}{-2} \text{ or } B = \frac{-42 - 40.25}{-2}$$

B = 0.875 or B = 41.13

The B intercepts are (0.875, 0) and (41.13, 0).

- Find the P intercept. Set B = 0.

$$P = -(0)^2 + 42 \bullet 0 - 36$$
$$P = -36$$

The P intercept is (0, –36).

c. Suppose the company needs to earn $200,000 in profit (P = 200). Graph the line P = 200 and find how many juice boxes the company needs to make to earn $200,000.

$$200 = -B^2 + 42B - 36$$
$$0 = -B^2 + 42B - 236$$
$$a = -1,\ b = 42,\ c = -236$$
$$B = \frac{-42 \pm \sqrt{42^2 - 4(-1)(-236)}}{2(-1)}$$
$$B = \frac{-42 \pm 28.64}{2(-1)}$$
$$B = 6.682,\ 35.32$$

The company needs to make 6.682 or 35.32 million juice boxes in order to earn $200,000 in profits.

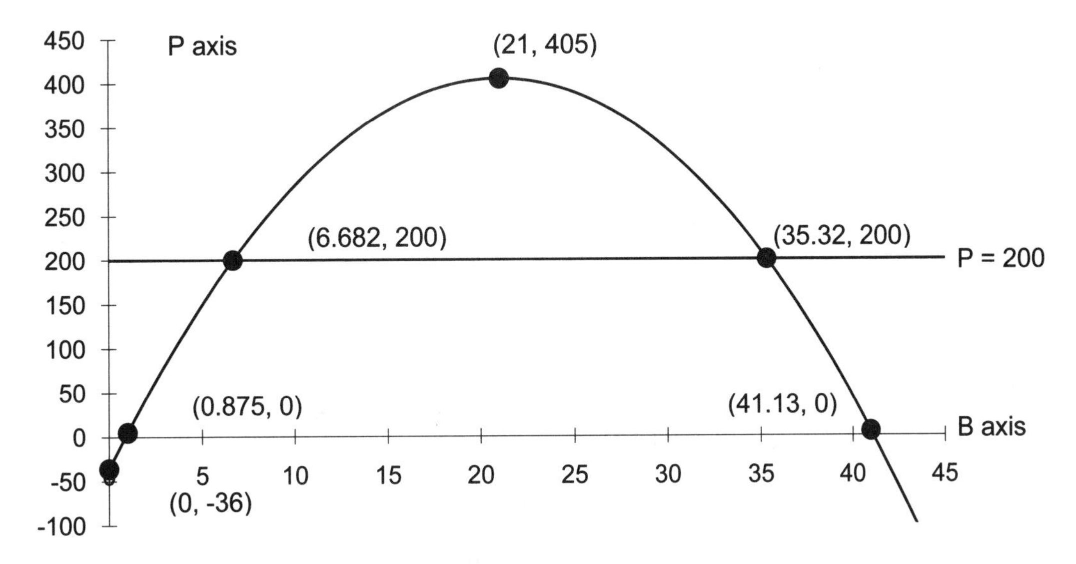

The vertex (21, 405) represents the maximum profit. The company will obtain its maximum profit of $405,000 when they sell 21 million juice boxes.

The B intercepts (0.875, 0) and (41.13, 0) tell us that the company will break even if they sell .875 or 41.13 million juice boxes.

The P intercept (0. –36) represents the company's start up costs of $36,000.

Section 4.4: Factoring:

Common Factors:

Example 6. Factor $24x^3 + 30x$.

$$24x^3 + 30x = 6 \bullet 4 \bullet x \bullet x \bullet x + 6 \bullet 5 \bullet x$$
$$= 6x(4x^2 + 5)$$

Trinomials:

Example 7. Factor $x^2 - 4x - 12$.

$x^2 - 4x - 12$, need two numbers that when added equal –4 and when multiplied equal –12.

$(x-6)(x+2)$.

Example 8. Factor $x^2 - 81$.

$x^2 - 81 = x^2 + 0x - 81$, need two numbers that when added equal 0 and when multiplied equal –81.

$= (x-9)(x+9)$

Solving quadratic equations by factoring.

If $a \bullet b = 0$ then $a = 0$ or $b = 0$.

Example 9. Solve $x^2 + 5x - 14 = 0$.

$$x^2 + 5x - 14 = 0$$
$$(x+7)(x-2) = 0$$
$$x - 2 = 0 \text{ or } x + 7 = 0$$
$$x = 2 \text{ or } x = -7$$

Study Tips:

1. Practice the review test starting on the next page by placing yourself under realistic exam conditions.
2. Find a quiet place and use a timer to simulate the length of the class period.
3. Write your answers in your homework notebook or make a copy of the test. You may then re-take the exam for extra practice.
4. Check your answers. The answers to the review test are on page 465.
5. There is an additional exam available on the MAT 011 web page, **www.mc3.edu/aa/career/MATHSCI/mat011/mat011.htm**
6. Do NOT wait until the night before to study.

CHAPTER 4 REVIEW TEST

Study Tip: Make sure you have all of your graphing materials: colored pencils, ruler, and graph paper.

1. Titanic Ship Company makes yachts. The cost of making x yachts per month is

$$C = x^2 - 32x + 72,$$

and the revenue from selling x yachts per month is

$$R = -x^2 + 8x.$$

C and R are in thousands of dollars.

a. Find the equation for profit. (Profit = Revenue - Cost)

b. Find the **vertex** and explain what it means in terms of making yachts.

c. Find the **x intercepts** and explain what they mean in terms of making yachts.

d. Find the **P intercept** and explain what it means in terms of making yachts.

e. Graph the function.

Vertex	
x intercepts	
P intercept	

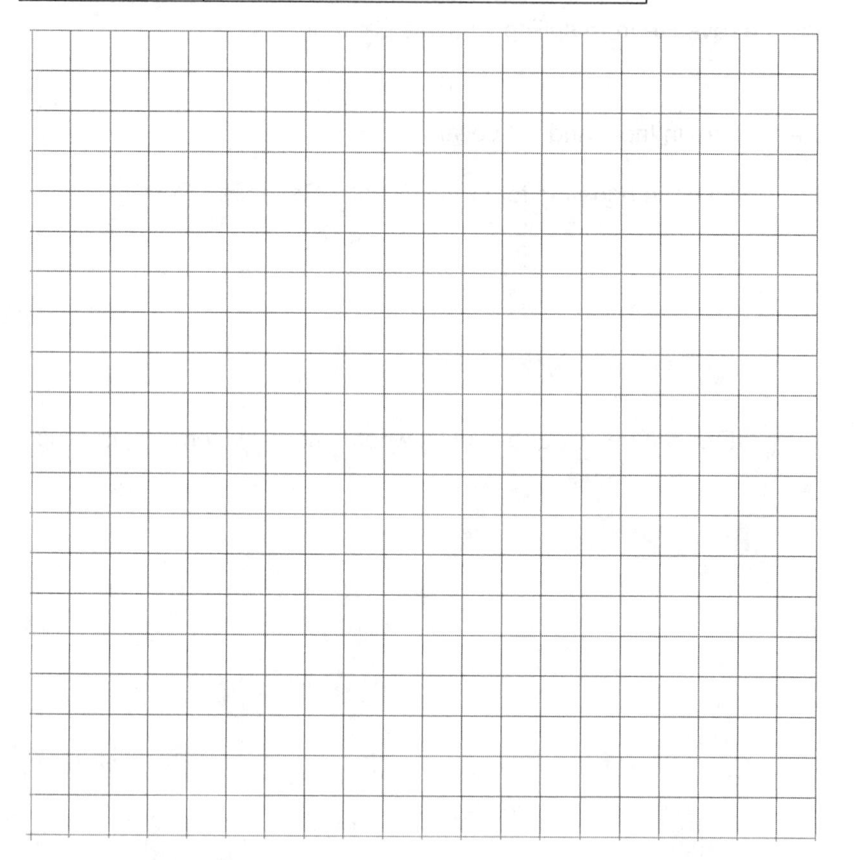

f. Suppose the Titanic Ship Company needs $35,000 in profits (P = 35). Graph this line on the graph created in part b and then use the quadratic formula to find where the line intersects the graph of the quadratic. Explain what the answers mean.

2. A rabbit breeder has 80 meters of chicken wire. He wants to form two rectangular hutches for his rabbits. One side of the hutch will be against a wall. (See the diagram below.)

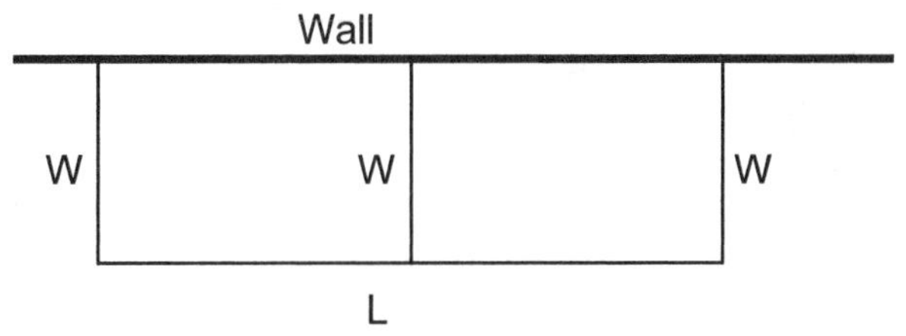

a. Find a formula for the area of the rabbit hutches (Make a table.)

b. Find the **vertex** and explain what it means in terms of the area of the hutch.

c. Find the **w intercepts** and explain what they mean in terms of the area of the hutch.

d. Find the **A intercept** and explain what it means in terms of the area of the hutch.

e. Graph the area equation. Make sure you label the axes and use an appropriate scale.

Vertex	
w intercepts	
A intercept	

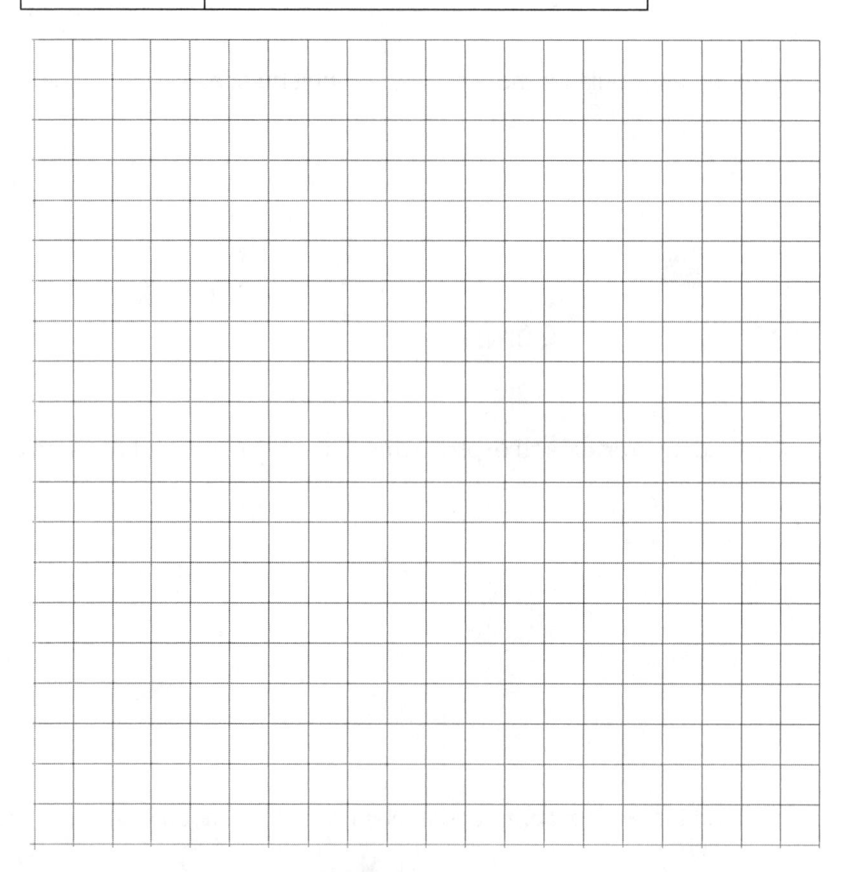

f. Suppose the breeder reads in *Breeding Rabbits Magazine* that he should have an area of 477 square feet (A = 477) Represent this idea in the graph of Part b. Use the quadratic formula to find where the line intersects the graph of the quadratic and explain what the solutions represent.

3. During the course of an experiment, the temperature of oxygen must be monitored. Using the data from the experiment, the following quadratic can model the temperature of the oxygen,

$$T = 0.3m^2 - 5.1m + 9$$

where T is measured in Celsius, and m represents the minutes that the experiment has run.

a. Find the **vertex** and explain what it means in terms of the temperature of the oxygen.

b. Find the **m intercepts** and explain what they mean in terms of the temperature of the oxygen.

c. Find the **T intercept** and explain what it means in terms of the temperature of the oxygen.

d. Graph the temperature equation. Make sure you label the axes and use an appropriate scale.

Vertex	
m intercepts	
T intercept	

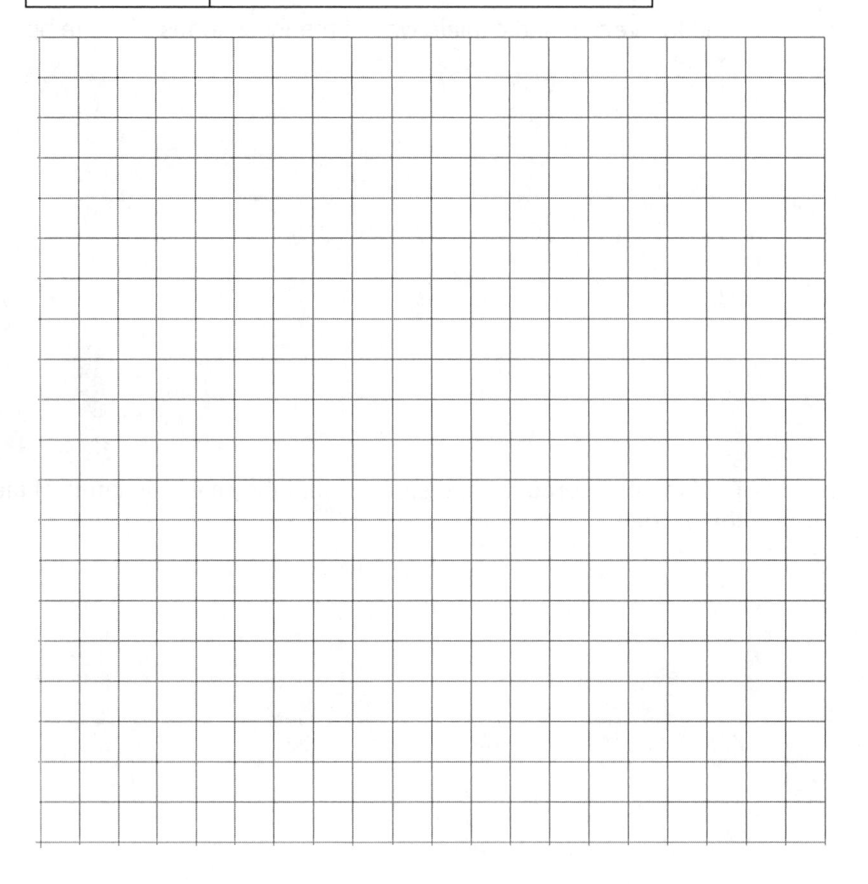

4. Simplify. $3\left(x^2+4x-8\right)-2\left(3x^2-5x+3\right)$

5. Multiply.

a. $(3x+5)(x-8)$

b. $(x-5)^2$

6. Factor.

a. $4x^2+8x$

b. $x^2+7x-18$

7. Solve. $x^2-8x+12=0$

8. Describe the steps in solving the following problem.

$4x^2 - 3x + 2 = 7$

$4x^2 - 3x - 5 = 0$ ______________________

a = 4 b = -3, c = -5 ______________________

$x = \frac{-(-3) \pm \sqrt{(-3)^2 - 4(4)(-5)}}{2(4)}$ ______________________

$x = \frac{-(-3) \pm 8.426}{2(4)}$ ______________________

$x = \frac{3 \pm 8.426}{8}$ ______________________

$x = \frac{3 + 8.426}{8}, \; x = \frac{3 - 8.426}{8}$ ______________________

x =1.428, x = -0.6783 ______________________

9. Find the mistake.

$x^2 - 5x + 2 = 4$

$x^2 - 5x - 2 = 0$

a = 1 b = -5, c = -2

$x = \frac{-(-5) \pm \sqrt{(-5)^2 - 4(1)(2)}}{2(1)}$

$x = \frac{-(-5) \pm 4.123}{2(1)}$

$x = \frac{5 \pm 4.123}{2}$

$x = \frac{5 + 4.123}{2}, \; x = \frac{5 - 4.123}{2}$

x =4.562, x = 0.4385

FINAL EXAM

REVIEW

FINAL EXAM REVIEW
STUDY TIPS

1. Know when and where your final exam is being held. It may not be at the same time as your class and may not be in the same room.

   My final is in Room ______________________________

   at ____

2. Arrive at least 15 minutes early for the final.

3. Make sure you have several sharpened pencils, your calculator, a ruler, and colored pencils.

4. Know what score you have to get on the final to get the grade you want for the course. If necessary, make an appointment with your teacher to discuss your grade.

5. Know when your teacher will be on campus during final exam week.

   My teacher will be in his/her office at ______________________________

6. Try to organize a study group with some of your classmates.

7. Find out if the Learning Assistance Lab is having a group study session for finals.

8. Study an hour or so a day. Do not try to pull an "all nighter" for the final.

9. To prepare for the final exam:
   a. Organize your note cards.
   b. Review the sample tests.
   c. Go over the tests you took. Go back and review the difficult sections; re-do the ones you had wrong.
   d. Review the sample problems starting on the next page.
   e. Practice the review final starting on page 387 by placing yourself under realistic exam conditions.
   f. Find a quiet place and use a timer to simulate test conditions.
   g. Write your answers in your homework notebook. You may then re-take the exam for extra practice.
   h. Check your answers. The answers to the review test are on page 466.
   i. Do NOT wait until the night before to study. The final can be very challenging.

SAMPLE PROBLEMS

Solving Equations: Solving equations is perhaps the most important skill taught in an algebra course. There were five types of equations covered this semester, linear, literal, inequalities, rational (equations with fractions), and quadratic.

- Linear Equations (Sections1.4 and 1.5: Solving Equations)

Example 1. Solve $4x-2(5x-8)=4x+12$

$4x-2(5x-8)=4x+12$

$4x-10x+16=4x+12$ Use the distributive property.

$-6x+16=4x+12$ Combine like terms.

$16=10x+12$ Add 6x to both sides.

$4=10x$ Subtract 12 from both sides.

$0.4=x$ Divide both sides by 10.

- Literal Equations (Section 1.7: Applications of Linear Equations, Literal Equations)

Example 2. Solve $6x+7y=15$ for y.

$6x+7y=15$

$7y=15-6x$ Subtract 6x from both sides.

$y=\frac{15-6x}{7}$ Divide both sides by 7.

- Inequalities (Section 2.1: Inequalities)

Example 3. Solve $24-7x \le 108$.

$24-7x \le 108$

$-7x \le 84$ Subtract 24 from both sides.

$x \ge -12$ Divide both sides by –7 and reverse the inequality.

Example 4. Solve $-5<7+3x<32$.

$-5<7+3x<32$

$-12<3x<25$ Subtract 7 from all three parts.

$-4<x<8.333$ Divide all three parts by 3.

- Rational Equations (Section 3.6: Solving Equations with Fractions)

Example 5. Solve $\frac{5}{3x}+\frac{7}{6}=\frac{26}{15}$.

$\frac{5}{3x}+\frac{7}{6}=\frac{26}{15}$ The LCD is 30x.

$\frac{5}{3x}\bullet\frac{30x}{1}+\frac{7}{6}\bullet\frac{30x}{1}=\frac{26}{15}\bullet\frac{30x}{1}$ Multiply all the terms by 30x

$5\bullet 10+7\bullet 5x=26\bullet 2x$ Reduce.

$50+35x=52x$ Multiply.

$50=17x$ Subtract 35x from both sides.

$\frac{50}{17}=x$ Divide both sides by 17.

- Quadratic Equations (Section 4.2: Applications of the Quadratic Formula)

Example 6. Solve $-2x^2 + 41x + 27 = 14$.

$-2x^2 + 41x + 27 = 14$	
$-2x^2 + 41x + 13 = 0$	Subtract 14 from both sides.
a = -2, b = 41, c = 13	Identify a, b, and c.
$x = \dfrac{-b \pm \sqrt{b^2 - 4ac}}{2a}$	Recall the quadratic formula.
$x = \dfrac{-41 \pm \sqrt{41^2 - 4(-2)(13)}}{2(-2)}$	Substitute a, b, and c into the quadratic formula.
$x = \dfrac{-41 \pm 42.25}{2(-2)}$	Simplify the square root.
$x = \dfrac{-41 + 42.25}{2(-2)}$ or $x = \dfrac{-41 - 42.25}{2(-2)}$	Write as two solutions.
$x = -.3125$ or $x = 20.81$	Simplify.

Graphing: Graphing is a way of visualizing a problem. A graph shows the "big" picture. There were two types of graphs presented in the course, lines (including horizontal and vertical) and quadratics.

- Graphing Lines

Example 7. Graph $y = -4x + 13$ by finding three points.
(Section 2.3: Graphing Lines by Plotting Points)

Pick three values for x and find their y coordinates.
(Two points are necessary to graph a line; a third point is used to check the work.)

1. x = -5, find y.	2. x = 3, find y.	3. x = 15 find y
$y = -4(-5) + 13$	$y = -4(3) + 13$	$y = -4(15) + 13$
$y = 33$	$y = 1$	$y = -47$
Plot the point (-5, 33).	Plot the point (3, 1).	Plot the point (15, -47).

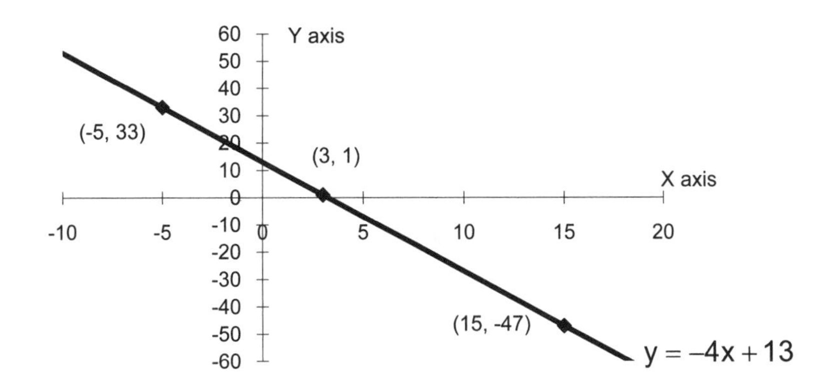

Example 8. Graph the line $4x + 0.2y = 64$ by finding the intercepts.

(Section 2.6: Graphing Lines by Plotting Its Intercepts)

Find the x intercept; set y = 0.

$$4x + 0.2(0) = 64$$
$$4x = 64$$
$$x = 16$$

The x intercept is (16, 0).

Find the y intercept; set x = 0.

$$4(0) + 0.2y = 64$$
$$0.2y = 64$$
$$y = 320$$

The y intercept is (0, 320).

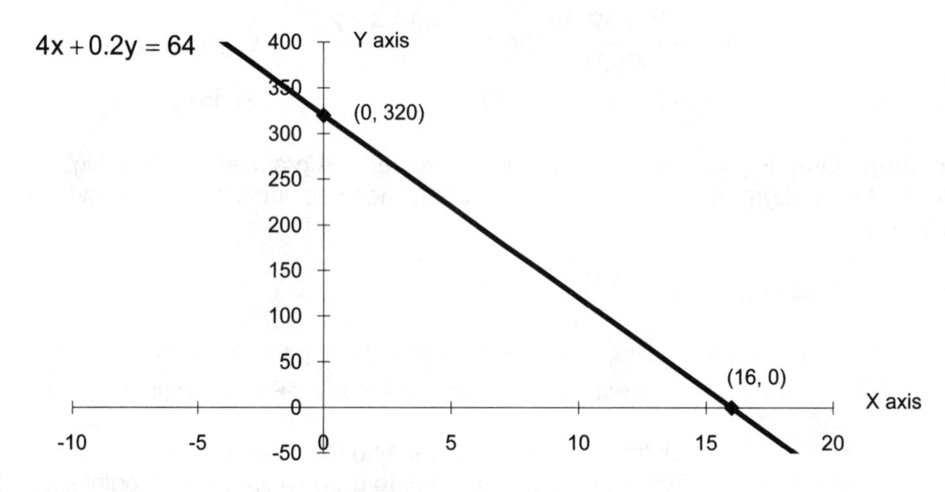

Example 9. Graph y = 8. (Section 2.8: Slope)

Since y is equal to a constant, then y = 8 is a horizontal line.

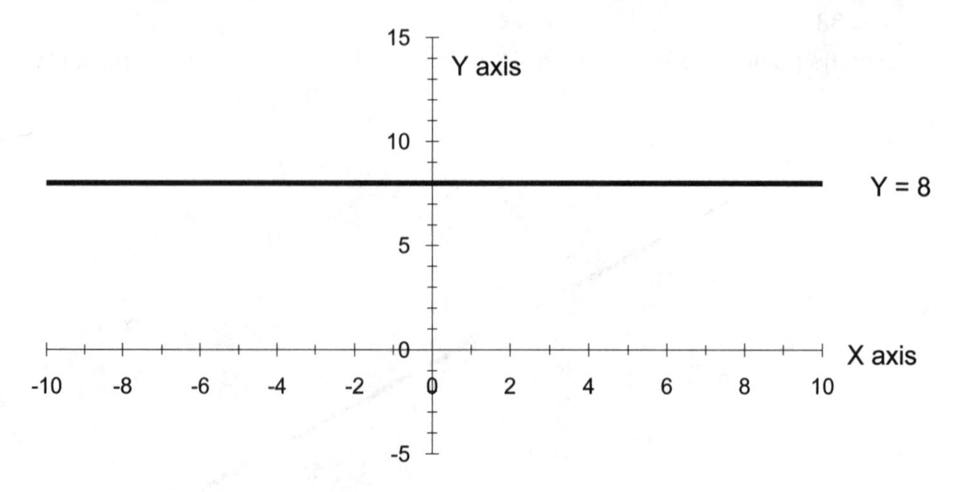

Example 10. Graph the line x = –3. (Section 2.8: Slope)

Since x is equal to a constant, then the line is vertical.

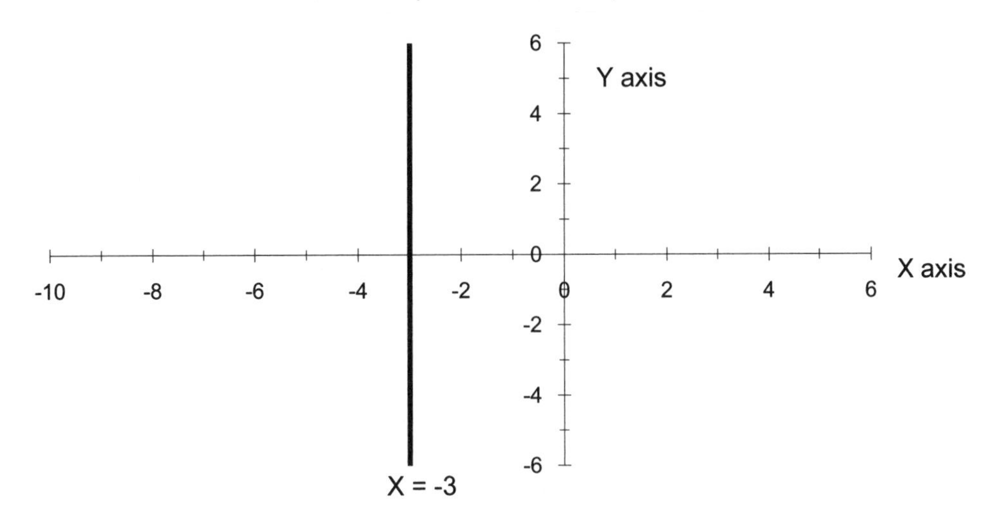

- Quadratics (Section 4.3: Quadratic Applications and Graphs)

Example 11. Graph $y = -2x^2 + 18x - 25$.

Find the vertex.

x coordinate:

$$x = \frac{-b}{2a}.$$

a = –2, b = 18

$$x = \frac{-18}{2(-2)}$$

$$x = 4.5$$

y coordinate:

$$y = -2(4.5^2) + 18(4.5) - 25$$

$$y = 15.5$$

The vertex is (4.5, 15.5).

Find the y intercept; set x = 0.

$$y = -2(0^2) + 18(0) - 25$$

$$y = -25$$

The y intercept is (0, –25).

Find the x intercept; set y = 0.

Solve $0 = -2x^2 + 18x - 25$

$$a = -2,\ b = 18,\ c = -25$$

$$x = \frac{-b \pm \sqrt{b^2 - 4ac}}{2a}$$

$$x = \frac{-18 \pm \sqrt{18^2 - 4(-2)(-25)}}{2(-2)}$$

$$x = \frac{-18 \pm 11.14}{2(-2)}$$

$$x = \frac{-18 + 11.14}{2(-2)} \text{ or } x = \frac{-18 - 11.14}{2(-2)}$$

$$x = 1.715 \text{ or } x = 7.285$$

The x intercepts are (1.715, 0) and (7.285, 0).

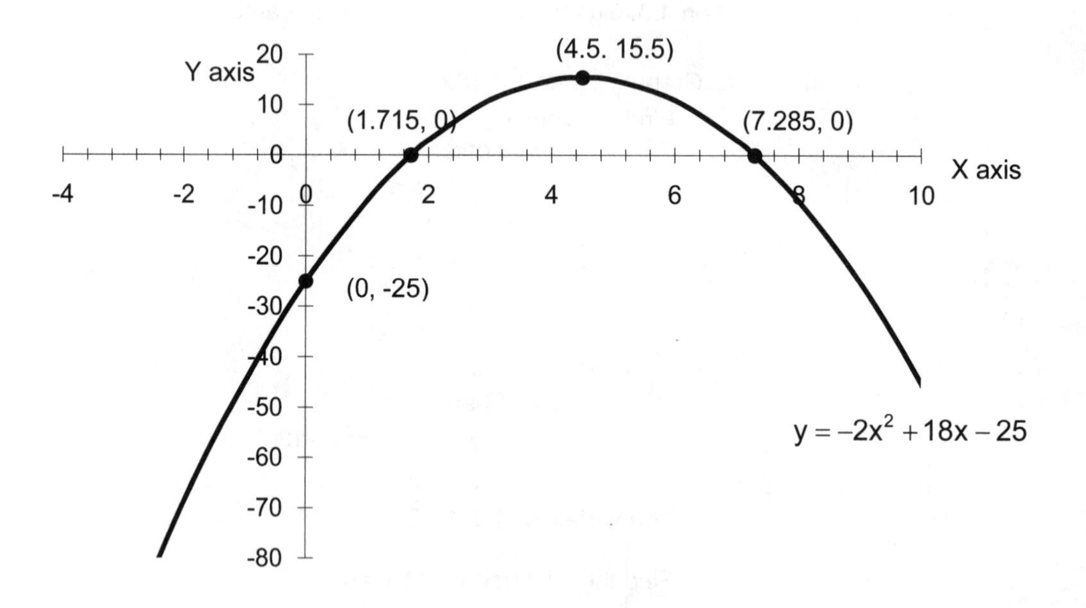

Applications: There are two reasons why applications were used in this course. One reason was to show you how algebra can be used in everyday life. The other reason was to give concrete examples to the mathematical ideas of the course.

- Tables

Example 12. A cell phone company charges $3.75 for the first 100 minutes and then 2 cents a minute after that.
(Sections 1.2 and 1.6: Introduction to Variables and Applications of Linear Equations)

a. Complete the table below and find an equation for the cost of the cell phone.

Minutes	**Calculation**	**Cost**
200	$0.02(200-100)+3.75$	$5.75
500	$0.02(500-100)+3.75$	$11.75
600	$0.02(600-100)+3.75$	$13.75
m	$0.02(m-100)+3.75$	C

$C = 0.02(m-100)+3.75$

b. If your cell phone bill were $4.25, how long were you the phone?

Find m when C = 4.25.

$$4.25 = 0.02(m-100)+3.75$$
$$4.25 = 0.02m-2+3.75$$
$$4.25 = 0.02m+1.75$$
$$2.50 = 0.02m$$
$$125 = m$$

Since the cost was $4.25, then you were on the phone for 125 minutes.

Example 13. Storm Cloud Umbrella Company is having a 20% off sale because of a prolonged drought. If the sale price is $7.45, what was the price of the umbrella before the sale?
(Section 1.8: Percentages)

Pre-Sale Price	**Calculation**	**Sale Price**
10.00	$10.00-0.20 \bullet 10.00$	$8.00
9.00	$9.00-0.20 \bullet 9.00$	$7.20
P	$P-0.20P$	S

$$S = P-0.20P$$
$$S = 0.80P$$

Find P when S = 7.45.

$$7.45 = 0.80P$$
$$9.31 = P$$

The pre-sale price of the umbrella was $9.31.

Example 14. 500 bacteria are initially present. If the bacteria grow at a rate of 4% a day, find a formula for the number of bacteria.
(Section: Introduction to Positive Exponents)

Day	Calculation	Number of Bacteria
1	$500 \bullet 1.04$	520
2	$500 \bullet 1.04^2$	541
3	$500 \bullet 1.04^3$	562
4	$500 \bullet 1.04^4$	585
D	$500 \bullet 1.04^D$	N

$$N = 500 \bullet 1.04^D$$

- Percentage (Section 1.8: Percentages)

Example 15. Dr. Scholastic computes her grades as follows:

Homework Average	20%
Group Work Average	10%
Test Average	50%
Project Average	5%
Final Exam	15%

Selena has a 92 homework grade, 88 group work grade, 98 test average, and a 95 project average. If Selena wants a 90 for the course, how well does she have to do on the final?

$$0.20 \bullet 92 + 0.10 \bullet 88 + 0.50 \bullet 98 + 0.05 \bullet 95 + 0.15E = 90$$
$$80.95 + 0.15E = 90$$
$$0.15E = 9.05$$
$$E = 60.33$$

Because Selena did well all semester, she just has to get a 60.33 to get a 90 for the year.

- Inequalities (Section 2.2: Applications of Inequalities)

Example 16. Smith/Jones offers you a sales position upon graduation from M.C.C.C. They will pay $12,000 a year plus 8% commission. If your wages need to be between $45,000 and $62,000, then how much do you have to sell?

The equation that relates wages and sales is

$$W = 0.08S + 12{,}000 \ .$$

Wages need to be between 45,000 and 60,000.

$$45{,}000 < 0.08S + 12{,}000 < 60{,}000$$
$$33{,}000 < 0.08S < 48{,}000$$
$$412{,}500 < S < 600{,}000$$

If wages have to be between $45,000 and $60,000, then you sales have to be between $412,500 and $600,000.

- Slope and Percent Change (Section 2.7: Introduction to Slope)

Example 17. Use the table to answer the following questions.

Year	Number of CD Players Sold
1998	2,345,000
2002	3,789,000

a. Find the slope or average rate of change for the given years.

$$\text{A.R.C.} = \frac{3{,}789{,}000 - 2{,}345{,}000}{2002 - 1998}$$

$$\text{A.R.C.} = 361{,}000$$

The average rate of change for the years 1998 to 2002 was 361,000 CD players per year.

b. Find the percent change in the number of CD players sold.

$$\text{A.R.C.} = \frac{3{,}789{,}000 - 2{,}345{,}000}{2{,}345{,}000} \bullet 100$$

$$\text{A.R.C.} = 61.6\%$$

CD sales increased by 61.6% from 1998 to 2002.

Proportions (Section 3.7: Ratio and Proportion Problems)

Example 18. Two people pool their money to buy lottery tickets. Dave contributes $35 while Sue puts in $45. If they win 3.78 million dollars, how much should Dave get?

	Tickets	Winnings
Share	35	?
Total	80	3.78

$$\frac{35}{80} = \frac{W}{3.78}$$

$$132.3 = 80W$$

$$1.654 = W$$

Dave's fair share is 1.654 million dollars.

Scientific Notation (Section 3.2: Negative Exponents and Scientific Notation)

Example 19. a. Write 3,400,000,000 in Scientific Notation.

The 3 is in the 10^9 place. Remember that the first zero on the right is the 10^0 place.

$3{,}400{,}000{,}000 = 3.4 \text{ X } 10^9$

b. Write $5.3 \text{ X } 10^{-4}$ in decimal notation.

The 5 is in the 10^{-4}. Remember that the first zero to the left of the decimal point is the 10^{-1}place.

$5.3 \text{ X } 10^{-4} = 0.00053$

- Summary of Linear Equations (Section 2.9: Applications of Graphs)

Example 20 You are going to rent a moving truck for the day. One company, Lite Trucks, charges 23.95 plus 35 cents per mile while a second company, Spacious Vans, charges a flat rate of 64.95.

a. Write the cost equations for each company.

Lite Trucks: $C = 0.35m + 23.95$
Spacious Vans: $C = 64.95$

b. Graph both equations on the same set of axes. Label each axis and choose an appropriate scale. Only graph the portion relevant to the problem.

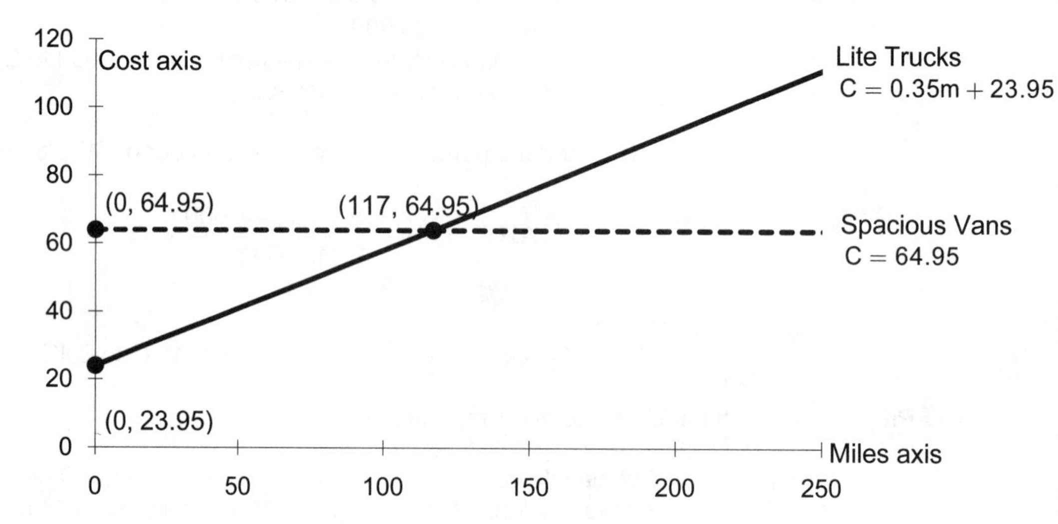

c. Find where the two lines intersect.

Solve $64.95 = 0.35m + 23.95$
$41 = 0.35m$
$117 = m$

The two companies will charge the same when you drive 117 miles.
The two lines intersect at (117, 64.95).

d. Use the graph to find when Lite Trucks costs more than Spacious Vans.

$m > 117$ Lite Trucks cost more when you drive more than 117 miles.

e. What does the C intercept mean in terms of the problem?

For Spacious Vans the C intercept is (0, 64.95).
For Lite Trucks the C intercept is (0, 23.95).
The C intercept is the cost of going zero miles.

f. What is the slope of each line, and what does it mean in terms of the problem?

The slope of Spacious Vans is zero.
The slope of Lite Trucks is 0.35.
The slope is the cost per mile.

- Summary of Quadratic Applications (Section 4.3: Quadratic Applications and Graphs)

Example 21. Q-Bees makes quilts. The cost equation for making quilts is represented by the equation $C = 0.7q^2 - 34q + 89$, and the revenue is represented by the equation $R = -0.3q^2 + 24q$. The units for q are thousands, and C and R are in hundreds.

a. Find the profit equation.

Profit = Revenue – Cost

$$P = (-0.3q^2 + 24q) - (0.7q^2 - 34q + 89)$$
$$P = -0.3q^2 + 24q - 0.7q^2 + 34q - 89$$
$$P = -q^2 + 58q - 89$$

b. Graph the profit equation. Explain what the vertex, q intercepts, and P intercept mean in terms of the problem.

Find the vertex.

Find the q coordinate.

$$q = \frac{-b}{2a}$$

a = –1, b = 58

$$q = \frac{-58}{2(-1)}$$
$$q = 29$$

Find the P coordinate.

$$P = -(29)^2 + 58(29) - 89$$
$$P = 752$$

The vertex is (29, 752).

Find the q intercepts. Set P = 0.

Solve $0 = -q^2 + 58q - 89$

a = –1, b = 58, c = –89.

$$q = \frac{-b \pm \sqrt{b^2 - 4ac}}{2a}$$
$$q = \frac{-58 \pm \sqrt{58^2 - 4(-1)(-89)}}{2(-1)}$$
$$q = \frac{-58 \pm 54.85}{2(-1)}$$
$$q = \frac{-58 + 54.85}{2(-1)} \text{ or } q = \frac{-58 - 54.85}{2(-1)}$$
$$q = 1.575 \text{ or } q = 56.43$$

The q intercepts are (1.575, 0) and (56.43, 0).

Find the P intercept. Set q = 0.

$$P = -(0^2) + 58(0) - 89$$
$$P = -89$$

The P intercept is (0, –89).

(The graph contains the answer to Part c.)

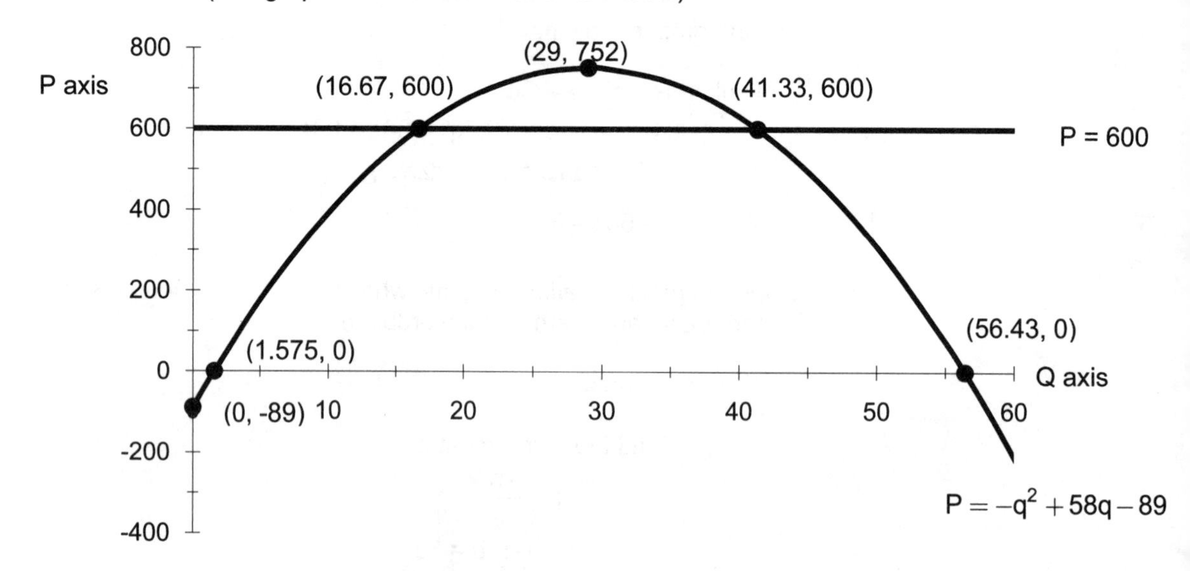

The vertex is (29, 752). If Q-Bees sell 29,000 quilts, then they will earn a maximum profit of $75,200.

The q intercepts are (1.575, 0) and (56.43, 0). If Q-Bees sells 1,575 or 5,643 quilts, then they will break even.

The P intercept is (0, –89). The start up costs for Q-Bees is $8,900.

c. Suppose that the company needs to earn a profit of $60,000, P = 600. Sketch the line P = 600 on the graph above and find where the line intersects the graph.

$$\text{Solve } 600 = -q^2 + 58q - 89$$
$$0 = -q^2 + 58q - 689$$
$$a = -1,\ b = 58,\ c = -689.$$
$$q = \frac{-b \pm \sqrt{b^2 - 4ac}}{2a}$$
$$q = \frac{-58 \pm \sqrt{58^2 - 4(-1)(-689)}}{2(-1)}$$
$$q = \frac{-58 \pm 24.66}{2(-1)}$$
$$q = 16.67 \text{ or } q = 41.33$$

Q-Bees will earn $60,000 if they sell 16,670 or 41,330 quilts.

Algebra Skills: Manipulation of algebraic expressions is good exercise for the mind. It forces you to follow abstract rules and perform prescribed actions.

- Exponents (Section 3.3: Properties of Exponents)

Example 22. Simplify each expression. Write with positive exponents only.

a. $(3x^4)^2$

$$(3x^4)^2 = 3^2(x^4)^2 = 9x^8$$

b. $\frac{7x^{-4}}{x}$

$$\frac{7x^{-4}}{x} = \frac{7}{x(x^4)} = \frac{7}{x^5}$$

c. $\frac{4x^5}{8x^2}$

$$\frac{4x^5}{8x^2} = \frac{x^3}{2}$$

- Multiplying and Dividing Fractions (Section 3.4: Introduction to Algebraic Fractions)

Example 23. Multiply or divide as indicated. Reduce to lowest terms.

a. $\frac{9x^2}{5} \bullet \frac{10}{6x^3}$

$$\frac{9x^2}{5} \bullet \frac{10}{6x^3} = \frac{3 \bullet 3 \bullet x \bullet x}{5} \bullet \frac{5 \bullet 2}{3 \bullet 2 \bullet x \bullet x \bullet x} = \frac{3}{x}$$

b. $\frac{8}{21x^3} \div \frac{16x^2}{7}$

$$\frac{8}{21x^3} \div \frac{16x^2}{7} = \frac{8}{21x^3} \bullet \frac{7}{16x^2} = \frac{8}{7 \bullet 3x^3} \bullet \frac{7}{8 \bullet 2x^2} = \frac{1}{6x^5}$$

- Factoring (Section 4.4: Factoring)

Example 24. Factor each of the following.

a. $8x^3 + 24x$

$$8x^3 + 24x = 8 \bullet x \bullet x \bullet x + 8 \bullet 3 \bullet x$$
$$= 8x(x^2 + 3)$$

b. $x^2 - 7x - 18$

We need two numbers that when added equal –7 and when multiplied equal –18.

$$x^2 - 7x - 18 = (x - 9)(x + 2)$$

c. $x^2 - 25$

$$x^2 - 25 = x^2 + 0x - 25$$

We need two numbers that when added equal 0 and when multiplied equal –25.

$$x^2 - 25 = (x - 5)(x + 5)$$

SAMPLE FINAL

1. Evaluate: $9^2 - [16 - (10 - 2)]$.

2. Simplify: $8x - 7 - 3(6x + 4y - 5)$

3. Solve for x: $\frac{x}{3} - \frac{5}{6} = \frac{1}{4}$

4. Solve $36 \leq 4 + 8x < 84$ and graph on a real number line.

5. Multiply:

a. $(x - 4)(x + 5)$

b. $(x + 7)^2$

6. Use the following bar chart to determine the total profit for the six years shown.

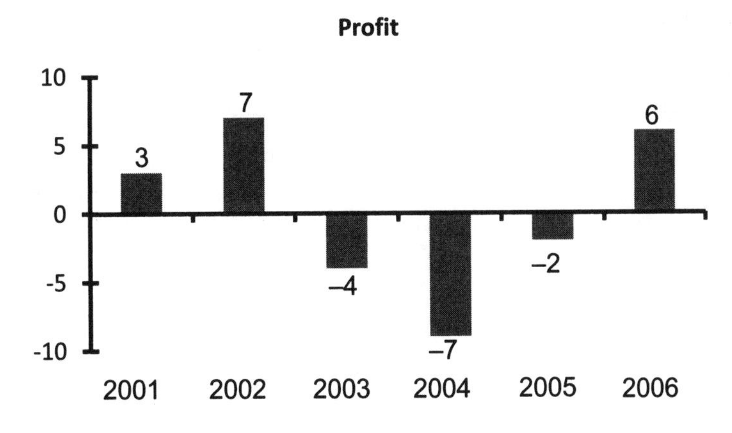

In #7 and #8, find an equation for each situation. (A table may be helpful.)

7. Two students want to open up a gift wrapping store in the mall. They spend $800 on wrapping paper, boxes, and ribbons; and they plan on charging $1.25 per package. Find an equation for the amount of money they will earn.

8. A phone company charges a basic rate of $2.25 plus 12 cents per minute after the first 15 minutes. Find an equation for the cost of making a phone call.

9. The equation $S = 23t + 71$ represents the number of stores, S, Z-Mart has opened at the end of t years, where t is the number of years since 2005.

   a. When will Z-Mart have more than 278 stores? (You must set up an inequality.)

   b. When will Z-Mart have between 232 and 416 stores? (You must set up an inequality.)

Use the following table in #10 and #11. The table indicates the population of the U.S. from 1800 to 1810.

YEAR	POPULATION IN MILLIONS
1800	5.3
1810	7.5

10. Find the percent increase from 1800 to 1810.

11. Find the average rate of change (slope) between 1800 and 1810.

12. a. Convert the number 4,300,000 to Scientific Notation.

b. Convert the number 2.4×10^{-4} to Decimal Notation.

13. Simplify using properties of exponents. Write with positive exponents only.

a. $x^5 \cdot x^2$

b. $\left(3x^4\right)^2$

c. $\dfrac{x^3}{x^6}$

d. $\dfrac{9x^{-3}}{x^2}$

e. x^0

f. $8x^{-4}$

Use this information for #14 and #15.
The following equation represents the average time of people commuting to work on public transportation. T is the time it takes to get to work, and D is the distance from home to work.

$T = 2.9D - 0.3$ (T is in minutes, and D is in miles)

14. How long it will take you to get to work if you live 15 miles from your job.

15. How far away do you live from work if it takes 30 minutes to get there.

16. Reduce the fraction: $\dfrac{-20x^6}{16x^2}$

17. Perform the indicated operation and reduce to lowest terms.

a. $\frac{15}{8x^3} \div \frac{3}{16x^2}$

b. $\frac{x^2}{8} \bullet \frac{x^3}{2}$

c. $\frac{7}{8x} - \frac{1}{4}$

18. Factor completely.

a. $8x^2 + 16x$

b. $x^2 - 4x - 21$

c. $x^2 - 81$

19. Solve for x:

a. $3x + 7 = 4(2x - 8)$

c. $\frac{9}{4x} - \frac{1}{8} = 9$

20. Which is a better buy, a 16 oz jar of peanut butter for $3.98 or a 20 oz jar of peanut butter for $4.99?

21. A math teacher, Dr. Ki, computes a student's grade for the course as follows:

10% for homework
65% for the average of 4 tests
25% for the final exam

Suppose Salena has an 82 homework average and a 67 test average. What does Salena have to get on the final exam to get a 70 average for the course?

For problems #22 to #25, use the following information.
You have the choice of two phone companies, Ringer and Buzz. Ringer charges 35¢ a phone call and 10¢ a minute while Buzz charges 15¢ a phone call and 14¢ a minute. The equation for the cost of making a phone call using Ringer is

$$C = 10m + 35 \text{ cents.}$$

The equation for the cost of making a phone call using Buzz is

$$C = 14m + 15 \text{ cents.}$$

22. **Use the equations to algebraically** find where the two lines intersect. In other words, determine the number of minutes when the two companies charge the same price. What will be that charge? Label this point on the graph.

23. Graph both equations on the same set of axes. Label your axes and choose an appropriate scale. Only graph the portion that is relevant to the problem.

24. What is the C intercept of the Ringer equation? What does it mean in terms of the problem?

25. What is the slope of the Ringer equation? What does it mean in terms of the problem?

26. Graph the equation y = 0.2x + 41 by finding the **x and y intercepts** and a third point. Choose an appropriate scale and label the axes.

27. Use the formula to fund the monthly payment of a loan.

$$P = A\left[\frac{i}{1-(1+i)^{-n}}\right]$$

P is the monthly payment
A is the amount of the loan
n is the number of payments
i is the interest rate per month

Find the monthly payments of a 36-month auto loan of $3,000 at 9% annual interest. (Hint: i = 0.09/12)

28. The height of an arrow shot straight up into the air from 6 feet above the ground with an initial velocity of 95 feet per second is represented by the equation

$$h = -16t^2 + 95t + 6$$

where h is the height in feet at *t* seconds.

When will the arrow be 100 feet above the ground?

Use the following information for #29 to #33.
AIE makes printing presses. The cost of making x presses in a month is

$$C = 0.5x^2 - 10x + 60$$

and the revenue from selling x printing presses a month is

$$R = -0.5x^2 + 14x$$

C and R are in thousands of dollars.

29. Find the equation for profit. (P = R - C)

30. Find the **vertex** and explain what it means in terms of making printing presses.

31. Find the **x intercepts** and explain what they mean in terms of making printing presses.

32 Find the **P intercept** and explain what it means in terms of making printing presses.

33. Graph the profit equation. Make sure you label the axes and use an appropriate scale.

Vertex	
x intercept	
P intercept	

DRILL AND PRACTICE PROBLEMS

SECTION 1.1 SIGNED NUMBERS

Perform the operations.

1. $-9 + 8 =$
2. $5 - 9 =$
3. $-3 - 4 =$
4. $7 - 11 =$
5. $8 - 3 =$
6. $-6 + 3 =$
7. $2 - 9 =$
8. $3 - 5 =$
9. $-7 + 2 =$
10. $12 - 15 =$
11. $-18 + 4 =$
12. $21 - 30 =$
13. $-24 + 30 =$
14. $18 - 22 =$
15. $-11 - 12 =$
16. $5 - 7 =$
17. $(-2) + (+5) + (-7) + (+3) + (-8) =$
18. $(+3) - (-4) + (-6) - (+5) + (-9) =$
19. $(+6) + (-3) - (-7) + (+2) - (+5) =$
20. $(+7) - (-2) - (+6) - (+8) + (-3) =$
21. $(-8) - (+2) + (-3) - (+5) + (+3) =$
22. $(-6) + (+3) - (-9) - (+4) + (-5) =$
23. $(-4) \bullet 5 =$
24. $-3 \bullet (-5) =$
25. $6 \bullet (-9) =$
26. $-3 \bullet (-7) =$
27. $7 \bullet (-5) =$
28. $9 \bullet (-8) =$
29. $-6 \bullet (-9) =$
30. $7 \bullet (-8) =$
31. $-8 \bullet 5 =$
32. $6 \bullet (-6) =$
33. $3 \bullet 8 =$
34. $-7 \bullet (-2) =$
35. $-4 \bullet 5 \bullet 8 \bullet -3 \bullet 0 \bullet 2 =$
36. $(-5)(+7)(+8)(-2) =$
37. $\frac{6}{-2} =$
38. $\frac{-24}{-8} =$
39. $\frac{-72}{-8} =$
40. $\frac{-27}{3} =$
41. $\frac{36}{6} =$
42. $\frac{-54}{6} =$
43. $\frac{-25}{-5} =$
44. $\frac{24}{-3} =$
45. $\frac{0}{-2} =$
46. $\frac{-48}{-8} =$
47. $\frac{6}{0} =$
48. $\frac{-35}{-7} =$
49. $(-3)^2$
50. $(-5)^2$
51. $(8)^2$
52. $(-4)^2$
53. $(7)^2$
54. $(0)^2$
55. $(-9)^2$
56. $(10)^2$
57. $6 \bullet (-4) + 12 =$
58. $2 - 3 \bullet 7 =$
59. $-4 - \frac{12}{-2} =$
60. $-6 - (+3)(-7) =$
61. $-6(7 - 3) =$
62. $5 - 8(9 - 2) =$
63. $-4(6 - 3) - 7 =$
64. $\frac{15}{-3} + 6 =$
65. $4^2 - 7^2 =$
66. $8^2 - 7(3 - 5) =$
67. $5^2 - 9(4 - 1) =$
68. $-3(-7) - 6^2 =$
69. $\frac{4(-2) - 7}{5 - 2} =$
70. $\frac{3^2 - 6}{12 - 2(8 - 2)} =$
71. $\frac{(-6)(+5) - (-2)(+15)}{6^2 - 7} =$

SECTION 1.3 SIMPLIFYING ALGEBRAIC EXPRESSIONS

Simplify.

1. $9x - 5 + 3x - 4 =$
2. $3 + 6x - x + 2 =$
3. $4x - 6 - 7 - 5x =$
4. $3 + 2(4x + 5) =$
5. $5 - 3(2x - 1) =$
6. $8(4 - 5x) + 2x =$
7. $4x + 5(2 - x) =$
8. $9 - (7 - 2x) =$
9. $x + 3(5 - 2x) =$
10. $3x - 4x + 6(2 - 3x) =$
11. $2 - 7(2x + 5) - 6x =$
12. $6(5 - 2x) - (x + 5) =$
13. $4(3x - 5) - 7(2 + 2x) =$
14. $7 - 3(2x + 6) + 2(5 - 2x) =$
15. $8(4x - 1) - (3 + 2x) =$
16. $3x + 2y - 5 + y - 2x =$
17. $x + 2y - 5y + 6x - 3 =$
18. $6(3x - 2y) + 2(4y + x) =$
19. $6z - 3(5 + x) - 4x + z =$
20. $4(3y + 2z) - 5(z - 2y) =$
21. $3 - 4z + 6y - 7 + 2y - 3z =$
22. $5x - 6x + 2(3x - 7) =$
23. $8y + 3y - 6(3 + 3x) =$
24. $3z - 6(4z - 7) + z =$

SECTION 1.4 SOLVING EQUATIONS

Solve.

1. $6x + 2 = 26$
2. $5x - 15 = 2x$
3. $8 - 5x = 18$
4. $3x + 7 = 5x - 2$
5. $6 - 3x = 8 - 7x$
6. $21x + 6 = 3x - 33$
7. $9 - 3x = 7x - 1$
8. $11x + 6 = -3x + 18$
9. $-4x + 5 = 7 - 6x$
10. $3(4x + 5) + 2 = 7$
11. $-7 - (3x + 8) + 3x = 5x$
12. $6(x - 5) + 5x - 7 = 23$
13. $4(3 - 2x) + 6x = 12 - 3(4x + 1)$
14. $7x - 2(6 - 5x) + 11 = 4(x + 5) - 3x + 8$
15. $\frac{x}{4} = 5$
16. $\frac{2x}{3} = 9$
17. $\frac{-5x}{2} = -15$
18. $3 + 4x = -6$
19. $9 - 5x = 11x$
20. $7x + 9 = -4x$
21. $9x - 1 = 3 + 5x$
22. $10 - x = 21 + 5x$
23. $35x + 21 = -48 + 21x$
24. $2(4 - 5x) = 3x - 12$
25. $5 - 7(2x + 4) = 21 + 4x$
26. $3x - 5(2x + 7) = 11 + x$
27. $32x + 11(5 - 12x) = 21$
28. $3(8x - 2x) + 21 - x = 7x$
29. $3 - 5(3x - 11) = 3x + 7$
30. $2(x - 3) - 5(11 - 2x) + 3 = 3x + 12$

SECTION 2.1 INEQUALITIES

Solve and graph the solution on the number line.

1. $3x + 5 > -7$
2. $7 - 5x < 24$
3. $12x + 45 > -23$
4. $23 - 4x \leq -24$
5. $12 \geq 21 - 2x$
6. $21 + 7x \geq -45$
7. $2(3x - 5) > -21$
8. $5x - 3(2x + 7) < -21$
9. $4x + 2(4x - 21) \geq 32$
10. $2x + 14 \geq 4x - 21$
11. $4x - 23 > 31 - 5x$
12. $3(4 - 3x) < 4x + 8$
13. $4 - 3(2x + 5) > 4x + 9$
14. $12 + 7x \geq 15 - 6(3 - 2x)$
15. $5x - 4(3x + 9) \leq -5$
16. $-5 \leq 3x + 9 < 8$
17. $21 \leq 4x + 12 < 45$
18. $-12 < 4x + 12 \leq -1$
19. $-24 < 5x + 15 < 24$
20. $-2 < 24 + 6x < 4$
21. $-5 \leq 5 + 4x < 15$
22. $-1 \leq 5x + 24 \leq 12$
23. $21 \leq 4 + 7x < 34$
24. $-3 < 5 + 2x < 6$

SECTION 2.3 GRAPHING LINES BY PLOTTING POINTS

Graph the line by finding two points. Find a third point to check.

1. $y = 2x + 5$
2. $y = -5x + 12$
3. $y = .25x - 6$
4. $y = 4.2x - 11$
5. $y = -.6x - 21$
6. $y = .01x + 46$
7. $y = 23x + 45$
8. $y = 6x - 21$
9. $y = -4x - 12$
10. $y = \frac{2}{3}x - 5$
11. $y = \frac{-4}{5}x - 9$
12. $y = \frac{7}{2}x + 6$
13. $y = \frac{-4}{7}x - 9$
14. $y = \frac{-5}{8}x - 4$
15. $y = \frac{2}{3}x + 5$
16. $3x + 5y = 14$
17. $6x - 5y = -6$
18. $7y + 4x = -23$
19. $6y - 4x = 21$
20. $0.5x + 7y = -45$
21. $0.6y - 5x = 42$
22. $4x - 7y = 32$
23. $6x + 2y = 23$
24. $12y - 11x = 45$

SECTION 2.4 GRAPHING LINES BY PLOTTING INTERCEPTS

Graph the lines by finding the x and y intercepts.

1. $y = 2x + 6$
2. $y = -4x + 12$
3. $y = 0.2x - 8$
4. $y = 3.2x - 10$
5. $y = -16x - 20$
6. $y = .01x + 32$
7. $y = 23x - 45$
8. $y = 6x - 28$
9. $y = -4x + 12$
10. $y = \frac{1}{3}x - 5$
11. $y = \frac{-4}{5}x + 9$
12. $y = \frac{-5}{2}x + 6$
13. $y = \frac{-3}{7}x + 9$
14. $y = \frac{-3}{8}x + 4$
15. $y = \frac{2}{3}x + 27$
16. $3x + 7y = 14$
17. $12x - 5y = -6$
18. $7y - 4x = -28$
19. $6y - 4x = 24$
20. $0.5x - 6y = -45$
21. $0.06x - 5y = 42$
22. $4x - 7x = -32$
23. $6x + 2y = 84$
24. $12y - 15x = 45$

Graph the horizontal or vertical line.

25. $y = -4$
26. $x = 6$
27. $y = 5$
28. $y = 15$
29. $y = -4$
30. $x = -4$
31. $x = 12$
32. $y = 1$
33. $y = 0$

SECTION 2.8 SLOPE

Find the slope of the line that contains the two points.

1. (4, 8) and (–7, 9)
2. (5, 9) and (6, –1)
3. (0, –1) and (–2, –6)
4. (–3, 6) and (–3, 9)
5. (4, 7) and (9, 12)
6. (–2, 8) and (5, 8)
7. (4.25, 6) and (–3, 1.22)
8. (1, 5) and (–4, 3.1)
9. (2.73, –.05) and (23, 19)
10. (4, 8) and (–3, 8)
11. (–23, 16) and (13, 39)
12. (–3, – 6) and (3, 9)

Use the slope intercept equation to find the slope of the line and the y intercept.

13. $y = 3.2x - 10$
14. $y = -16x - 20$
15. $y = .01x + 32$
16. $y = 23x - 45$
17. $y = 6x - 28$
18. $y = -4x + 12$
19. $y = \frac{1}{3}x - 5$
20. $y = \frac{-4}{5}x + 9$
21. $y = \frac{-5}{2}x + 6$

SECTION 3.3 PROPERTIES OF EXPONENTS

Simplify. Write with positive exponents only.

1. $x^3 \bullet x^4 =$
2. $x^{-3} \bullet x^2 =$
3. $3x \bullet x^2 =$
4. $x^3 \bullet x^{-4} =$
5. $7x^5 \bullet x^3 =$
6. $x \bullet 5x =$
7. $(3x^2)^4 =$
8. $(5x^3)^2 =$
9. $(-3x^5)^4 =$
10. $(-4x^5)^2 =$
11. $(6x^3)^5 =$
12. $(-5x^{-3})^2 =$
13. $4x^{-3} =$
14. $2x^{-1} =$
15. $21x^{-7} =$
16. $\dfrac{2}{3x^{-4}} =$
17. $\dfrac{2x^{-4}}{5} =$
18. $\dfrac{1}{7x^{-5}} =$
19. $\dfrac{3x^4}{12x^2} =$
20. $\dfrac{30x^5}{6x^3} =$
21. $\dfrac{24x^2}{8x^2} =$
22. $\dfrac{7x^2}{56x^6} =$
23. $\dfrac{36x^8}{72x^5} =$
24. $\dfrac{21x}{7x^4} =$
25. $\dfrac{18x^{-4}}{12x^{-2}} =$
26. $\dfrac{9x^{-3}}{36x^{-5}} =$
27. $\dfrac{6x^{-2}}{42x^{-3}} =$
28. $(-4x^4)^{-2} =$
29. $(-2x^{-5})^{-3} =$
30. $(3x^2)^{-2} =$
31. $(7x^{-3})^{-1} =$
32. $(3x^{-7})^{-3} =$
33. $(6x^2)^{-3} =$
34. $\left(\dfrac{2}{x^3}\right)^4 =$
35. $\left(\dfrac{3x^2}{5}\right)^3 =$
36. $\left(\dfrac{6}{5x^2}\right)^{-4} =$
37. $\left(\dfrac{7x^{-3}}{3}\right)^2 =$
38. $\left(\dfrac{6x^{-1}}{5}\right)^{-3} =$
39. $\left(\dfrac{5x^{-2}}{4}\right)^{-2} =$
40. $(3x^9)^0 =$
41. $4y^3 \bullet 3x^4 \bullet 2x^3 \bullet 5y =$
42. $(3xy^2)(2x^3y^2) =$
43. $(3x^2y^4)^3 =$
44. $(5x^3y^2)^4 =$
45. $2x^2(4xy^2)^4 =$
46. $\dfrac{21x^3y^2}{7xy^3} =$
47. $\left(\dfrac{3x^{-5}y^2}{2x^{-3}y^4}\right)^3 =$
48. $\left(\dfrac{5x^2y^{-3}}{3x^{-3}y^3}\right)^{-2} =$

SECTION 3.4 INTRODUCTION TO ALGEBRAIC FRACTIONS

Reduce.

1. $\frac{6x^3}{12x^2} =$

2. $\frac{-18x^4}{6x^2} =$

3. $\frac{24x^3}{4x^3} =$

4. $\frac{8x^3}{56x^5} =$

5. $\frac{9x^9}{72x^4} =$

6. $\frac{-21x}{3x^3} =$

7. $\frac{4yx^3}{12x^5y^2} =$

8. $\frac{32x^3y^2}{16x^4y} =$

9. $\frac{5x^3y^4}{25x^2y} =$

Multiply or divide as indicated and reduce to lowest terms.

10. $\frac{1}{6} \bullet \frac{2}{5} =$

11. $\frac{2}{3} \div \frac{8}{9} =$

12. $\frac{6}{15} \bullet \frac{25}{8} =$

13. $\frac{2x}{5} \div \frac{15x}{4} =$

14. $\frac{6}{5x} \bullet \frac{15}{2x^2} =$

15 $\frac{18}{7x} \bullet \frac{21x^3}{6} =$

16. $\frac{12}{x^3} \bullet \frac{4}{x} =$

17. $\frac{81}{2x^3} \div \frac{27}{4x} =$

18. $\frac{6x^2}{25} \div \frac{4x^3}{15} =$

19. $\frac{30}{21x^4} \div \frac{15}{7x^2} =$

20. $\frac{16}{3x^2} \bullet \frac{9x}{8} =$

21. $\frac{32x}{4} \bullet \frac{5x^2}{15} =$

22. $\frac{28x^3}{4} \bullet \frac{1}{7x} =$

23. $\frac{45}{5x^2} \div \frac{9}{2x^2} =$

24. $\frac{16x^3}{32} \bullet \frac{8}{2x^5} =$

25. $\frac{9}{2x} \bullet \frac{10x^3}{5} =$

26. $\frac{5}{27x^4} \bullet \frac{18x^2}{15} =$

27. $\frac{4x^3}{3x} \div \frac{x}{14} =$

28. $\frac{18}{x^3} \div \frac{6}{5x^2} =$

29. $\frac{x}{3} \div \frac{x}{15} =$

30. $\frac{4x}{6x^3} \bullet \frac{12x}{15} =$

31. $\frac{3x}{2y^2} \bullet \frac{8y}{x} =$

32. $\frac{7x}{4y} \div \frac{21x^2}{16y^3} =$

33. $\frac{y^3}{4x^2} \bullet \frac{8x}{y} =$

34. $\frac{27x^3}{15y^2} \div \frac{3y}{x^2} =$

35. $\frac{6x^4}{8y^2} \bullet \frac{16x^2}{4y} =$

36. $\frac{30y^2}{40x} \div \frac{9y^3}{8x^2} =$

SECTION 3.5 ADDING AND SUBTRACTING ALGEBRAIC FRACTIONS

Combine into a single fraction and reduce to lowest terms.

1. $\frac{4}{5}+\frac{7}{5}=$

2. $\frac{4}{9}-\frac{1}{9}=$

3. $\frac{6}{11}+\frac{5}{11}=$

4. $\frac{3}{x}-\frac{4}{x}=$

5. $\frac{5}{2x}+\frac{1}{2x}=$

6. $\frac{8}{3x^2}-\frac{4}{3x^2}=$

7. $\frac{5}{9}-\frac{1}{6}=$

8. $\frac{3}{6}+\frac{5}{8}=$

9. $\frac{5}{9}-\frac{5}{12}=$

10. $\frac{x}{4}-\frac{x}{6}=$

11. $\frac{3x}{2}+\frac{5x}{8}=$

12. $\frac{x}{18}-\frac{5x}{12}=$

13. $\frac{3}{x}+\frac{5}{x^2}=$

14. $\frac{5}{4x}+\frac{1}{2x}=$

15. $\frac{5}{8x}-\frac{3x}{10}=$

16. $\frac{7}{12y^3}+\frac{2}{20y}=$

17. $\frac{3}{24m^3}-\frac{5}{16m}=$

18. $\frac{y^2}{14}-\frac{y}{21}=$

19. $\frac{5w}{27}+\frac{4w}{36}=$

20. $\frac{5}{12x^2}+\frac{9}{20x}=$

21. $\frac{15}{16z^2}+\frac{2}{40z^3}=$

22. $\frac{2}{x^2}+3=$

23. $7-\frac{4}{w^3}=$

24. $\frac{7x}{15}-\frac{1}{3x^2}=$

25. $\frac{x-5}{6}-\frac{7}{9}=$

26. $\frac{5}{2x}+\frac{6+x}{6x}=$

27. $\frac{9}{16y}+\frac{7y-5}{20}=$

28. $\frac{11+w}{9w}-\frac{4}{w^3}=$

29. $\frac{1}{4}-\frac{7+y}{10y}=$

30. $\frac{x+4}{30x}-\frac{7-x}{24}=$

SECTION 3.6 SOLVING EQUATIONS WITH FRACTIONS

Solve each equation.

1. $\frac{2}{3}+\frac{5}{6}=\frac{x}{9}$

2. $\frac{x}{6}-\frac{x}{8}=\frac{1}{12}$

3. $\frac{x}{4}+\frac{x}{2}=6$

4. $\frac{2}{3x}+\frac{1}{x}=10$

5. $\frac{1}{2x}+\frac{1}{x}=-12$

6. $\frac{x}{4}-\frac{x}{6}=\frac{1}{8}$

7. $\frac{3}{5}-\frac{2}{3}=\frac{x}{9}$

8. $\frac{2}{3}+\frac{1}{6}=\frac{1}{x}$

9. $\frac{1}{x}=\frac{1}{3}-\frac{5}{6}$

10. $\frac{1}{8}+\frac{1}{12}=\frac{1}{x}$

11. $\frac{4}{7}-\frac{7}{x}=0$

12. $\frac{3}{5}+\frac{5}{3}=\frac{x}{9}$

13. $\frac{5}{x}=\frac{6}{x}-\frac{1}{3}$

14. $\frac{5}{3x}+\frac{2}{x}=1$

15. $\frac{5}{2x}+\frac{7}{6}=5$

16. $\frac{4}{15x}-\frac{7}{20}=\frac{23}{5x}$

17. $\frac{5x}{24}-\frac{3}{8}=\frac{x}{3}$

18. $\frac{7}{2x}+\frac{1}{5x}=\frac{4}{5}$

19. $\frac{x+1}{5}-\frac{x-2}{4}=1$

20. $\frac{x+1}{3}-\frac{x-1}{2}=3$

21. $\frac{x+3}{18}+\frac{x-2}{6}=\frac{5}{3}$

22. $2-\frac{3}{5x}=\frac{3}{2}$

23. $\frac{7}{6}-3x=\frac{x}{10}$

24. $\frac{4x+5}{12}-\frac{2x-1}{24}=\frac{5}{6}$

SECTION 4.1 INTRODUCTION TO QUADRATICS

Simplify.

1. $3x^2 + 5x - 7 - x^2 + 3x - 6$
2. $-4x^2 + 7x + 8 + 3x^2 - 7x + 1$
3. $-2x^2 + 6 - 5x^2 - 4x + 5$
4. $x^2 - 11x + 21 - 3x^2 - 9x + 16$
5. $2(x^2 - 9x + 3) + 5(3x^2 + x - 8)$
6. $5(2x^2 + 5x - 6) + 4(x^2 - 7x - 3)$
7. $4(9x^2 + 2x + 1) - 7(5x^2 + 3)$
8. $6(2x^2 + 3x - 5) - 3(7x^2 - 6x + 1)$
9. $4(3x^2 + 5x - 1) - (6x^2 - 3x + 28)$
10. $(5x^2 + x - 12) - (2x^2 + 11x - 12)$

Multiply.

11. $(x + 3)(x + 1)$
12. $(x + 6)(x + 2)$
13. $(x + 4)(x + 8)$
14. $(x + 7)(x + 9)$
15. $(2x + 5)(x + 7)$
16. $(x + 5)(3x + 4)$
17. $(x - 4)(x - 2)$
18. $(x - 6)(x - 3)$
19. $(5x - 1)(x - 7)$
20. $(5x - 7)(3x - 5)$
21. $(x + 2)(x - 7)$
22. $(x + 9)(x - 9)$
23. $(2x + 1)(2x - 1)$
24. $(6x + 3)(7x - 8)$
25. $(x + 4)^2$
26. $(x + 3)^2$
27. $(x - 2)^2$
28. $(5x - 8)^2$
29. $(3x + 9)^2$
30. $(x - 11)^2$

SECTION 4.2 THE QUADRATIC FORMULA

Solve using the quadratic formula.

1. $-2x^2 - 4x + 30 = 0$
2. $3x^2 - 4x = 0$
3. $x^2 - 9x + 20 = 0$
4. $x^2 - 2x - 14 = 0$
5. $-x^2 + 5x - 3 = 0$
6. $-4x^2 - 11x - 6 = 0$
7. $6x^2 - 39 = 0$
8. $-3x^2 + 6x + 9 = 0$
9. $x^2 + 6x - 17 = -26$
10. $x^2 - 8x - 4 = -20$
11. $12x^2 + 7x - 12 = 0$
12. $30x^2 - 11x - 30 = 0$
13. $18x^2 - 33x + 130 = -136$
14. $-9x^2 - 6x - 3 = 1$

SECTION 4.3 GRAPHING QUADRATICS

Graph each quadratic by finding the vertex, x intercepts, and y intercept.

1. $y = x^2 - 6x + 8$
2. $y = -x^2 + x + 2$
3. $y = -x^2 + 2x + 3$
4. $y = x^2 + 5x + 4$
5. $y = x^2 + 7x + 10$
6. $y = -x^2 + 4x + 3$
7. $y = -x^2 + 4x$
8. $y = x^2 + 2x - 8$

SECTION 4.4 FACTORING

Factor.

1. $3x + 6$
2. $18x - 12$
3. $30x - 15$
4. $42x - 7$
5. $24x^2 - 18x$
6. $25x^4 - 15x^2$
7. $-15x^3 + 9x$
8. $32x - 18x^2$
9. $40x^2 - 16x$
10. $-21x^4 + 49x^2$
11. $6x^5 - 40x^3$
12. $-4x^2 + x$
13. $x^2 + 7x + 6$
14. $x^2 + 6x + 8$
15. $x^2 + 3x - 40$
16. $x^2 + 2x - 24$
17. $x^2 - 8x + 15$
18. $x^2 - 10x + 9$
19. $x^2 - 6x + 9$
20. $x^2 - 3x - 18$
21. $x^2 - x - 30$
22. $x^2 - 3x - 4$
23. $x^2 + 5x - 50$
24. $x^2 - 13x + 30$
25. $x^2 - 9x + 14$
26. $x^2 - 9x + 20$
27. $x^2 - x - 56$
28. $2x^2 + 20x + 32$
29. $3x^2 + 30x + 63$
30. $2x^3 + 14x^2 + 12x$
31. $x^2 - 49$
32. $x^2 - 36$
33. $x^2 - 4$
34. $x^2 - 1$
35. $x^2 - 100$
36. $x^2 - 121$
37. $3x^2 - 75$
38. $5x^2 - 45$
39. $x^3 - 16x$

ANSWERS

ANSWERS TO HOMEWORK AND REVIEW TESTS

Section 1.1 Signed Numbers page 15

Skill Building

3. The subtraction key is [–]. The negative key is [(-)].

Practice Exercises

4.	$–20	5.	$30	6.	$–290	7.	$10	8.	$–58
9.	a. 2	b.	–13	c.	–9	d.	15	e.	–7
	f. 7	g.	–29	h.	-5	i.	–32	j.	11
	k. –14	l.	–9	m.	–8	n.	–15	o.	3
10.	a. 12	b.	–17						
11.	[(-)]								
12.	a. –4.4	b.	0.71	c.	0.59	d.	–7/12	e.	18.2 f. –5/24
13.	7.667 °F	14.	–1.5 °C	15.	Average elevation is 2,109.6 feet.				
16.	a. –9	b.	34	c.	–3	d. The profit increased in b but decreased in c.			

e. What is the difference between the profit in 2002 and 2000?

f. The National Silver Company average –1.8 million dollars between 1999 and 2003.

17.	a. –42	b.	30	c.	–15	d.	63	e.	–6
	f. -5	g.	0	h.	undefined	i.	indeterminate	j.	5
	k. –16/15	l.	60	m.	–96	n.	0	o.	–2/5
18.	a 26.37	b.	49.32	c.	–2.953	d.	1.769		
19.	a. -10	b.	-10	c.	1	d.	29	e.	–31
	f. –10	g.	–4	h.	–1	i. .	0.5 or 1/2		
20.	a. –36	b.	–24	c.	–3	d.	–162		

Reading and Writing Mathematics

21. Add the two numbers and use the common sign.

22. Find the difference (or subtract) of the two numbers and use the sign of the larger number.

23. Add the 5 numbers then divide by 5.

24. The product or quotient of two numbers with like signs is always positive.

25. The product or quotient of two numbers with unlike signs is always negative.

26. Zero. 27. The result is indeterminate.

28. First: Inside Parentheses, ( ). Second: Exponents,
Third: Multiplication and Division (left to right), Fourth: Addition and Subtraction (left to right)

29. a. Should have simplified inside parentheses first, not read left to right.

b. "-" means subtract, should have been 16 – 49.

Section 1.2 Introduction to Variables page 29

Skill Building Exercises

1.

Width	Length	Area	Perimeter
7 in	8 in	56 in^2	30 in
9 in.	12 in	108 in^2	42 in
8 in.	10 in	80 in^2	36. in
11 in.	19 in	209 in^2	60 in

2. a. 0°C b. –20.55°C c. 37°C

Practice Exercises

3.a

Hours	Calculation	Income
40	8(40) – 160	160
60	8(60) – 160	320
80t	8(80) – 160	480
h	8h – 160	I

b. I = 8h - 160
c. 55 hours
d. I = 9h - 200

4.a

Calls	Calculation	Phone Bill
10	0.13(10) + 7.46	8.76
15	0.13(15) + 7.46	9.41
20	0.13(20) + 7.46	10.06
C	0.13C + 7.46	B_r

b. B_r = .13C + 7.46
c. B_B = .17C + 6.17
e. about 32 calls

5. a.

AGE	CALCULATION	VALUE
2	56,000 – 2,700(2)	$50,600
5	56,000 – 2,700(5)	$42,500
10	56,000 – 2,700(10)	$29,000
A	56,000 – 2,700A	V

b. V = 56,000 – 2,700A
c. Approximatley 15 years
d. V = 86,000 – 3,400A

6. b.

Base	Height	Area
5	10 - 5	$(1/2)(5)(5) = 12.5$
8	10 – 8	$(1/2)(8)(2) = 8$
b	10 - b	$(1/2)(10-b)(b)$

a. 2cm
c. $A = (1/2)b(10-b)$
d. Stick is only 10 cm
e. 5 cm

7 a.

Min.	Calculation	Cost
2	25	25
5	25	25
12	8(12 – 10) + 25	41
30	8(30 – 10) + 25	185
m	8(m – 10) + 25	c

b. $c = 8(m - 10) + 25$

Reading and Writing Mathematics

8. In part a, he should add 120, not subtract 120.
   In part b, the equation should be $w = 42.50t + 120$
   In part c, 36 is the number of tables, so he should have computed 42.50(36) + 120
   In part d, the equation should be $w = 37t + 105$.

9. Don't cross out, erase your mistakes.
   In the calculation column, subtract 250 and show this step.
   In part b, the formula should include the variable for income, I.
   Should answer part c with a sentence.
   No variable for income in part d.

<u>Section 1.3 Simplifying Algebraic Expressions page 43</u>

Skill Building Exercises

1. a. $8x$ and $-21x$ b. -8 and 5

2. a. -7 b. -1

Practice Exercises

3. a. $5x$ b. $17x - 13$ c. $\frac{7}{6}x - \frac{3}{5}$ d. $6x + 15$

   e. $-12x + 38$ f. $2x + 1$ g. $19x + 5$ h. $-x - 16$

   i. $-7x + 4$

Reading and Writing Mathematics

4. Like Terms have the same variable and exponent.

5. Factors are separated by multiplication or division.

6. Add their coefficients.

7. $a(b + c) = ab + ac$

8. a. Multiplied the coefficients b. Combined unlike terms

   c. Did not multiply the 6 and the –5 d. $-3 * -4 = 12$

   e. A negative times a negative is a positive f. $12x - 3x = 9x$

Section 1.4 Solving Equations, page 53

Basic Skills Exercises

1. $-6x + 28$
2. $11x - 16$

Practice Exercises

3. Both companies charge the same for 33 minutes.

4. a. $x = -6$ b. $x = 11$ c. $x = 4$ d. $x = 5$

 e. $x = \frac{-7}{4}$ or -1.75 f. no solution g. $x = 1$

 h. every number is a solution i. $x = \frac{-19}{5}$ or -3.8

Reading and Writing Mathematics

5. a. Distributive Property
 Combine like terms
 Subtract 3X from both sides
 Combine like terms
 Subtract 20 from both sides
 Combine like terms
 Divide both sides by –6
 Simplify

 b. Distributive Property
 Combine like terms
 Subtract 7X from both sides
 Combine like terms
 Conclusion

6. a. Sixth line: $7 - 2$ should be $7 + 2$

 b. Second line: Should have combined like terms.

8. If we end with a false equation, for example $3 = 9$, then the original problem has no solution.

9. If we end with a true equation, for example $5 = 5$, then every number is a solution to the original equation.

11. Better to write $+ ^{-}15$ as –15.
 Didn't write the right hand side of the equation in the second line, $-2x - 15$.
 When subtracting 4x from both sides, it is difficult to see what –4x is being added to on the right hand side. The same problem occurs when adding 15 to both sides.
 When dividing both sides by –6, use two division lines than one long line.
 Instead of circling the answer, write $x = -4$.
 It is generally better to write the algebraic steps horizontally than vertically. See example 1 on page 51.

Section 1.5 Applications of Linear Equations page 63

Skill Building Exercises

2. a. $x = 40$ b. $x = -160.\overline{6}$

Practice Exercises

3. a.

Miles	Calculation	Cost
20	0.16(20) + 25	$28.50
m	0.16m + 25	c

b. c = 0.16m + 25

c = 29.96, It will cost $29.96 to drive 31 miles.

d. m = 37.5, You can drive 37.5 miles when spending $31.

e. m = 250, You can drive 250 miles when spending $65.

4. a.

Years	Calculation	Value
10	450,000 – 33,000(10)	$120,000
t	450,000 – 33,000t	v

b. v = 450,000 – 33,000t

c. v = 351,000, The equipment is worth $351,000 in the year 2008.

d. t = 4.545, In the year 2010 the equipment is worth $300,000.

e. t = 10.6, In the year 2016 the equipment is worth $100,000.

5. b. $C_R = 0.08m + .5$ $C_B = 0.10m + .25$

c. m = 12.5, The two companies will cost the same when you are on the phone for 12.5 minutes.

6. a.

Company A			Company B		
Sales	Calculation	Wages	Sales	Calculation	Wages
$100,000	0.075(100,000) + 5,000	$12,500	$100,000	0.05(100,000) + 9,000	$14,000
S	0.075S + 5,000	W	S	0.05S + 9,000	W

b. $W_A = 0.075S + 5000$ $W_B = 0.05S + 9000$

c. S = 160,000, The two companies will pay the same wage if you sell $160,000 in merchandise

7. a.

Sales	Calculation	Wages
$1,500	0.15(1,500 – 1,000)	$75
$2,000	0.15(2,000 – 1,000)	$150
S	0.15(S – 1,000)	W

b. W = 0.15S – 150

c. W = 1350, You will earn $1,350 if you sell $10,000 in merchandise.

d. S = 2800, You sold $2,800 in merchandise when you earn $270 in wages.

e. S = 23,480, You sold $23,480 in merchandise when you earn $3,372 in wages.

8. a.

Min.	Calculation	Cost
3000	0.35(3000 – 2000) + 129.99	479.99
3500	0.35(3500 – 2000) + 129.99	654.99
4550	0.35(4550 – 2000) + 129.99	1005
m	0.35(m – 2000) + 129.99	C

b. C = 0.35m – 570.01

c. m = 3,215

d. m = 4,821 e. c = 129.99

9. a.

Minutes	Calculation	Cost
2¢		22¢
5¢		22¢
7¢	10(7 – 5) + 22	42¢
12¢	10(12 – 5) + 22	92¢
m	10(m – 5) + 22	C¢

b. C = 0.10m - 0.28

c. m = 23, You were on the phone for 23 minutes if it costs $2.02.

d. m = 1, You were on the phone for 41 minutes if it costs $3.81.

10. The companies will never charge the same. Nader is always cheaper.

Reading and Writing Mathematics

11. Creating a table and finding the equation was covered in Section 1.2 Introduction to Variables.
Section 1.1 Signed Numbers was needed to simplify the arithmetic.
Section 1.3 Simplifying Algebraic Expressions was needed to solve the equations.
Section 1.4 Solving Basic Equations was needed to solve the equations in part b and c.

Section 1.6 Literal Equations, page 75

Skill Building Exercises

1. a. v = 45.60 b. t = 9.167 or 9

Practice Exercises

2. a. t = 6.237, Q-Mart will have 1,500 stores in the year 2006.
b. t = 10.9, Q-Mart will have 2,600 stores in the year 2011. c. $t = \frac{s-28}{236}$

3. $T = \frac{W + 54.6}{1.6}$

4. a. r = 0.05, The interest rate is 5%. b. $r = \frac{FV - P}{Pt}$

5. a. $L = \frac{P-2W}{2}$ b. $r = \frac{D}{t}$ c. $y = \frac{12 - 3x}{-4}$ d. $y = \frac{9 - 6x}{4}$

6. $s = \frac{V - v^2}{2a}$ 7. $t = \frac{v - v_0}{a}$ 8. $r = \frac{C - P}{P}$

Reading and Writing Mathematics

9. a. Subtracted 2L from both sides.
Divided both sides by 3.
b. Added 3x to both sides.
Multiplied both sides by 5/4.
Multiplied on the left hand side and used the distributive property on the right.

10. Combined 8w – 12 to get -4w.

11. Didn't show that -4y was subtracted from both sides.
Didn't show that -15 was subtracted from both sides.
Didn't show that -4 was divided both sides.
It is better to do the algebra horizontally. See example d on page 69.

Section 1.7 Percentages page 85

Skill building Exercises

1. a. 0.42 b. 0.03 c. 0.0025 d. 0.987

2. a. $41,562.40 b. $13,500 c. 49.3%

Practice Exercises

3. a.

Susan	Joe	Mary	Pat
3.35	3.50	4.00	3.75
3.75	3.92	4.48	4.20

b. N = 1.12C

4. Your salary increased by 15%.

5. There was a 20% discount on the item.

6. a.

Retail Price	Discount	Sales Price
$35	$11.20	$23.80
$45	$14.4	$30.60
R	0.32R	0.68R

b. The current price is $55 when the sales price is $37.40.

7. a. George has an 82.75 average for the course.

b. Darrel has an 88.4 average.

c. Rachel has to get a 92.6 on the final to have a 90 average for the course. 92.6

8. a. Harold has to get a 90.25 on the final to get a 75 for the course.

b. Thomas has to get a 159 on the final to have a 90 average for the course. He can't get an A for the course.

Reading and Writing Mathematics

9. a. The markup was 20%. The 1.20 is 120% which comes from adding 100% and 20%.
b. The discount was 15%. The 0.85 is 85% which comes from subtracting 15% from 100%.
c. The coefficient is greater than one because the retail price is higher than the wholesale.
d. The coefficient is less than one because the sale price is lower than the retail.

10. In the last row of the table, the student didn't subtract the discount from the current price, 1.00C – 0.20C = 0.80C

Chapter 1 Review page 91

1 a

Depth	Calculation	Cost
50	20(50) + 350	$1,350
70	20(70) + 350	$1,750
90	20(90) + 350	$2,150
d	20d + 350	c

b. c = 20d + 350

c. d = 190, If it cost $4,150, then the well was 190 feet deep.

2. a.

Miles	Calculation	Cost
10	1.80(10 – 3) +1.35	$13.95
15	1.80(15 – 3) +1.35	$22.95
20	1.80(20 – 3) +1.35	$31.95
m	1.80(m – 3) +1.35	c

b. c = 1.80m – 4.05

c. m = 17.53, If it cost $27.50, then the ride was 17.53 miles

3. a. Otto's average for the course is an 81.8

b. Tito has to get a 64 on the final to get a 70 for the course.

4. a. \$2.28 is the price per gallon if the price per barrel is \$87.50

b. \$132.32 is the price per barrel when \$3.27 is the price per gallon.

5 a.

Current Salary	Calculation	New Salary
1	1 + 0.12*1	1.12
3	3 + 0.12*3	3.36
C	CS + 0.12CS	N

b. N = 1.12C

c. Your current salary is \$4.69 per hour if your new salary will be \$5.25 per hour.

6. a.

Retail Price	Calculation	Sale Price
10.00	10 – 0.20(10)	8.00
20.00	20 – 0.20(20)	16.00
R	OP – 0.20OP	S

b. S = 0.8R

c. R = 101.25, The original price was \$101.25 if the sale price is \$81.00.

7. a. The company made 3.2 million more in 2002 than in 2000.

b. The difference in profit between 2003 and 2001 was 4.6 million dollars.

8. $-4x + 14$

9. a. $x = -3$

9 b. $x = 13$

10. The company made 250 cameras with a total cost of \$21,000.

11. $W = \dfrac{P-2L}{2}$

12. Steps
Distributive Property
Combine Like Terms
Add 2 to both sides
Combine Like Terms
Subtract 4x from both sides
Combine Like Terms
Divide both sides by 7
Answer

13. At line 5, 8x +3x = 3x +3x +27, 3x should be subtracted from both sides, not added.

Section 2.1 Inequalities, page 103

Skill Building Exercises

2. a.

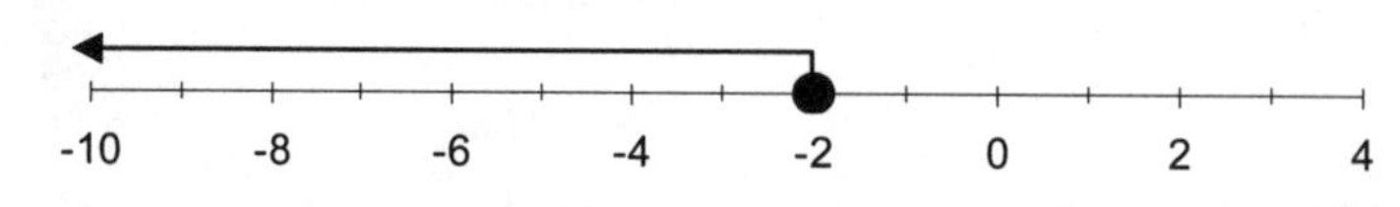

b.

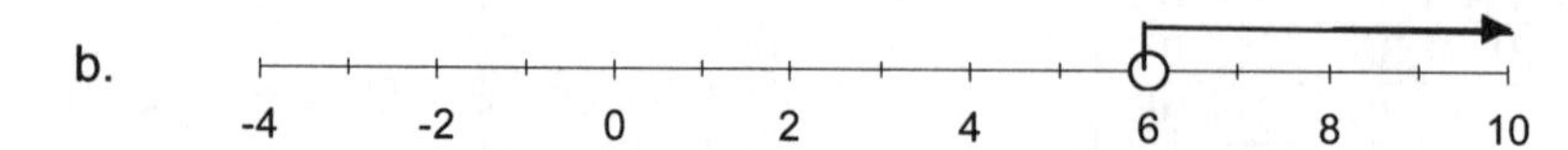

c.

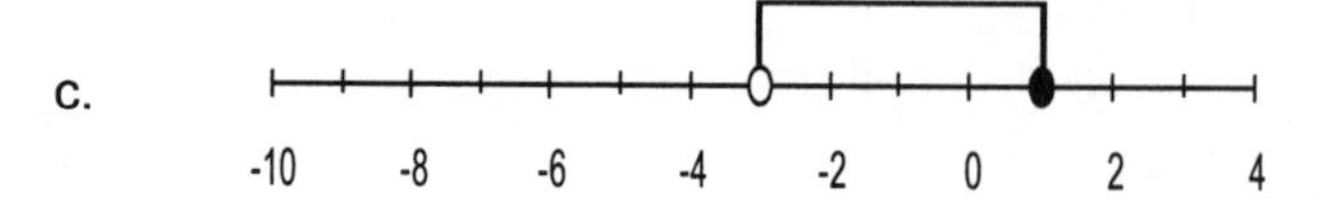

3. a. $x = -14$

b. $x = 5.243$

4. a. Yes b. Yes c. No

Practice Exercises

5. $82.8 \leq E < 122.8$, Al has to score between an 82.8, including 82.8, and 100 to get a B for the course.

6. a. $x < -9$ b. $x < 20$ c. $x \geq -8$ d. $x \leq -3$ e. $x < 6.33$ f. $x \leq 7.75$

g. $-6 < x \leq 4$ h. $-3 \leq x \leq 5.5$ i. $2 \leq x < 6.5$ j. $-4 \leq x \leq 3.333$ k. $-8 < x < 7$

7. a. $y < \frac{5-2x}{3}$ b. $y \leq \frac{8-6x}{-5}$

Reading and Writing Mathematics

8. a. Subtract 6 from both sides.
Subtract x from both sides.
Divide both sides by –4 and change the direction of the inequality

b. Subtract 6 from all three parts
Divide all three parts by –2 and change the directions of the inequalities
Realign answer to reflect direction of number line.

9. a. Didn't change the direction of the inequality b. Didn't subtract 9 from 12

10. a. When dividing or multiplying by a negative number, the inequality needs to be reversed.

b. The procedure for solving a single inequality problem is the same as an equality problem except when multiplying or dividing by a negative number.

c. For a double inequality problem, whatever is done to one part must be done to all three parts.

Section 2.2 Applications of Inequalities, page 113

Skill Building Exercises

1 a. $x \geq -7$ b. $-1.8 \leq x < 0.4$

2 a.

Years	Calculation	Value
5	350,000 – 25,000(5)	225,000
10	350,000 – 25,000(10)	100,000
t	350,000 – 25,000t	v

b. $v = 350{,}000 - 25{,}000t$

Practice Exercises

3. a. $t > 10.8$, The equipment will be worth less than $80,000 after the year 2015.

b. $3.6 < t < 7.2$, The equipment will be worth between $170,000 and $260,000 between the years 2009 including 2009, and 2012, including 2012.

4. $c < 250{,}000$, Company A will pay more than Company B when your sales commission is less than $250,000.

5. a. 308.3, The population of the U. S. in 2010 will be approximately 308,300,000.

b. $t > 36.12$, The population of the U. S. will be more than 325,500,000 after the year 2016.

c. $27.04 < t < 44.84$, The population of the U. S. will be between 300 and 350 million people between the years 2007 and 2024.

6. b. $p = 8.50h - 200$

c. $h > 47.05$, They will have to work more than 47 hours to earn more than $200.

d. $23.52 \leq h \leq 82.35$, The girls will have to work between 23.52 hours, including 23.5 hours and 82.35 hours, including 82.35 hours to break even but not earn more than $500 for the summer.

7. b. $C_W = 0.50m + 28$, $C_E = 0.75m + 20$

c. $m < 32$, Wrecker costs more than Ertz when you drive less than 32 miles.

8. b. $W_A = 0.12(s - 50{,}000) + 8000$, $W_B = 0.05s + 15000$

c. $s > 185{,}714$, Company A pays more than Company B for sales above $185,714.

d. The formula for Company A is not valid for s = 20,000 because Company A only pays commission for sales over $50,000. If your sales are $20,000 Company A pays $8,000.

9. $C_W = 0.11(m - 4) + 0.15$, $C_D = 0.14(m - 5) + 0.10$, $m < 10.3$, Disconnect costs less than WHAT?! when you are on the phone for less than 10.3 minutes. To use the formula for WHAT?!, $m > 4$ and for Disconnect $m > 5$.

Reading and Writing Mathematics

10. a. Put ( ) in calculation column
b. Mixed dollars and cents in the cost column
c. Didn't label equations
d. It is better to simplify the equations before setting up the inequality.
e. It is better to write .15 as 0.15.

Section 2.3 Plotting Points page 127

Skill Building Exercises

1. 3 2. 7 3. 3 4. 7

Practice Exercises

5.

Revenue
400
300
200
100
0
1920 1940 1960 1980 2000
Year

6.

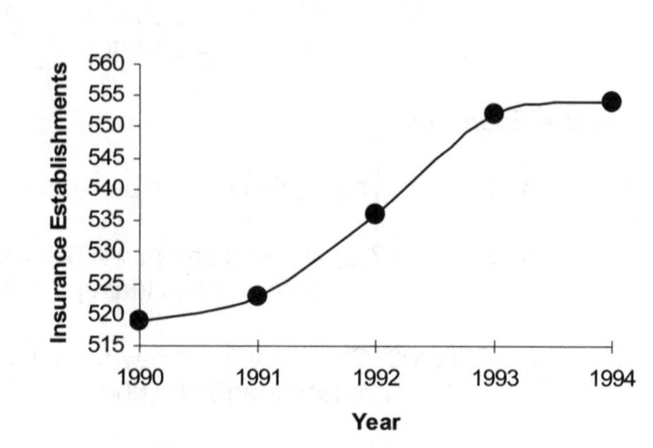

7.

a.

Time	Average
11:00	9.333
12:00	17.33
1:00	19.67
2:00	11
3:00	5
4:00	7
5:00	12.67
6:00	15.67
7:00	13.67
8:00	7.33

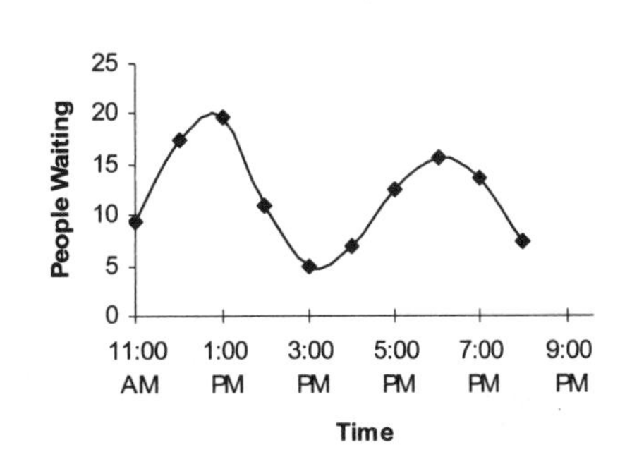

c. I would not include the 4 from Day 2 at 6:00 in my study.

8. a.

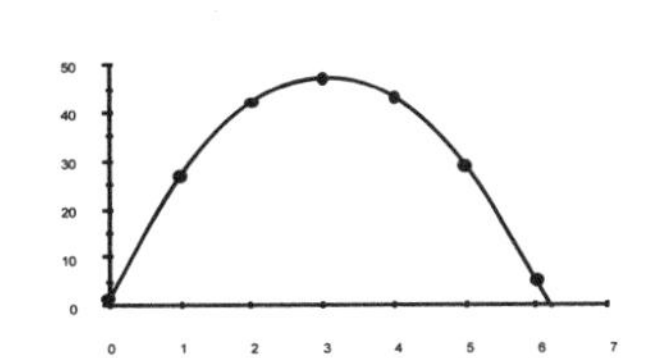

b. (0, 6)

c. (2, 42)

d. (0.6, 20) (5.4, 20)

e. (3, 47)

f. (6.2, 0)

g. (4.5, 35)

h. between 0 and 1 sec.

i. between 5 and 6 seconds

Reading and Writing Mathematics

9. The scale along the vertical axis is wrong.

Section 2.4 Interpreting Graphs page 137

Skill Building Exercises

1. A. (0, –40) B. (4, 0) C. (7, 10) D. (9, 5) E. (10, 0)

2. B and E. 3. A 4. C

Practice Exercises

5. a. –14°, 11° b. 3AM, 3 PM c. 8:30AM to 9:30PM d. Before 8:45 AM e. 3:00 PM

f. 10° g. 3 AM to 3 PM h. Before 3AM and after 3PM

6. a. 8500 b. July c. 9000 d. Between April and July

e. Jan. to April and July to Dec. f. The lake was stocked

7. a. 5 min 30 sec b. WRONG #

c. Buzz d. Min > 5.5

Reading and Writing Mathematics

8.

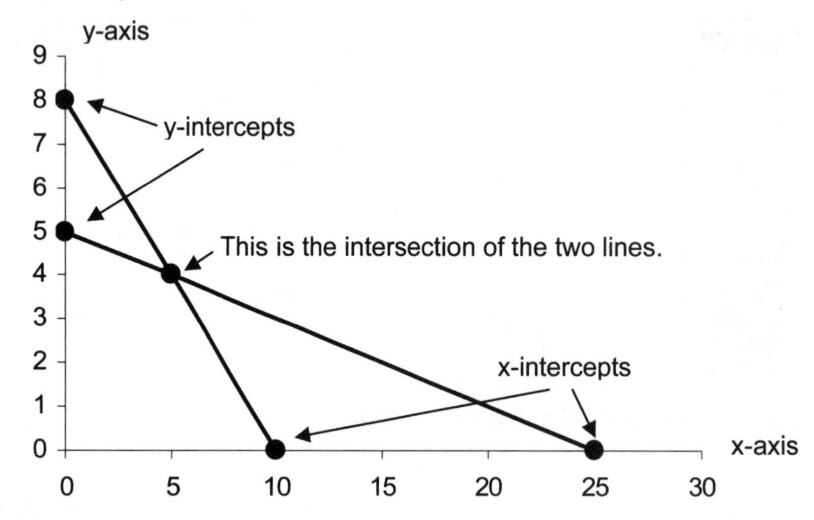

9.

a.	ordered pairs	b.	intersection	c.	independent
d.	vertex	e.	dependent	f.	intercept
g.	coordinates	h.	Cartesian coordinate system		

Section 2.5 Graphing Lines by Plotting Points page 151

Skill Building Exercises

1.

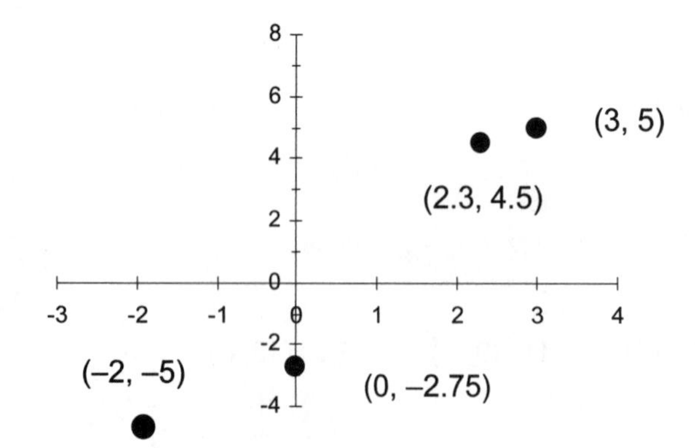

2. y = 30, y = –12, y = –42

3. y = 10, y = 7, y = –2

4 a.

x	y	Point (x, y)
0	–3.333	(0, –3.333)
6	4.667	(6, 4.667)
–6	–11.33	(–6, –11.33)

b. $y = \frac{4}{3}x - \frac{10}{3}$

Practice Exercises

5. a. (20,25) (50,40) (100,65)

b. C = 0.50h + 15

c.

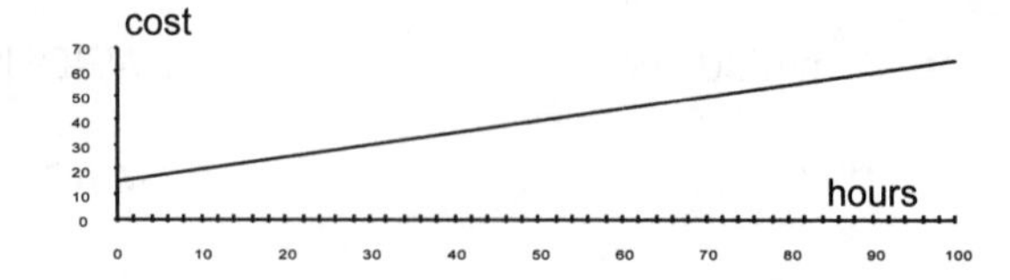

6. a. (time, value)

b. v = –30,000t + 250,000

c.

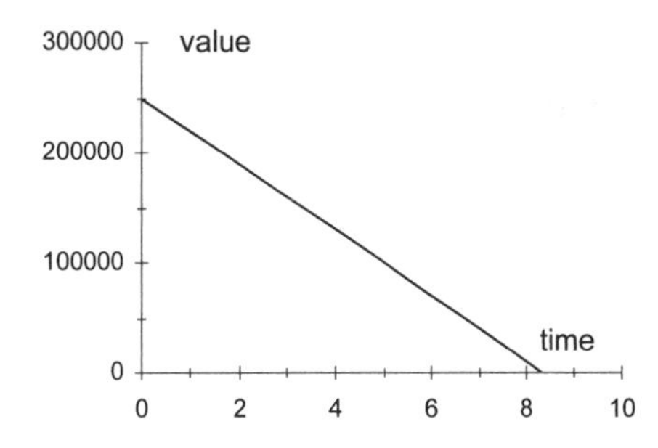

7. a. Yes b. No c. Yes d. Yes

8. a.

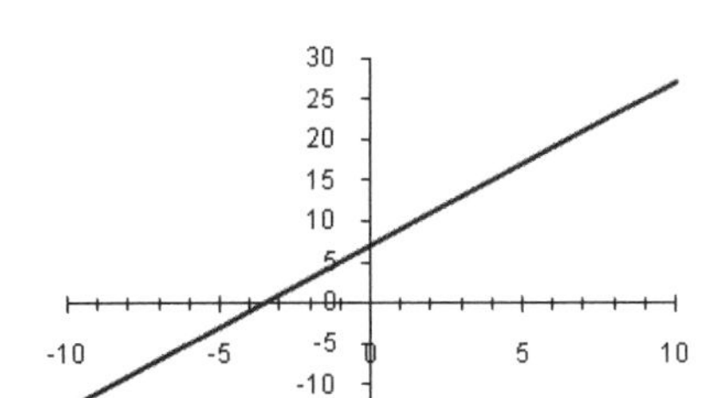

b.

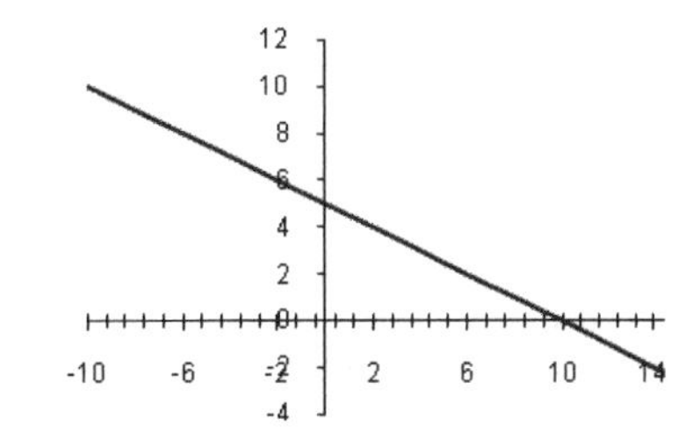

c.

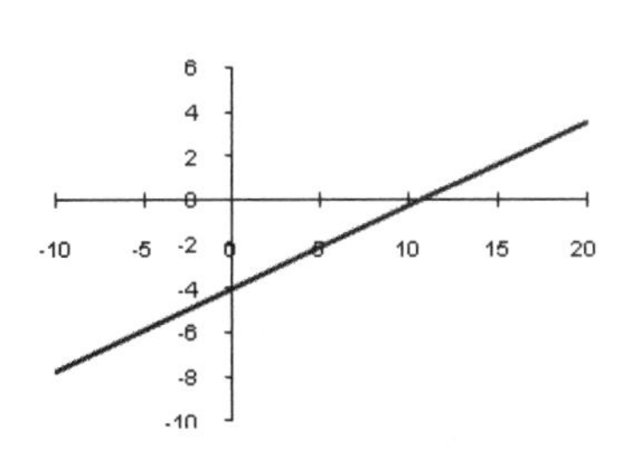

d.

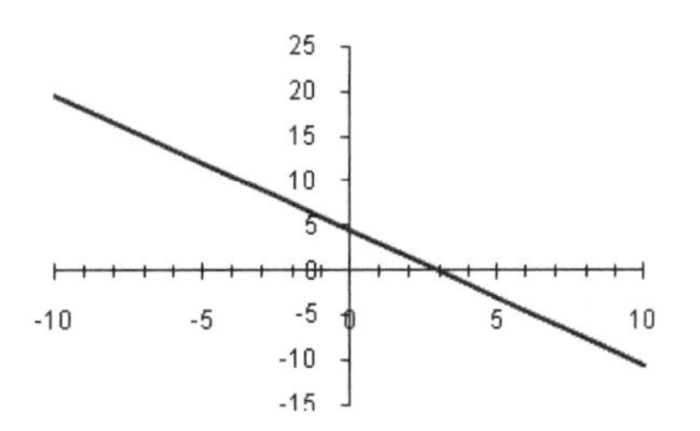

Reading and Writing Mathematics

9. Switched the x and y coordinates when graphing.

11. He didn't pick multiples of 7 for x.
He didn't write the ordered pairs that were graphed.
He didn't label the axis on the graph.
He didn't write the equation of the line on the graph.
He didn't label the points that were graphed.

<u>Section 2.6 Graphing Lines by Plotting Intercepts page 165</u>

Skill Building Exercises

1. x = 2.667 2. y = –3.8

Practice Exercises

3. a. (73, 0) Joe has to work 73 hours to break even. b. (0, –1095) Joe loses $1,095.

c.

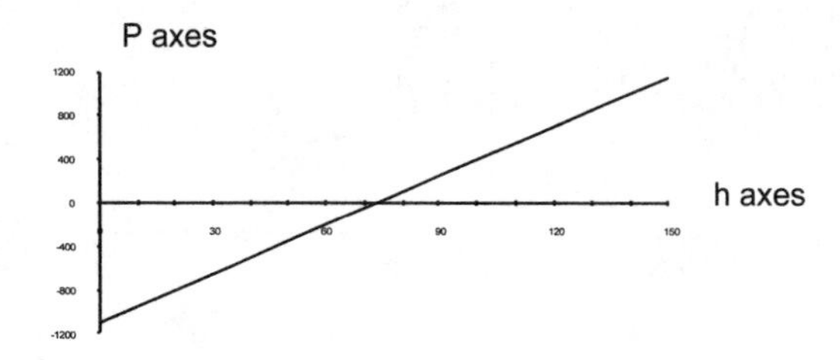

4. a. t = 9 (9, 0) The minivan will be worthless in 9 years.

b. v = 20,700 (0, 20700), The minivan is worth $20,700 in 2007.

c.

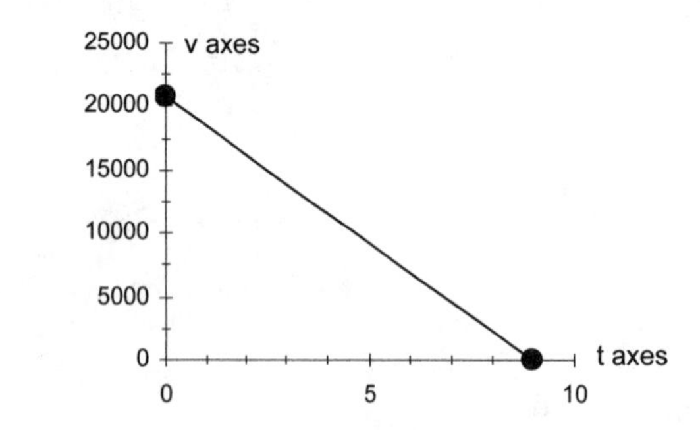

5.

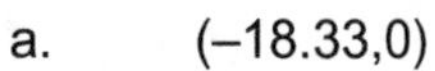

a. (–18.33,0) (0,11)

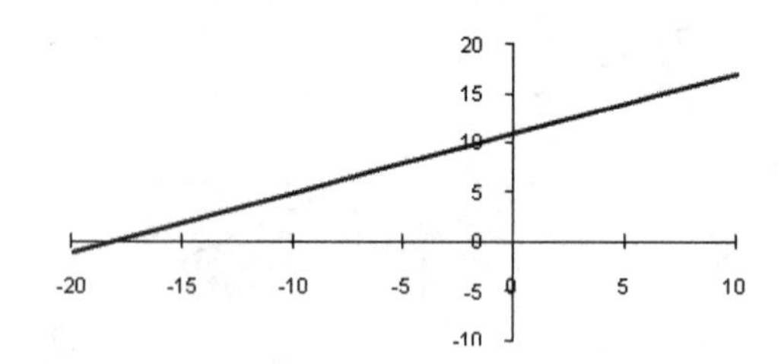

b. (9.09,0) (0,.0806)

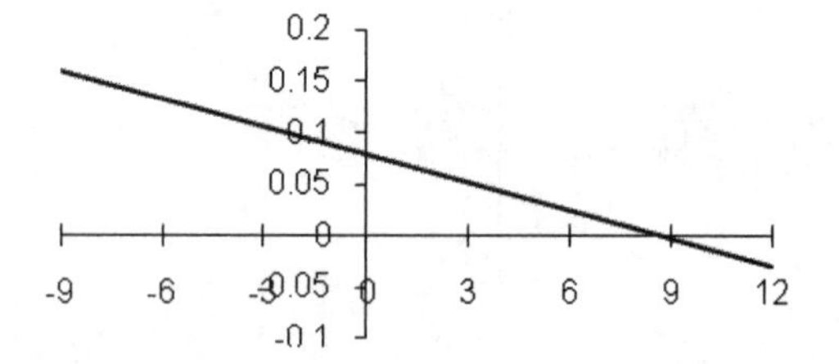

c. (4,0) (0,-600)

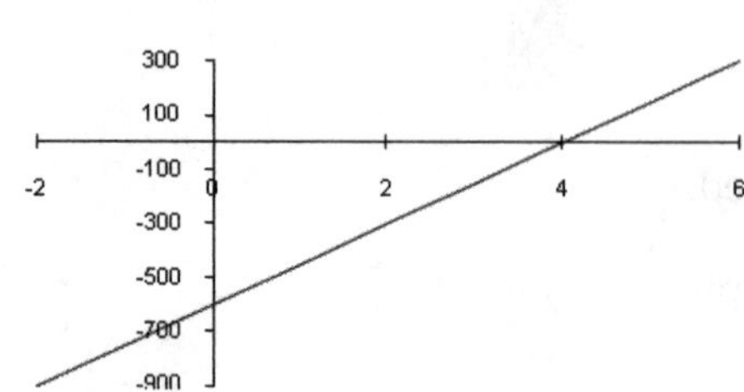
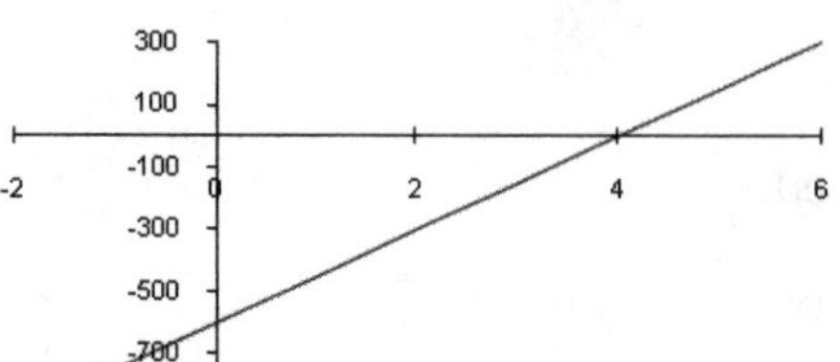

d. (-6.66,0) (0,-5)

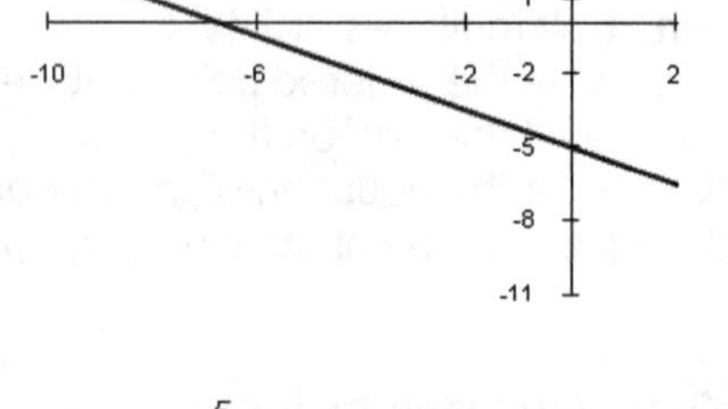

7 a.

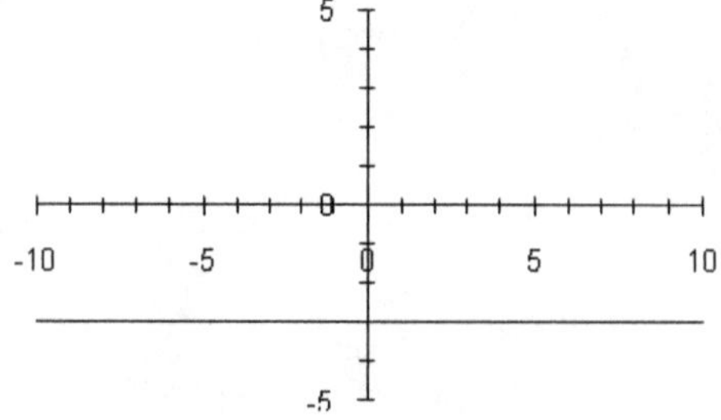

b.

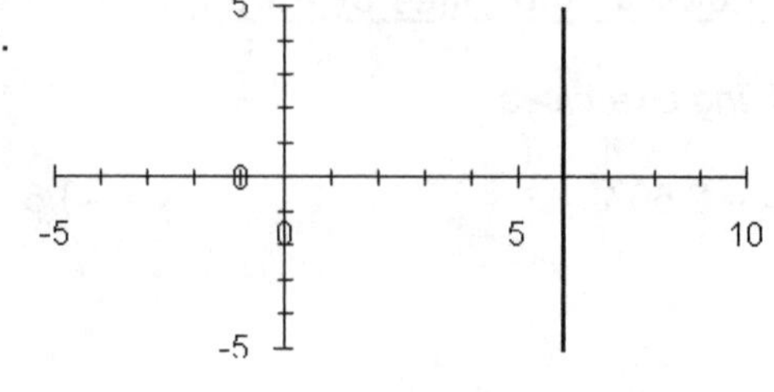

c

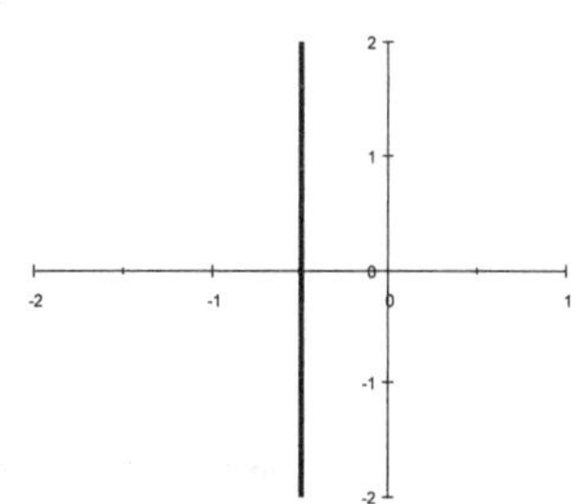

d.

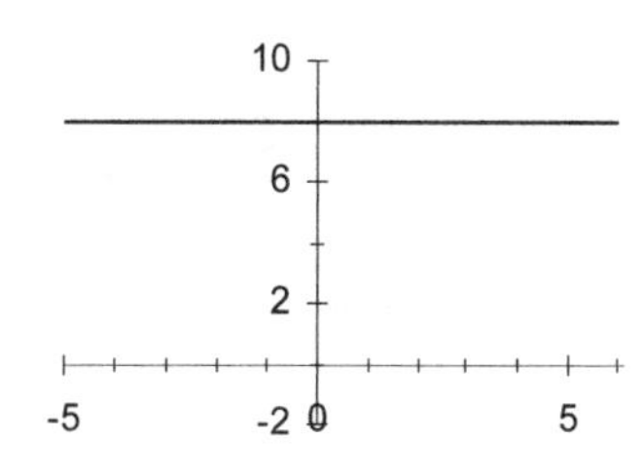

8.

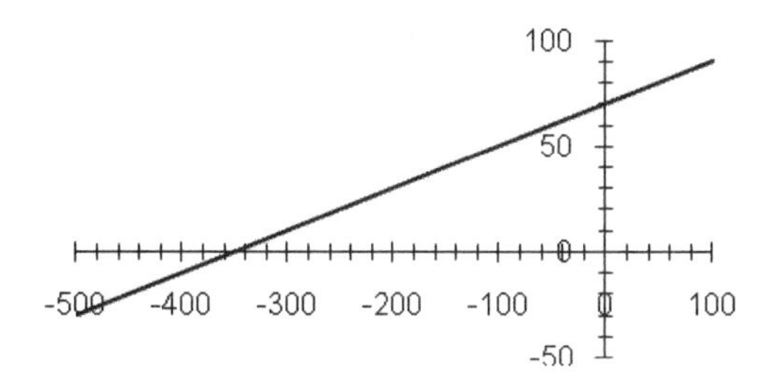

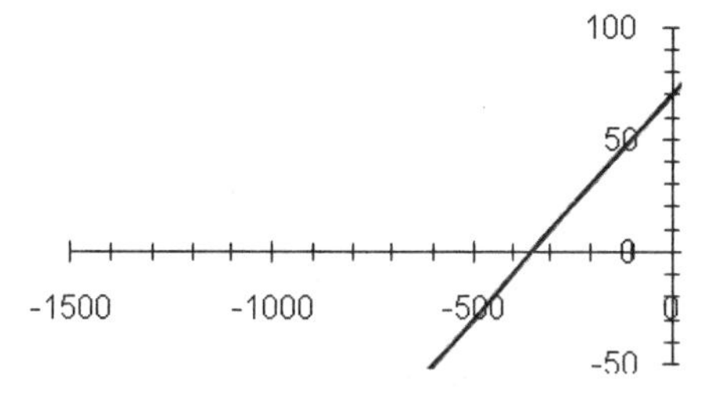

The graph on the right looks steeper only because of the scale of the graph. The two graphs represent the same equation.

Reading and Writing Mathematics

9. The student didn't write down the intercepts, (0, –3) and (2, 0) so he didn't graph the intercepts just the point (2, –3) which is not on the line $3x + 2y = 6$.

10. The student graphed the points (–22, 0) and (0, 55). He should have graphed (0, –22) and (55, 0). He switched the coordinates.

11. a. Set $y = 0$ and solve for x.

    b. Set $x = 0$ and solve for y.

12. He started to find the x intercept.
    He needs to complete the following steps to finish the question:
    1. Write the x intercept as an ordered pair.
    2. Find the y intercept by setting $x = 0$.
    3. Write the y intercept as an ordered pair.
    4. Choose an appropriate scale for the x and y axis.
    5. Plot the x and y intercepts.
    6. Label the graph (the points, the line and the axis).

Section 2.7 Introduction to Slope page 179

Skill Building Exercises

1. The independent variable is years or t and the dependent variable is value or v. The slope of the line is negative.

2. The independent variable is year and the dependent variable is minimum wage.

Practice Exercises

3. L. H. = $\frac{1.89}{12}$ = 0.1575, F.S. = $\frac{2.68}{18}$ = 0.1489 F.S. is the better buy.

4. Slope of U-Haul's ramp is 0.5556, Slope of Darrel's ramp is 0.375.

5. a.

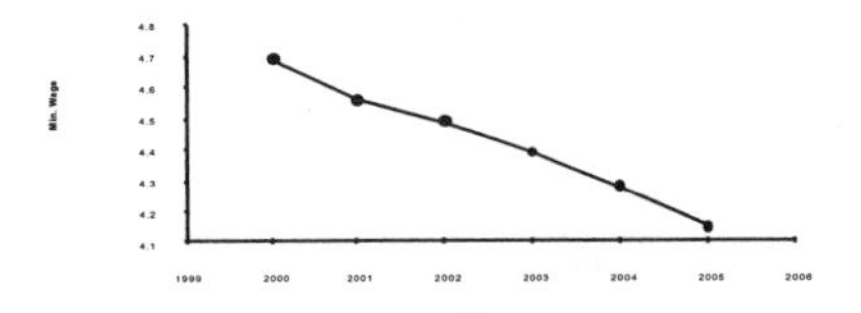

b. The average rate of change between 2000 and 2005 is –0.108 dollars per year.

c. The average rate of change between 2004 and 2005 is –0.13 dollars per year.

d. An estimate for the minimum wage in 2006 could be $4.02.

e. The percent change in minimum wage between 2000 and 2005 was –11.51%.

f. The minimum wage adjusted for inflation decreased between the years 2000 and 2005.

6. a.

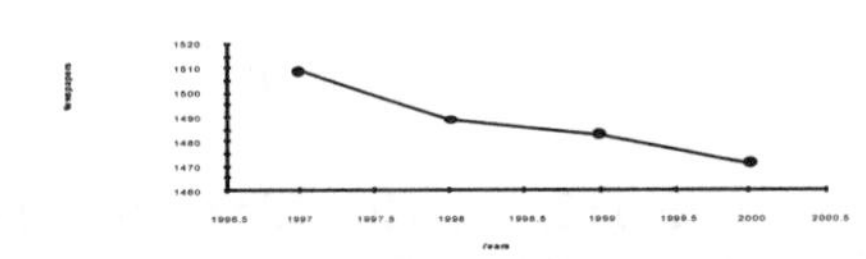

b. The average rate of change between 1997 and 2000 is –12.67 newspapers per year.

c. The average rate of change between 1999 and 2000 is –12 newspapers per year.

d. The percent change in newspapers between 1999 and 2000 was –0.8092%.

e. The number of daily newspapers in the U. S. has been decreasing since 1997.

7.

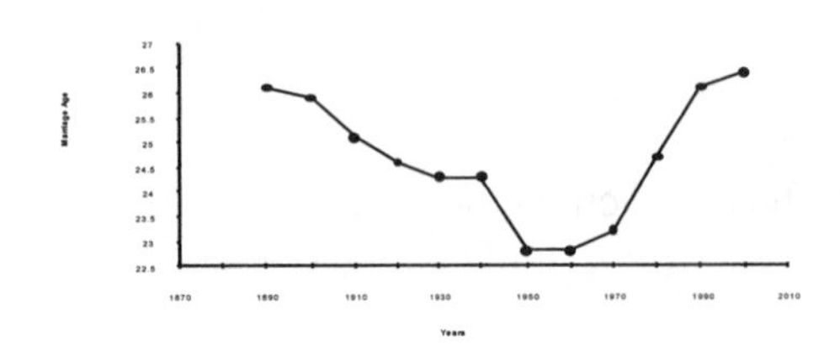

a. 1940 to 1950

b. –0.15

c. 1970 to 1980 (1980 to 1990 looks similar.)

d. Average rate of change from 1970 to 1980 was 0.15 .

e. 1930 to 1940 and 1950 to 1960

f. The age men first get married is increasing by 0.3 years.

g. 26.7 (answer not unique)

8. a. It appears that Medicare Costs grew faster.

b. Doctor's charges grew at a rate of 2.3 billion dollars per year while Medicare grew 1.3 billion per year.

9. a. Second graph

b. Both lines have the same slope, 35/3.

10. For PPL: 100(390 – 55)/55

Reading and Writing Mathematics

11. a. Measures how steep a line is.
    b. Measures average rate of change.
    c. Determines if a quantity is increasing or decreasing.

12. To compute slope, divide by the difference in the independent variables. To compute percent change, divide by the original value of the dependent variable.

13. Both use the difference in the dependent variable in the numerator.

15. The first mistake is in part a; the order of the subtraction in the numerator is switched. The second mistake occurs in part b; the student should have divided by amount in 1985.

16. In part a, it would have been better to write the formula for slope using the data.
    In part a, the answer didn't have any units.
    In part a, it is best to write a sentence explaining what slope means in terms of the data.
    In part b, there aren't any parentheses around the numerator.
    In part b, there isn't a sentence explaining what the percent change means.

Section 2.8 Slope page 193

Skill Building Exercises

1. a. –5   b. 9   c. –4   2. 5 is the x coordinate and 9 is the y coordinate.

Practice Exercises

3. a. $m = \frac{5}{2}$ b. $m = \frac{-3}{7}$ c. $m = 0$

4. a. $m = -.5$ b. $m = 0$ c. $m = .44$ d. undefined   e. $m = .8$

5. a. $m = 7$, (0,5)   b. $m = -2/3$, (0, –2)

6. a. m= –1,825 The truck depreciates $1,825 a year. (0, 73250) The truck originally cost $73,250.

   b.

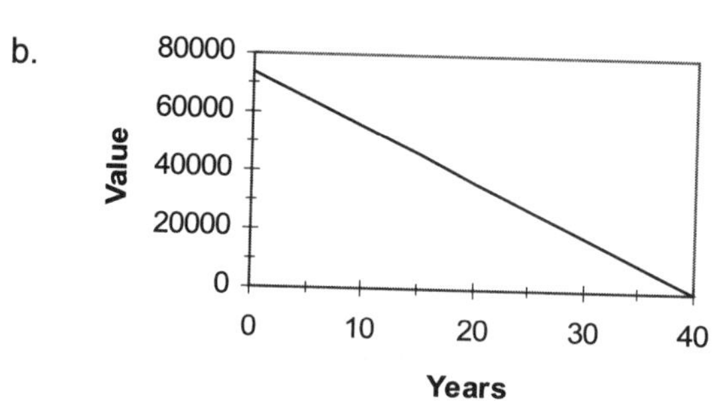

7. a. m = 0.10 They make 10% commission. (0, 22000) The base salary is $22,000.

   b.

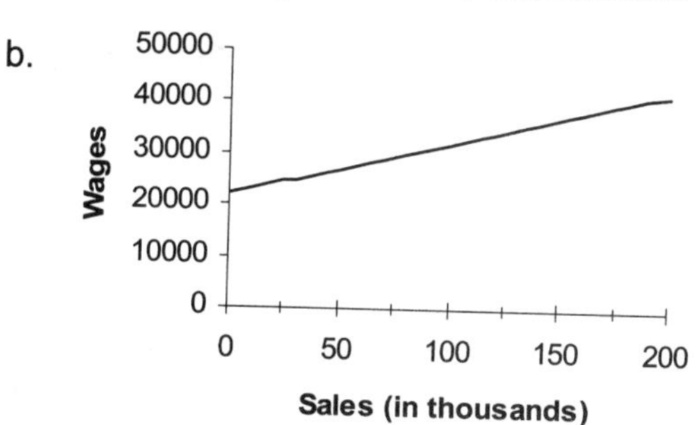

Reading and Writing Mathematics

8. a

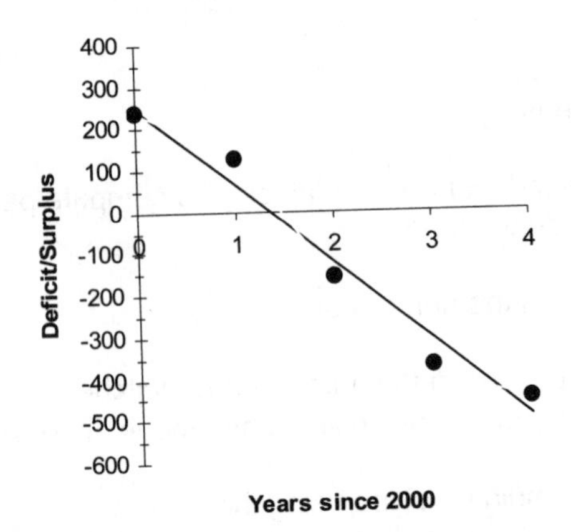

b.

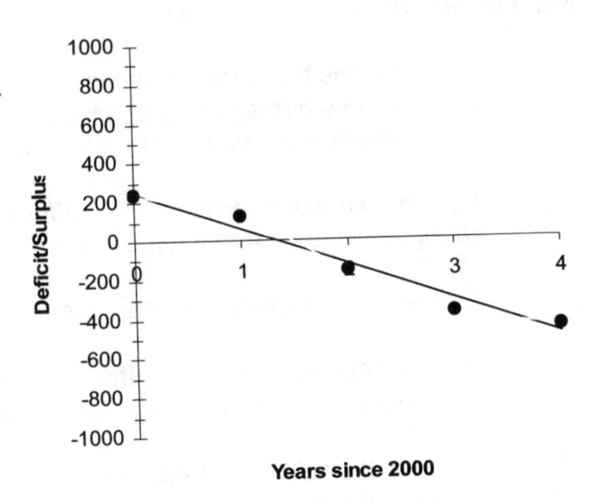

c. $m = -188$ The budget surplus is decreasing 188 billion dollars per year.
(0, 250) There was approximately a 250 billion dollar surplus in 2000.

9. a. Should be $\frac{1-3}{-6-(-2)}$

b. The student computed the change in x divided by the change in y.

Section 2.9 Applications of Graphs page 211

Skill Building Exercises

1. $x = 33.25$

2. a. $m = 0.5$

b. (0, 20)

c

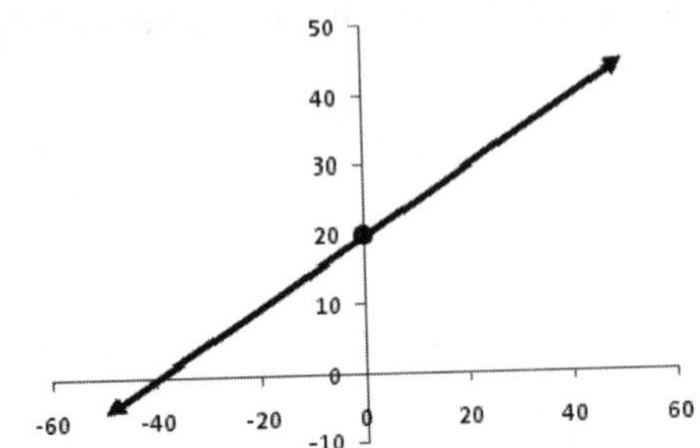

3. a. $m = 0$

b. (0,15)

c.

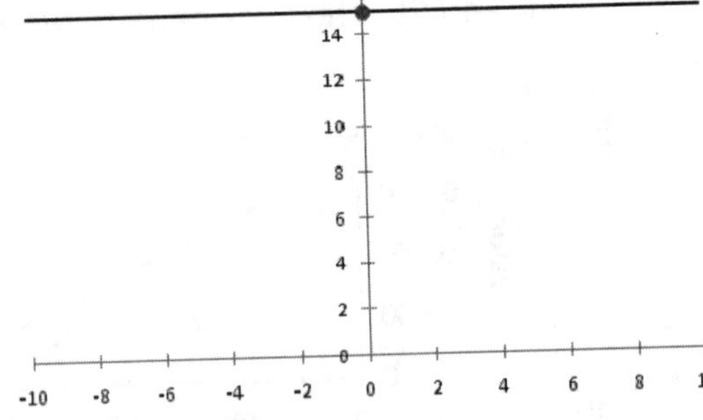

4. The intersection is the point where two lines cross, the intercept is the point where a line crosses an axis.

Practice Exercises

5. a. $h = 1.7d + 4$

b.

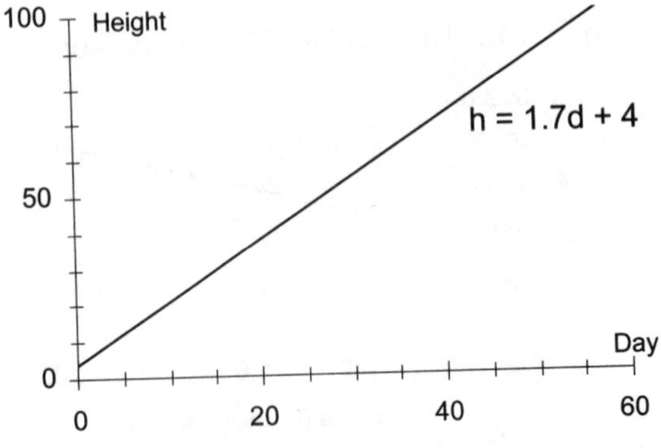

c. The plant is 27.8 inches after 14 days.

d. The plant is106 inches after 60 days.

e. The plant is 208 inches after 120 days. This is probably too tall.

f. The sunflower will be 5 feet tall after 33 days.

6. a. Golden: m = 35, Classic: c = 0.80m + 15

b. m = 25, c = 35 The two companies charge $35 when you drive 25 miles.

c.

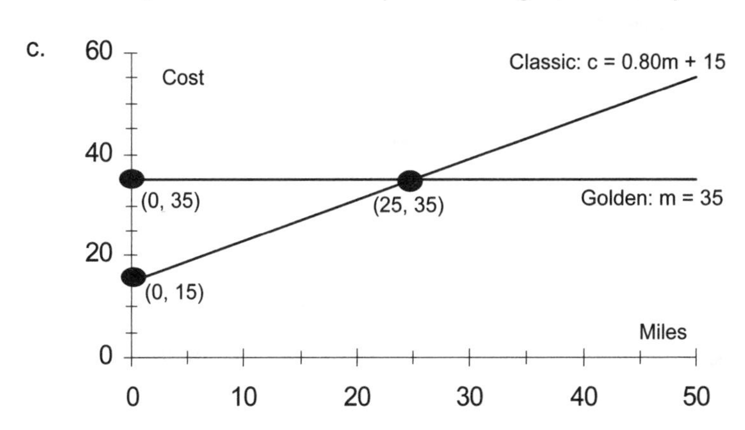

d. $0 \leq m < 25$ Golden is more expensive when you drive between 0 and 25 miles.

e. $m > 25$ Classic is more expensive when you drive more than 25 miles

f. Golden: (0, 35) Classic: (0, 15) Cost if you don't drive anywhere.

g. The slope is 0.80 for Classic and 0 for Golden. Slope is the cost per mile.

7. a. $C_R = 0.18m + 0.50$, $C_B = 0.27m + 0.25$

b. m = 2.7, C = 1.00 The two companies charge $1.00 when you talk for 2.8 minutes.

c.

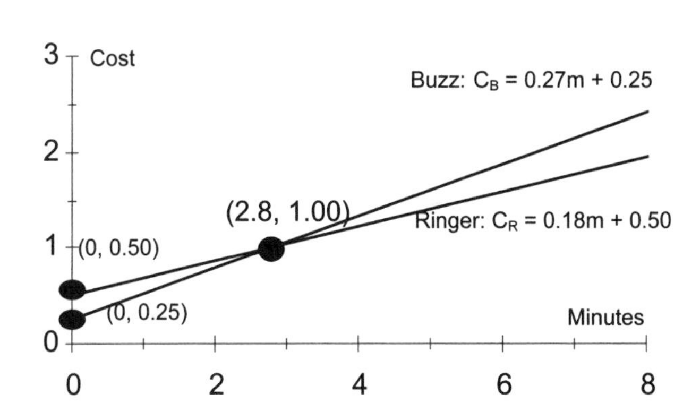

d. $0 \leq m < 2.7$ Ringer is more expensive when you talk between 0 and 2.7 minutes.

e. $m > 2.7$ Buzz is more expensive than Ringer when youtalk more than 2.7 min.

f. Ringer: (0, 0.50) Buzz: (0, 0.25) The initial charge for the phone call.

g. Slope for ringer is 0.18, and the slope for Buzz is 0.27.

8. a. $W_M = 0.08\,S + 5{,}000$, $W_C = 0.04\,S + 10{,}000$ c.

b. S = 125,000, W = 15,000, Both companies pay $15,000 when you sell $125,000.

c.

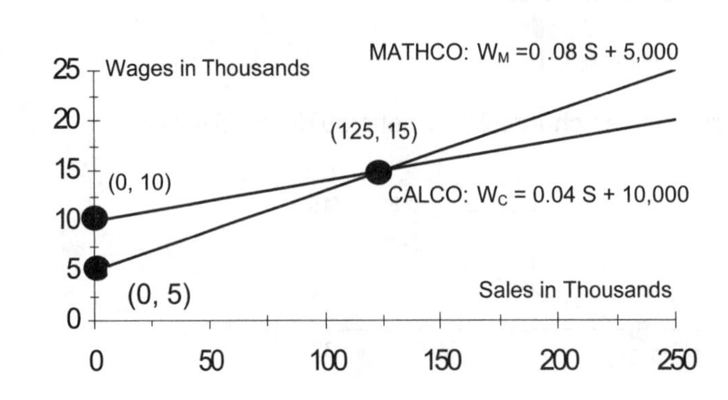

d. S > 125,000, MATHCO pays more when you sell more than $125,000.

e. $0 \leq S < 125000$, CALCO pays more when you sell between $0 and $125,000.

f. MATHCO (0, 5000)
Your wages from MATHCO will be $5,000 a year if you sell nothing.

CALCO (0, 10000)
Your wages from CALCCO will be $10,000 a year if you sell nothing.

g. Slope for MATHCO is 0.08, and the slope for CALCO is 0.04. Slope is the commission.

9. a. $V_D = -2{,}000t + 32{,}000$, $V_M = -3{,}000t + 42{,}000$

b. (10, 12000) In ten years both machines will cost $12,000.

c.

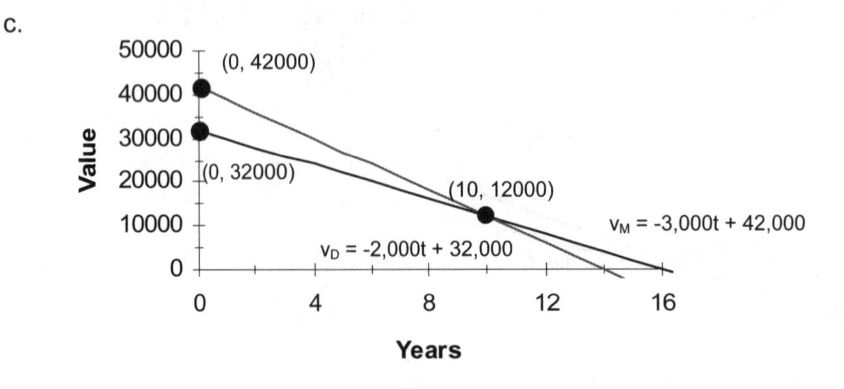

d. After 10 years.

e. Before 10 years.

f. (0, 32000), (0, 42000) The initial cost of the machines.

g. (16, 0), (14, 0) How long until the copiers are worthless.

h. Slopes are –2,000 and –3,000. How much the copiers depreciate per year.

10. a. $c = 0.20(m-3) + 0.50$

b. $m < 3$

c. $c = 0.50$

d.

c axis
2
1.5
1
0.5
0
m axis
0
5
10

11. a. $W = 0.10(S - 50000) + 10000$

b. $S < 50000$

c. $10,000

d.

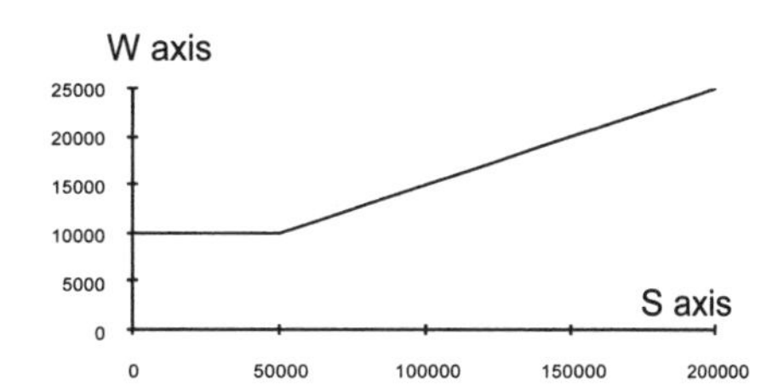

Reading and Writing Mathematics

12. In part a. the equations should be $w = 0.06s + 10,000$ and $w = 0.04s + 25,000$.
In part d, $s > 75,000$
In part f, the student gave the point of intersection, not the wage intercepts.
In part g, the slope is the commission.

13. In part a, didn't set the equations equal to C.
In part c, didn't label the graph.
In part c, the graph is too small.
In part d, didn't write a sentence.

<u>Chapter 2 Review Test page 226</u>

1. a. $x \le 1.25$ b. $x \le 3$ c. $1.71 \le x < 3.57$

2. a. $m < 3461$ b. $1538 < m < 7307$

3. a.

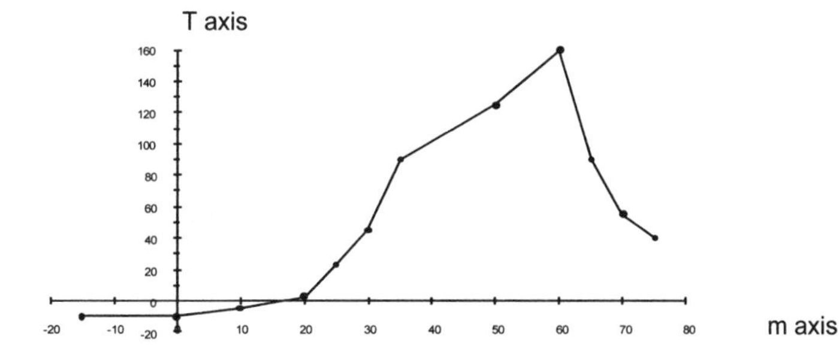

b. The dinner was placed in the oven around 20 minutes.

c. The dinner was taken out of the oven around 60 minutes.

d. The dinner was 100 degrees around 45 min. and 62 min

4.

a.

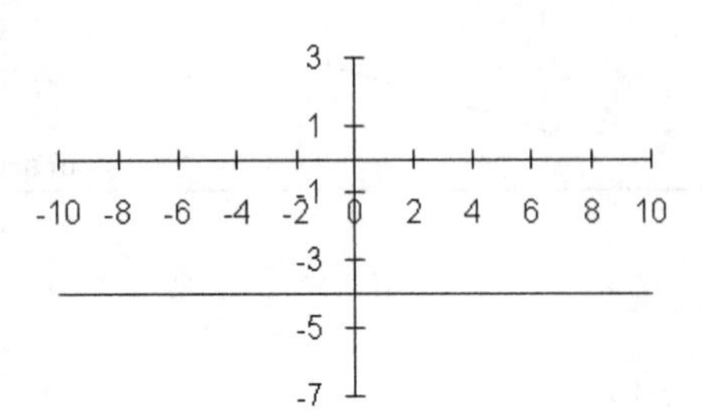

b.

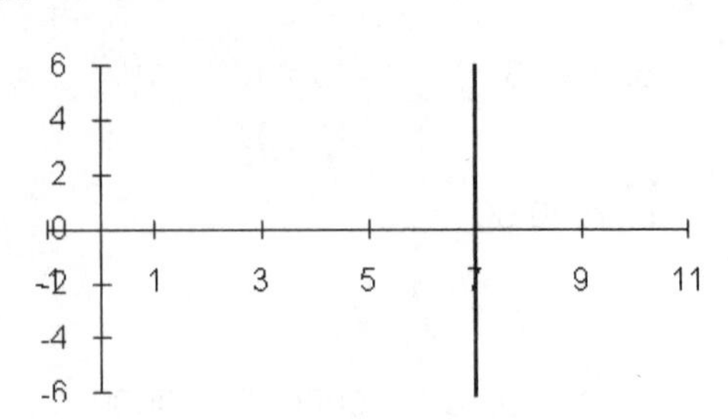

5.

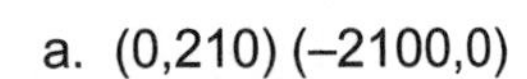
a. (0,210) (–2100,0)

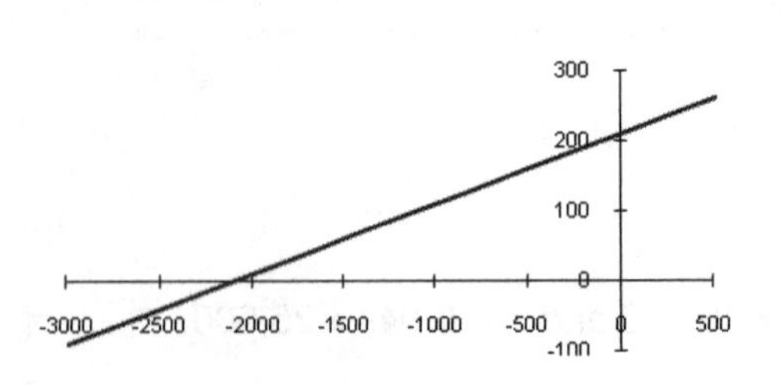

b. (0,2) (0.05263,0)

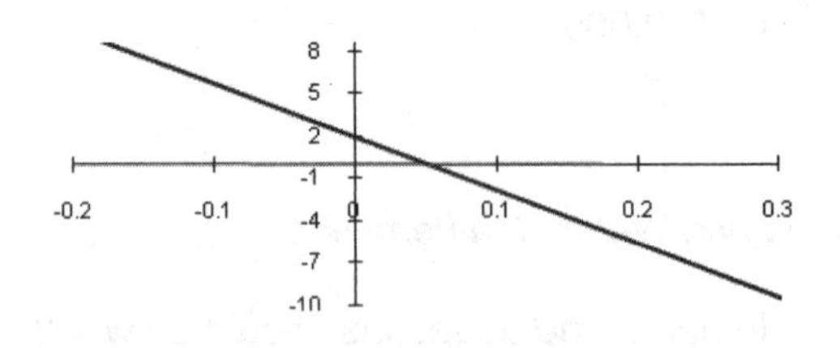

c. (0,2.85) (5,0)

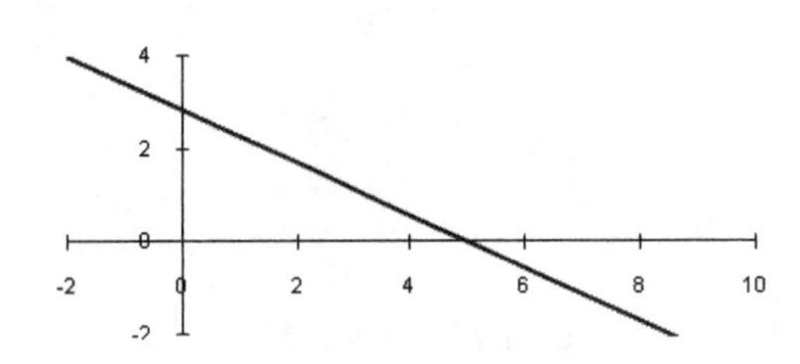

d. (0,8) (–6,0)

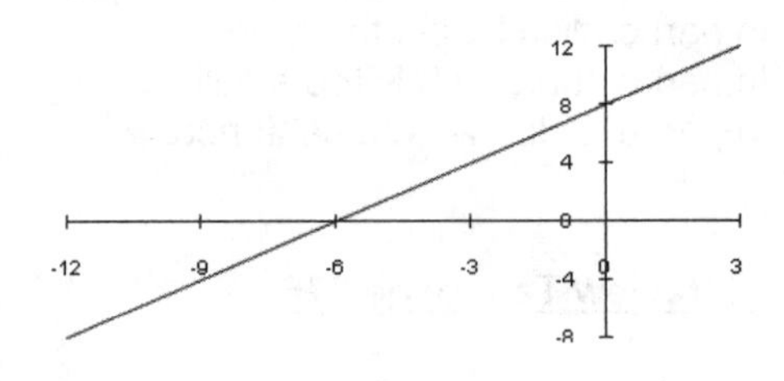

6.	a. –12º	b. 2º	c. 8:30 AM, 11:00PM
	d. 8 and 10 AM	e. 10º at 3 PM	f. –12º at 3 AM
	g. 3 AM TO 3 PM	h. midnight to 3 AM and 3 PM to midnight	
7.	a. 4.025	b. 25.8%	c. m = 4.025
8.	a. m = –3, (0,7)	b. m = .15, (0, –6)	
9.	a. m = –13/8	b. m = 0	

10. a. The slope is 0.1. The slope represents the commission.

b. If you sell nothing, your wages are $20,000. The point is (0, 20000), and is the w intercept.

11. The student graphed the equation by plotting points, not by finding the intercepts.

12. a. Limo: $c = 32$ Ultra: $c = 0.26m + 19$

b. $m = 50$, $c = 32$, Both companies charge $32 when you drive 50 miles.

c.

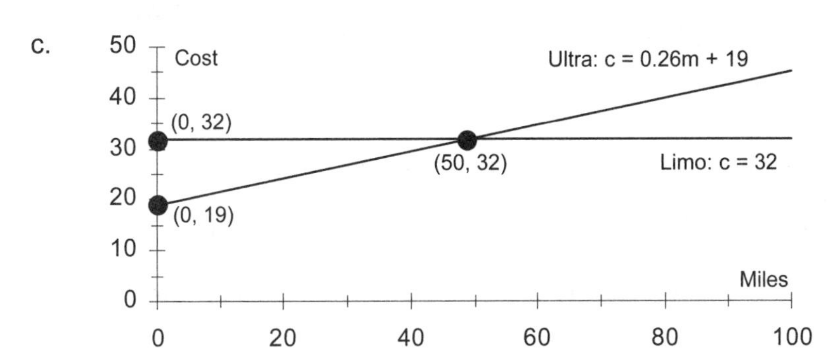

d. $0 \leq m \leq 50$ Limo is more expensive when you drive less than 50 miles.

e. $m > 50$, Ultra costs more when you drive more than 50 miles.

f. Limo: (0, 32) Ultra: (0, 19) Rental charge without any miles

g. Slope of Limo is 0, Slope of Ultra is 0.26. Slope is the cost per mile.

Section 3.1 Introduction to Positive Exponents page 243

Skill Building Exercises

1. a. 9 b. –9

Practice Exercises

2. a. 7776 b. 478.212 c. 5,244.67 d. 0.02799
   e. 0.003906 f. 0.006934

3. a. 36 b. 164,206.5 c. 104.9 d. 65.61
   e. 2,138 f. 1,100.8 g. –67.24 h. –2,015
   i. –6.25 j. –216 k. –216 l. –16,807
   m. –16807 n. –0.729 o. 0.004096

4. a. The luminosity of a sun with 5 times the mass of our sun is 279.5 times the luminosity of our sun.

   b. The luminosity of a sun with half the mass of our sun is 0.08839 times the luminosity of our sun.

5. a.

Time	Calculation	Bacteria
1 day	1000(1.05)	1,050
2 days	1,050(1.05) = 1000(1.05)(1.05)	1,103
3 days	$1000(1.05^3)$	1,158
4 days	$1000(1.05^4)$	1,216
n days	$1000(1.05^n)$	B

b. $B = 1{,}000(1.05)^n$

c. There will be 2,654 bacteria in 20 days

d. 7,040 bacteria in 40 days.

e. Between 14 and 15 days there will be 2,000 bacteria

6. a.

Hour	Calculation	ML
1st	$14(0.60)$	8.4
2nd	$14(0.60^2)$	5.04
3rd	$14(0.60^3)$	3.024
4th	$14(0.60^4)$	1.814
nth	$14(0.60^n)$	d

b. $d = 14(0.60)^h$

c. There will be 0.2351 milliliters of the drug 8 hours later.

d. In about 2.5 hours there will be less than 4 milliliters in the bloodstream.

7 a. $4930.72 b. $6336.19 c. $6112.47 d. $2241.74

e. It will take approximately 138 months or 11 1/2 years for the account to grow to $15,000.

Reading and Writing Mathematics

8. $(-5)^8$ means multiply –5 times itself 8 times, since it is an even number of multiplications the product will be positive.
-5^8 means multiply 5 times itself 8 times then multiply by negative 1, so the result is negative.

9. $-b^n$ means multiply b times itself n times then multiply by negative 1.
$(-b)^n$ means multiply -b times itself n times.

10. $b > 1$ 11. $b < 1$

13. Substitute the values for Future Value and interest.
Simplify inside parentheses.
Calculate the exponent
Divide both sides by 3.307

Section 3.2 Negative Exponents and Scientific Notation page 257

Skill Building Exercises

1. a. 16 b. –16 c. 16

Practice Exercises

2. a. 0.001953 b. 0.1041 c. 625 d. -0.01234

e. 0.01234 f. -0.001953 g. -0.001953 h. 3,125

3. a. 2.356×10^{13} b. 4.35×10^{-8} c. 6.789×10^{13}

4. a. $866.66 b. $9033.42 c. $804.62

d. $104,635.35, $136,276.91

5. a. 7.8×10^4 b. 1.67×10^{-6} c. 6.35×10^{-3} d. 1.16×10^6

6. a. 786,000,000 b. 0.0000000008673 c. 0.033 d. 20,320

7. 9,460,000,000,000 kilometers

8. 9.460×10^{16} kilometers

Reading and Writing Mathematics

9. Compute the values for interest and number of payments
   Substitute the values for i and n into the formula.
   Simplify inside parentheses.
   Compute the exponent.
   Simplify the denominator.
   Divide.
   Divide both sides by 0.01933

10. A negative exponent means take the reciprocal.

11. The 2 is in the 10^9 place value.

12. The exponent is negative.

13. The EE key is used for scientific notation and the carat key is used for computing exponents.

14. It is the way the calculator writes a number in scientific notation.

Section 3.3 Properties of Exponents page 267

Skill Building Exercises

1. a. 2 b. -5 c. –10

Practice Exercises

2. a. $8x^8$ b. $2x$ c. x^6y^{15} d. $\frac{625}{x^{12}}$

   e. $\frac{6}{x}$ f. $\frac{5x^3}{2}$ g. $\frac{x^3}{2}$ h. $\frac{y^2}{9x^2}$

   i. 1 j. $\frac{216}{x^6}$ k. $\frac{8y^{15}}{x^{12}}$ l. $\frac{1}{49x^{10}}$

3. a. $T = \frac{10^{10}}{M^{2.5}}$ years b. 312,500,000 years c. $5.657 \bullet 10^{10}$ years

Reading and Writing Mathematics

5. a. Should be $81x^8$ b. Should be $12x^3$ c. Should be $\frac{-7}{x^2}$

Section 3.4 Introduction to Algebraic Fractions page 277

Skill Building Exercises

1. 3/4

2. a 10/21 b. 49/32

Practice Exercises

3. a. \$6,800 b. \$22,800 c. \$118,800

d. Undefined; it is not possible to have 100% pure water.

4. a. \$33,200 b. \$74,700 c. \$157,700

d. undefined, 100% of the particle pollution cannot be removed.

5. a. $\frac{3}{2}$ b. $\frac{9}{5}$ c. $\frac{1}{4x}$ d. $\frac{2y^3}{5x}$ e. $-\frac{5}{8x^3}$ f. $-\frac{x^2}{2}$

6. a. $\frac{4}{3}$ b. 4 c. $\frac{7}{9y^2}$ d. x e. $\frac{1}{x}$ f. $-\frac{2x^2}{3}$

7. a. 132 feet per second b. About a half second.

8. 182.88 cm

Reading and Writing Mathematics

9. Only factors can be cancelled. The numerator involves addition not multiplication.

10. The student cancelled before taking the reciprocal of $\frac{25}{6x}$.

Section 3.5 Adding and Subtracting Fractions page 285

Skill Building Exercises

1. 53/45

Practice Exercises

2. $\frac{1}{5x}$ 3. $\frac{9-10x}{15x}$ 4. $\frac{31m}{21}$ 5. $\frac{8y-9}{12y}$

6. $\frac{15-2m^2}{24m^3}$ 7. $\frac{20y+9}{12y^2}$ 8. $\frac{8n^2-15}{36n^4}$ 9. $\frac{9+8x}{6x^2}$

10. $\frac{3x^2-4x}{12}$ 11. $\frac{1+35x^3}{5x^3}$

Reading and Writing Mathematics

12. a. Cannot combine unlike terms, $4x^2$ and 15.

b. Cannot add fractions by simply adding the numerators and denominators.

13. Multiply the numerator and denominator by the factor that will give the LCD.
Multiply the fractions.
Write as a single fraction.

14. Label the Least Common Denominator
Do not cross out, it looks like your canceling
Write all fractions with a denominator.
Use equal signs.

Section 3.6 Solving Equations with Fractions page 293

Skill Building Exercises

1. a. $x = 4$ b. $x = 1/8$

Practice Exercises

2. $x = \frac{-7}{6}$ or $-1.1\overline{6}$
3. $x = \frac{4}{11}$ or $0.\overline{36}$
4. $x = \frac{-24}{19}$ or -1.263
5. $x = \frac{-4}{9}$ or $-0.\overline{4}$
6. $x = \frac{14}{17}$ or 0.8235
7. $x = -\frac{15}{62}$ or -0.2419
8. $x = \frac{-11}{7}$ or -1.5714
9. $x = \frac{9}{14}$ or 0.6429

10. a. $x > -2.5$ b. $x \geq -0.1$

11. a. $F > 46.4$ b. $28.4 < F < 53.6$ c. $F = \frac{9C + 160}{5}$

Reading and Writing Mathematics

12. Multiply all terms by the LCD, 36.
Reduce or cancel.
Multiply.
Combine like terms.
Divide both sides by the coefficient of x, 46.

13. Multiply all terms by the LCD, 8.
Reduce or cancel.
Multiply and use the distributive property.
Combine like terms.
Subtract 17 from both sides.
Divide both sides by the coefficient of x, –2.

14. a. Didn't cancel correctly, the first term should be 30 not 30x.
. b. Didn't apply the distributive property correctly, –15 should be + 15.

15. Label the LCD.
Use equal signs.
Rewrite the problem when multiplying by the LCD.
Don't do the distributive property mentally.

Section 3.7 Ratio and Proportion Problems page 305

Skill Building Exercises

1. a. $x = \frac{24}{9}$ or $\frac{8}{3}$ or $2\frac{2}{3}$ or 2.667 b. $x = \frac{12}{35}$ or 0.3429

Practice Exercises

2. The 75 ounce laundry detergent is the better buy.

3. The 15 ounce can of tuna is the better buy.

4. The number of bears in the forest is approximately 36.

5. The car can go 264 miles on 12 gallons.

6. The number of people in Reading without medical insurance is approximately 3,038.

7. It will take about 23 minutes to print 81 pages.

8. One person should get 3.36 million, the second person should get 4.032 million and the third person should get 5.208 million.

9. a. The area of the 10 inch pizza is 314.2 square inches; the 14 inch pizza is 615.8 square inches. The difference is 301.5 square inches.

   b. The ten inch pizza costs 7.6 cents per square inch, and the 14 inch pizza costs 4.5 cents per square inch. The better buy is the 14 inch pizza.

   c. You get 14.15 square inches per dollar for the 12 inch pizza. A fair price for the 6 inch pizza is $2.00.

Chapter 3 Review Test page 312

1. a. x^7 b. $\frac{1}{x^2}$ c. 1 d. x^{10}

   e. $8x^6$ f. $\frac{1}{x^5}$ g. x^7 h. $\frac{9}{x^5}$

2. a. 0.064 b. –167.96 c. 167.96

3. a. 2.15×10^{13} b. 5.022×10^{-13}

4. a. 8.3×10^6 b. 6.14×10^{-4}

5. a. 420000 b. .0031

6. a. $\frac{6x^6}{y^5}$ b. $\frac{2}{49x^3}$ c. $\frac{15x-14}{6x^2}$ d. $\frac{33+5x}{15x}$

7. Steve should get $700,000 and Sarah $1,050,000.

8. a.

Day	Calculation	Population
I. D.		500
1	500(1.07)	535
2	$500(1.07)^2$	572
3	$500(1.07)^3$	613
n	$500(1.07)^n$	p

   b. $p = 500(1.07)^n$

   c. There will be 3,806 bacteria in 30 days.

   d. There will be 28,973 bacteria in 60 days.

9. a. The monthly payments are $1609.25. b. You can afford a $10,087 car.

10. 16,220,160 millimeters

11. a. x = 9 b. x = –2

Section 4.1 Introduction to Quadratics page 327

Skill Building Exercises

1. a. 9 b. –144 c. 704

2. a. $x - 1$ b. $-3x + 7$

Practice Exercises

3. a. 80 feet b. 704 ft
 c. 1104 ft d. 1040 ft
 e. 80 ft f. –192 ft
 g. t = 8 seconds h. 16.3 secs.
 i.

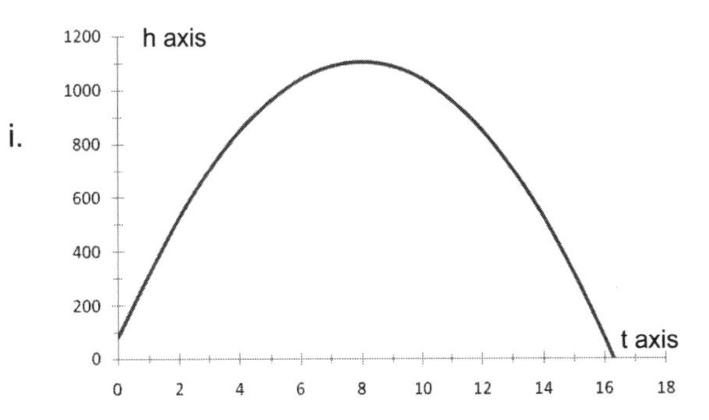

4. a. $-4x^2 + 12x - 3$ b. $-4x^2 + 3x - 20$ c. $-19x^2 + 13x - 7$
 d. $-18x + 18$ e. $-6x^2 - 25x + 14$ f. $-11x^2 + 6x - 15$

5. $P = -4x^2 + 17x - 72$

6. a. $x^2 + 5x + 6$ b. $x^2 + x - 12$ c. $x^2 - 11x + 28$ d. $x^2 - 64$
 e. $x^2 - 81$ f. $6x^2 + 7x - 3$ g. $x^2 + 6x + 9$ h. $x^2 - 10x + 25$

Reading and Writing Mathematics

7. Terms are added or subtracted, like terms have the same variable with the same exponent.

8. To add or subtract like terms, add or subtract their coefficients. A coefficient is the number multiplying the variable.

9. a. The student did not distribute the –1 through the second term. The first step should be $9x^2 + 12x - 21 - 2x^2 + 5x - 4$.
 b. The student raised each term, x and 6 to the second power. The student should have multiplied $(x + 6)(x + 6)$ using FOIL.
 c. The student incorrectly combined two unlike terms, $10x^2$ and $2x$, to get $12x^2$.

10. Used the Distributive Property
 Combined Like Terms

Section 4.2 Applications of Quadratic Formula page 341

Skill Building Exercises

1. a. 6.481 b. 5.745 c. 11.87

2. $ax^2 + bx + c = 0$

3. a. $a = 4, b = -6, c = 7$ b. $a = -2, b = 5, c = -12$ c. $a = 2, b = 0, c = -5$

Practice Exercises

4.

Width	Length	Area
50	$\frac{360-2(50)}{2}=130$	130(50) = 6500
70	$\frac{360-2(70)}{2}=110$	110(70) = 7700
90	$\frac{360-2(90)}{2}=90$	90(90) = 8100
W	$\frac{360-2W}{2}=L$	$\left(\frac{360-2W}{2}\right)W=A$

The pasture should be 80 by 100 yards

5. The flare is in the air for 9.028 seconds.

6. The company must make and sell 90 or 180 items to earn a profit of $10,000 per week.

7. a. According to the model, 13.8% of teenagers smoked marijuana in the year 2001.

   b. 22.56 = t or year 2003, 6.737 = t or year 1987 The model indicates that in 1987 and 2003 16% of teenagers smoked marijuana.

8. The company will earn a weekly profit of $300 if they make and sell 60 or 20 items.

9. The temperature of the oxygen is 7 degrees at 6.582 and 1.418 minutes.

Reading and Writing Mathematics

10. a. $\frac{-b \pm \sqrt{b^2-4ac}}{2a}$

    b. The formula is used to solve to quadratic equations, $ax^2 + bx + c = 0$.

11. Subtract 8 from both sides.
Identify the numbers for the quadratic formula.
Substitute the numbers into the quadratic formula.
Compute the square root portion of the quadratic formula.
Simplify the denominator.
Separate into two parts.
Simplify each part.

12. Computed the square root incorrectly. It should have been 2.522.

13. Didn't write A = W(1,000 – 4W)
Should have written $0 = 1000W - 4W^2 - 60{,}000$ as $0 = -4W^2 + 1000W - 60{,}000$
Didn't write down the entire quadratic formula.
Didn't find the corresponding values for L.
Didn't write a sentence for the answer.

Section 4.3 Quadratic Applications and Graphs page 367

Skill Building Exercises

1. $x = 2.605$ and $x = 33.40$

2. $P = 237$

3. (0, –87)

Practice Exercises

4.

a. $P = -x^2 + 36x - 87$

b. vertex (18,237) The maximum profit is \$237,000 and it occurs when the company makes and sell 18 thousand pretzels.

c. x intercepts (2.605, 0) (33.39, 0)
The company will break even when they sell 2,605 or 33,390 pretzels.

d. P intercept (0, –87) The company will loose \$87,000 dollars if they don't sell any pretzels.

e.

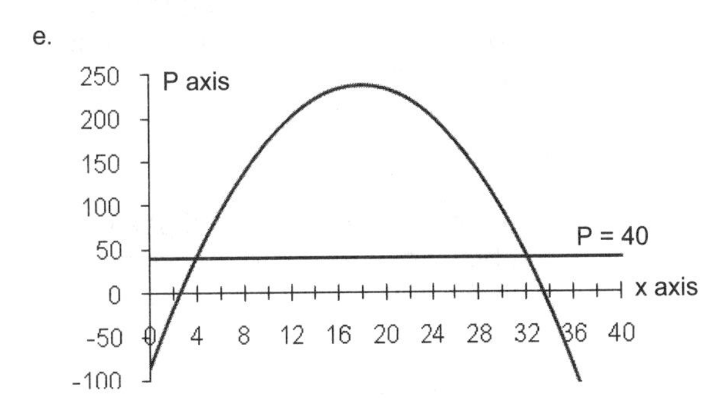

f. (3.964, 40), (32.04, 40)
The company will earn \$40,000 in profit if they sell 3,964 or 32,040 pretzels.

5.

a. $P = -7x^2 + 77x - 35$

b. vertex (5.5, 176.8) The maximum profit is \$17,680 and it occurs when 5.5 thousand doughnuts are sold.

c. x intercepts (0.475, 0)(10.53, 0) In order to break even the company must sell 475 or 10,530 doughnuts.

d. P intercept (0, –35) If they don't sell any doughnuts, they loose \$3,500.

e.

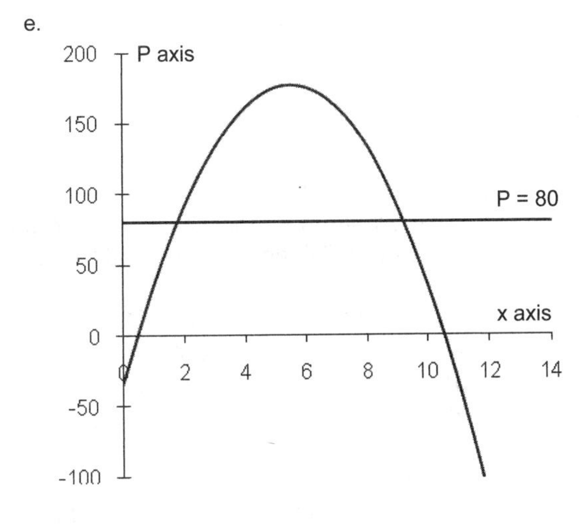

f. (9.218, 80) or (1.782, 80)
The company will earn \$8,000 in profit if they sell 9,218 or 1,782 doughnuts.

6.

a. vertex (6.25, 625) The maximum height of the rocket is 625 feet and the rocket reaches that height in 6.25 seconds

b. x intercepts (0, 0), (12.5, 0) The rocket is in the air 12.5 seconds.

c. h intercept (0, 0) The rocket is launched from the ground.

e.

f. (1.75, 300) and (10.75, 300)

The rocket is 300 feet in the air at 1.75 and 10.75 seconds.

7. a. $A = w(1800 - 2w)$
$= -2w^2 + 1800w$

b. Vertex (450, 405000). The maximum pasture is 405,000 square feet and is obtained with a width of 450 feet.

c. w intercepts (0, 0) and (900, 0) When the width is 0 or 900, then the area is 0 square feet.

d. A intercept is (0, 0).

e.

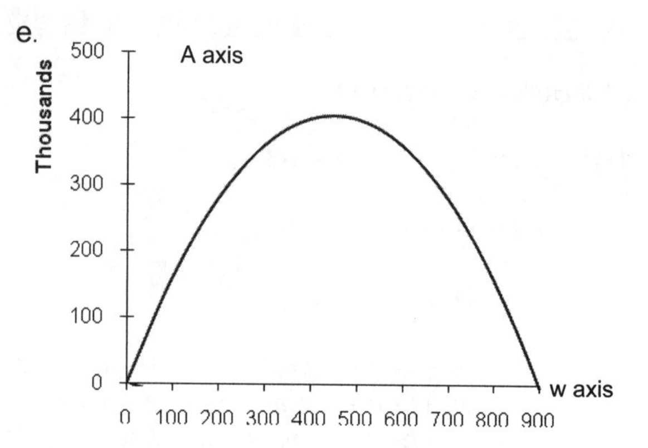

f. The maximum size of the pasture is obtained when the dimensions are 450 by 900 feet.

8. a. Vertex (215, –1.931).
The minimum high temperature for the year occurred on the 215th day and was –1.931° C.

b. d intercepts (94, 0) and (337,0)
On the 94th and 337th day of the year the high was zero.

c. T intercept (0, 4.1)
The high temperature on the last day of 2004 was 4.1° C.

d.

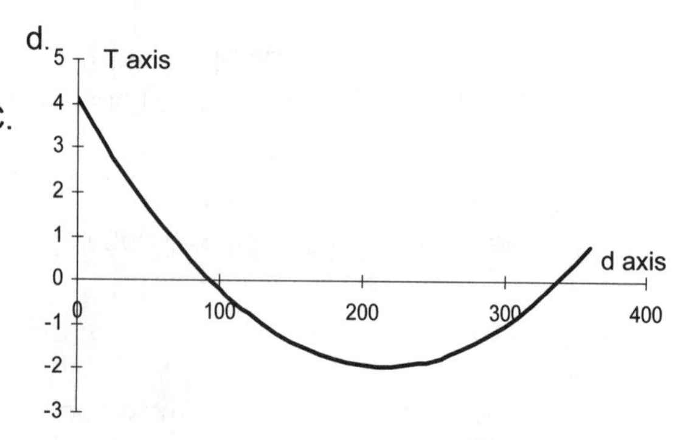

9. a. Vertex (36, -18.8).
The minimum temperature of hydrogen was –18.8 ° C and occurred at the 36th minute

b. m intercepts (55.4, 0), (16.61, 0)
The temperature of hydrogen was 0° C at the 55.4 and 16.61 minute mark of the experiment.

c. T intercept (0, 46).
46° C was the temperature at the start of the experiment.

d.

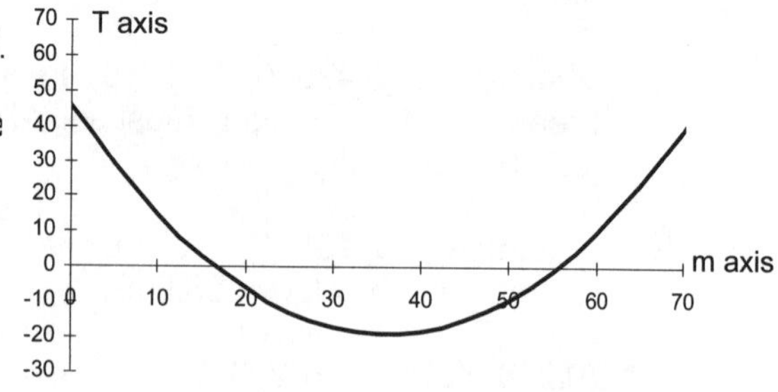

Reading and Writing Mathematics

10. The vertex is either the highest or lowest point of the graph.

11. $x = \frac{-b}{2a}$

12. Substitute the x coordinate of the vertex into the equation you are trying to graph.

13. x intercepts, y intercept, and the vertex

14. It depends if the coefficient of the squared term is positive or negative.

15. Point D. (19, 0)

16. Didn't write the first step, $P = (-1.4g^2 + 64g) - (0.6g^2 - 28g + 425)$, in finding the profit equation.
Didn't write the profit equation equal to P.
In part b, she didn't set anything equal to a variable.
In part b, she didn't write any of the points as ordered pairs.
The graph didn't contain the axis and the points weren't labeled on the graph.

Section 4.4 Factoring page 379

Skill building Exercises

1. a. 18 b. 4 c. 2x

2. 9 and 4

3. 6 and –5

Practice Exercises

4. a. $3(2x + 3)$ b. $7(2x - 1)$ c. $-10(x - 5)$

d. $2x(4x - 3)$ e. $9x(3x - 2)$ f. $5x^2(3x - 1)$

g. $(x + 6)(x + 1)$ h. $(x - 5)(x - 3)$ i. $(x - 3)(x - 3)$

j. $(x - 6)(x + 3)$ k. $(x + 10)(x + 3)$ l. $(x - 5)(x - 10)$

m. $(x - 10)(x + 10)$ n. $(x - 6)(x + 6)$ o. $(x - 9)(x + 9)$

5. a. $x = -1, -6$ b. $x = -5, 10$ c. $x = -1.667, 0$

Reading and Writing Mathematics

6. An algebraic expression is factor if when evaluating it the last operation is multiplication.

7. a. $2x(x + 4)$ b. $(x - 3)(x + 1)$

8. a. The second factor should be $(2x + 1)$

b. The second factor should be $(x + 3)$.

Chapter 4 Review Test page 385

1. a. $P = -2x^2 + 40x - 72$

b. vertex (10,128) The maximum profit will be \$128,000 when they make 10 yachts per month.

c. x intercepts (2, 0) and (18, 0) The company will break even if they sell 2 or 18 yachts

d. y intercept (0, –72) If they don't sell any yachts they will loose \$72,000.

e.

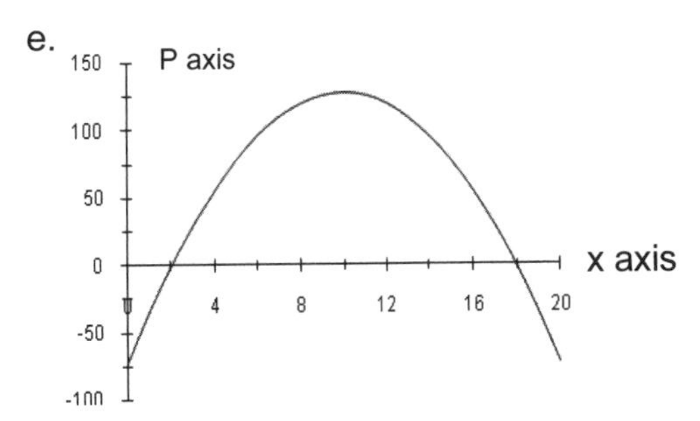

f. (3.181, 35) (16.82, 35)
In order for the company to make \$35,000 for the month they must sell 3 or 17 yachts.

2.

a. $A = W(80 - 3W)$
$= -3W^2 + 80W$

b. vertex (13.3, 533.3) The maximum size of the pen will be 533.3square meters when the width is 13.3 meters.

c. W intercepts (0, 0) (26.67, 0)

d. A intercept (0, 0)

e.

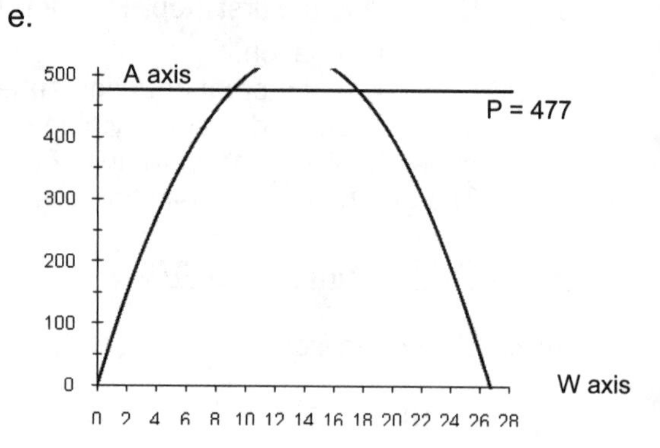

f. (9,477)(17.67, 477) To have a pen with an area of 477 square meters the width must be 9 or 17.67 meters.

3.

a. Vertex (8.5, –12.68) The minimum temperature of –12.68C will occur at the 8.5th minute.

b. m intercepts (2, 0), (15, 0)
The temperature will be zero at the 2 and 15 minutes.

c. T intercept (0, 9) The temperature was 9C at the start of the semester.

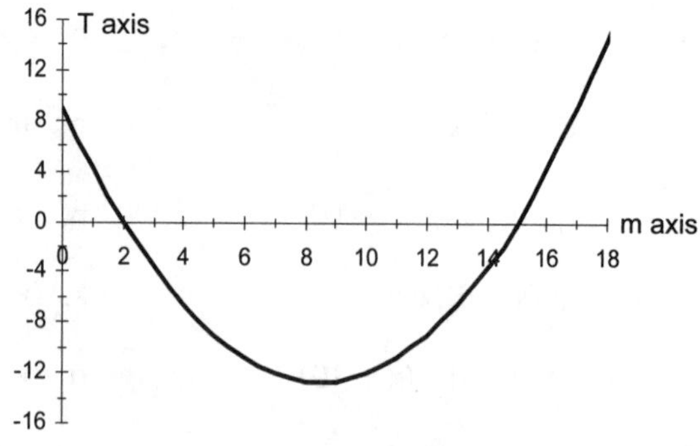

4. $-3x^2 + 22x - 30$

5. a. $3x^2 - 19x - 40$ b. $x^2 - 10x + 25$

6. a. $4x(x+2)$ b. $(x+9)(x-2)$

7. $x = 6, 2$

8. Subtract 7 from both sides.
Identify a, b and c for the quadratic equation.
Substitute a, b, and c into the quadratic formula.
Evaluate the square root using a calculator.
Simplify the denominator
Separate into the two solutions
Simplify the fractions using a calculator

9. $$x = \frac{-(-5) \pm \sqrt{(-5)^2 - 4(1)(2)}}{2(1)}$$ Should have substituted –2 instead of 2.

Final Review Test page 407

1. 73

2. $-10 - 12x + 8$

3. $x = -1.75$

4. $4 \leq x < 10$

5. a. $x^2 - 2x - 35$ b. $x^2 + 14x + 49$

6. The total profit for the six years is 3 million dollars.

7 $P = 1.25g - 800$

8. $c = 0.12(m - 15) + 2.25$

9. a. $t > 9$, Z-Mart will have more than 278 stores after the year 2014.

   b. $7 < t < 15$, Z-Mart will have between 232 and 416 stores between 2012 and 2020.

10. The percent increase in the U. S. population between the years 1800 and 1810 was 41.5%

11. The population of the U. S. increased an average of 0.22 million people per year

12. a. 4.3×10^6 b. 0.00024

13. a. x^7 b. $9x^8$ c. $\frac{1}{x^3}$

    d. $\frac{9}{x^5}$ e. 1 f. $\frac{8}{x^4}$

14. It will take 43.2 minutes to get to work if you live 15 miles away.

15. You live10.45 miles away if it takes 30 minutes to get to work.

16. $\frac{-5x^4}{4}$

17. a. $\frac{9}{x^5}$ b. $\frac{x^5}{16}$ c. $\frac{7-2x}{8x}$

18. a. $8x(x+2)$ b. $(x - 7)(x+3)$ c. $(x - 9)(x + 9)$

19. a. $x = 7.8$ b. $x = 0.2466$

20. The 16 oz jar costs 24.88 cents per ounce and the 20 oz jar costs 24.95 cents per ounce. So the 16 oz jar is the better buy.

21. Selena has to get a 73 on the final to get a 70 for the course.

22. (5, 85) Both companies charge 85 cents for a 5 minute phone call.

23.

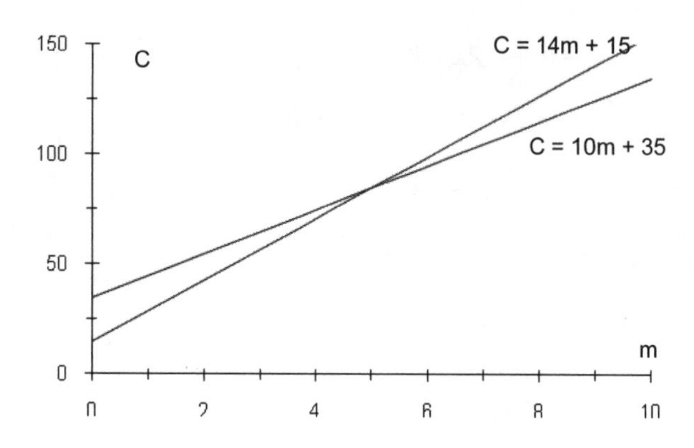

24. (0, 35), The basic rate for Ringer is 35 cents.

25. Slope is 10, Ringer charges 10 cents per minute

26. The x intercept is (–205, 0).

The y intercept is (0, 41).

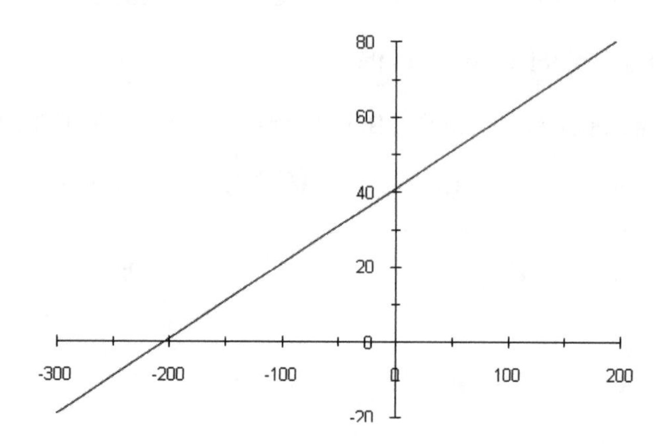

27. The monthly payments will be $95.38.

28. The arrow will be 100 feet in the air in 1.25 or 4.68 seconds.

29. $P = -x^2 + 24x - 60$

30. Vertex (12, 84) The maximum profit will be 84 thousand when they sell 12 presses.

31. X intercepts (2.84, 0) (21.17, 0) The breakeven points are 3 and 21

32. P intercept (0, 0 –60). The start up costs are 60 thousand dollars.

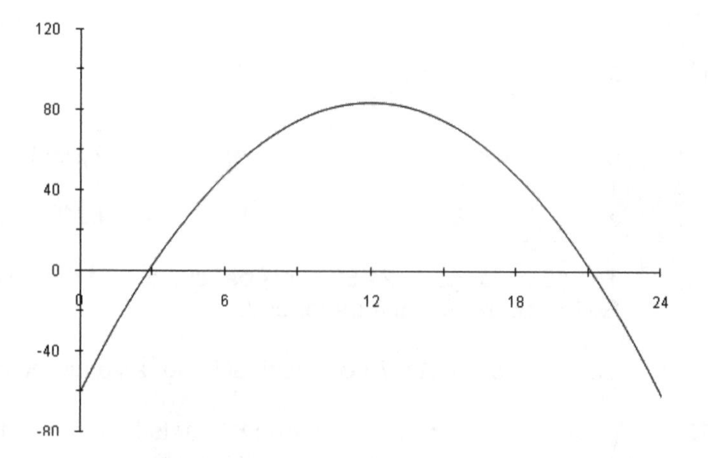

Signed Numbers, Drill and Practice page 415

1. -1 2. -4 3. -7 4. -4 5. 5 6. -3 7. -7 8. -2 9. -5 10. -3 11. -14

12. -9 13. 6 14. -4 15. -23 16. -2 17. -9 18. -13 19. 7 20. -8 21. -15

22. -3 23. -20 24. 15 25. -54 26. 21 27. -35 28. -72 29. 54 30. -56 31. -40

32. -36 33. 24 34. 14 35. 0 36. 560 37. -3 38. 3 39. 9 40. -9 41. 6

42. -9 43. 5 44. -8 45. 0 46. 6 47. undefined 48. 5 49. 9 50. 25

51. 64 52. 16 53. 49 54. 0 55. 81 56. 100 57. -12 58. -19 59. 2 60. 15

61. -24 62. -51 63. -19 64. 1 65. -33 66 78 67. -2 68. -15 69. -5 70. undefined

71. 0

Simplifying Algebraic Expressions, Drill and Practice page 416

1. $12x-9$	2. $5x+5$	3. $-x-13$	4. $8x+13$
5. $-6x+8$	6. $-38x+32$	7. $-x+10$	8. $2x+2$
9. $-5x+15$	10. $-19x+12$	11. $-20x-33$	12. $-13x+25$
13. $-2x-34$	14. $-10x-1$	15. $30x-11$	16. $x+3y-5$
17. $7x-3y-3$	18. $20x-4y$	19. $-7x+7z-15$	20. $22y+3z$
21. $8y-7z-4$	22. $5x-14$	23. $11y-18x-18$	24. $-20Z+42$

Solving Linear Equations, Drill and Practice page 417

1. $x = 4$	2. $x = 5$	3. $x = -2$	4. $x = 4.5$
5. $x = .5$	6. $x = -2.167$	7. $x = 1$	8. $x = 0.8571$
9. $x = 1$	10. $x = -0.8333$	11. $x = -3$	12. $x = 5.455$
13. $x = -0.3$	14. $x = 1.813$	15. $x = 20$	16. $x = 13.5$
17. $x = 6$	18. $x = -2.25$	19. $x = 0.5625$	20. $x = 0.8182$
21. $x = 1$	22. $x = -1.833$	23. $x = -4.929$	24. $x = 1.538$
25. $x = -2.444$	26. $x = -5.75$	27. $x = 0.34$	28. $x = -2.1$
29. $x = 2.833$	30. $x = 7.777$		

Inequalities, Drill and Practice page 418

1. $x > -4$
2. $x > -3.4$
3. $x > -5.667$
4. $x \geq 11.75$
5. $x \geq 4.5$
6. $x \geq -9.429$
7. $x > -1.833$
8. $x > 0$
9. $x \geq 6.167$
10. $x \leq 17.5$
11. $x > 6$
12. $x > 0.3077$
13. $x < -2$
14. $x \leq 3$
15. $x \geq -4.429$
16. $-4.667 \leq x < -0.3333$
17. $2.25 \leq x < 8.25$
18. $-6 < x \leq -3.25$
19. $-7.8 < x < 1.8$
20. $-4.333 < x < -3.333$
21. $-2.5 \leq x < 2.5$
22. $-5 \leq x \leq -2.4$
23. $2.429 < x < 4.286$
24. $-4 < x < 0.5$

Graphing Lines by Plotting Points, Drill and Practice page 419

1.

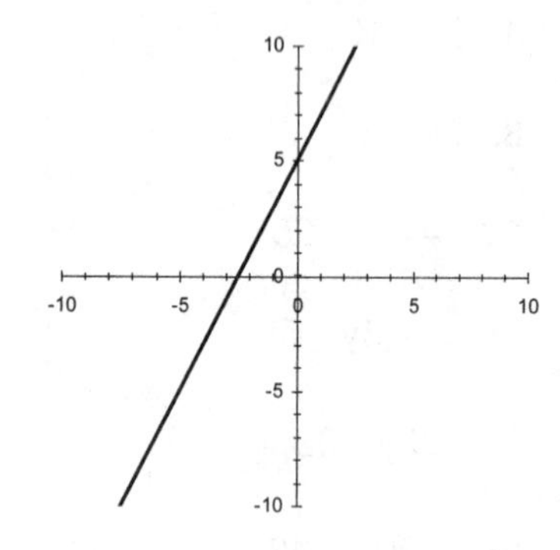

2

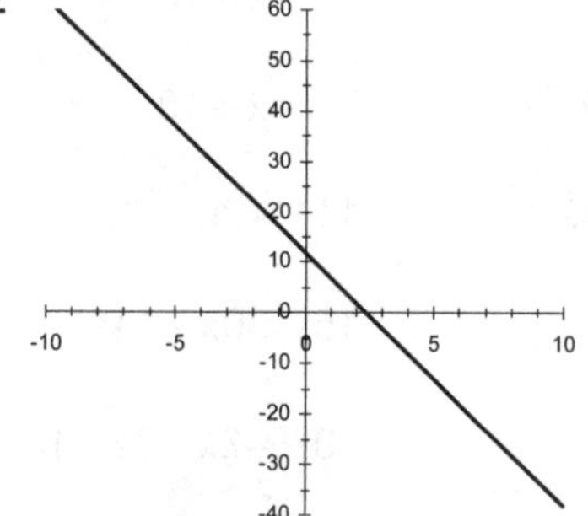

3

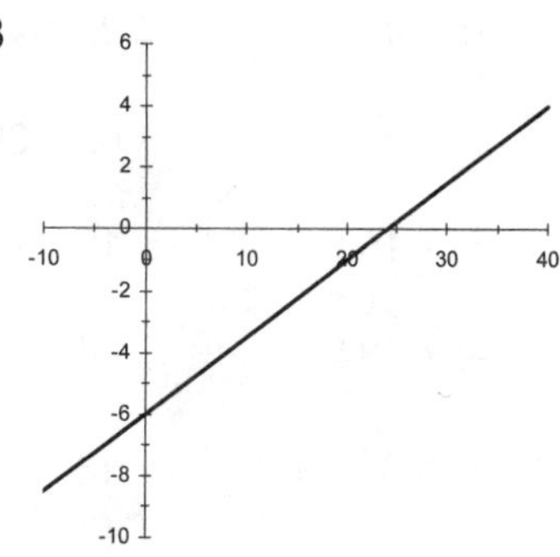

4.

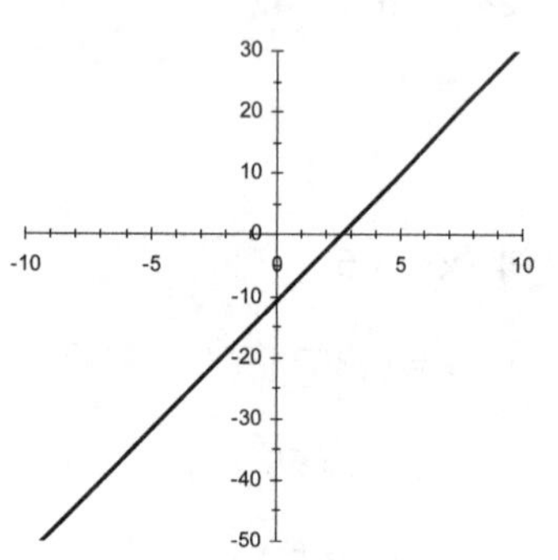

5.

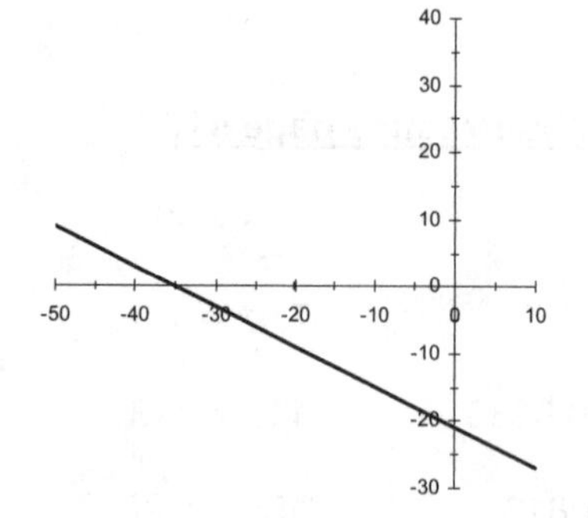

6

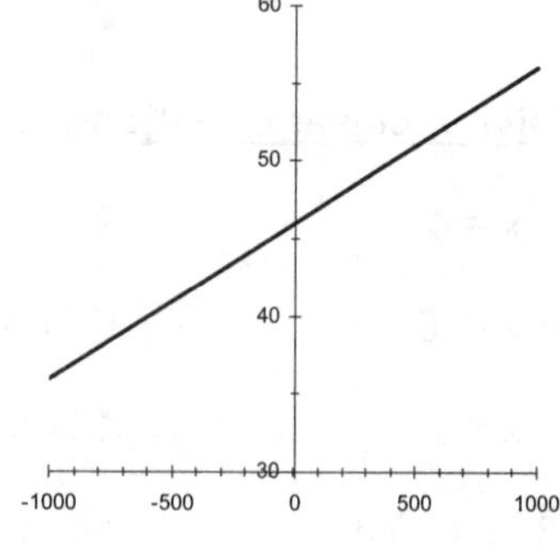

7.

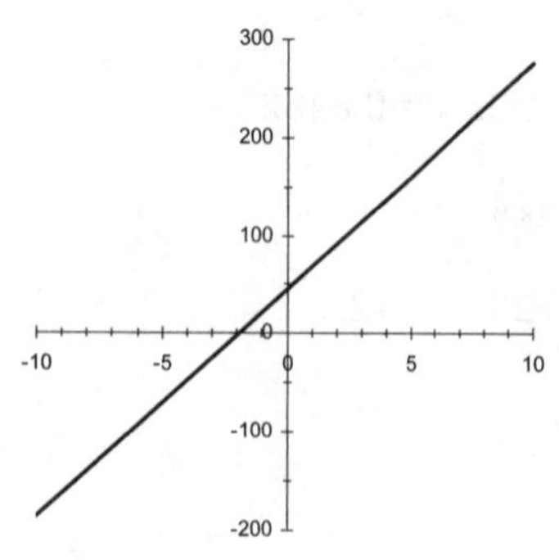

8.

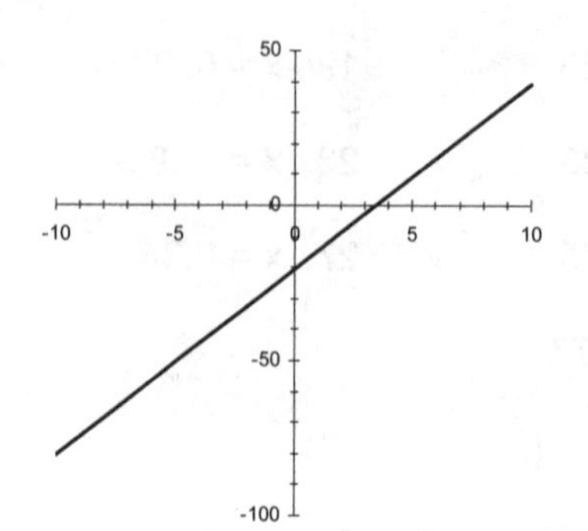

9.

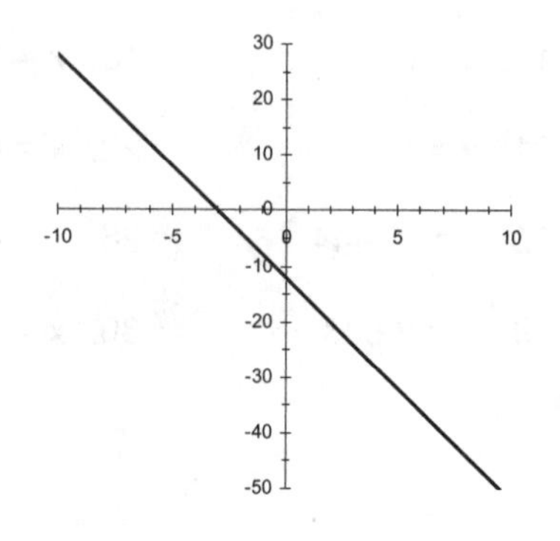

10.

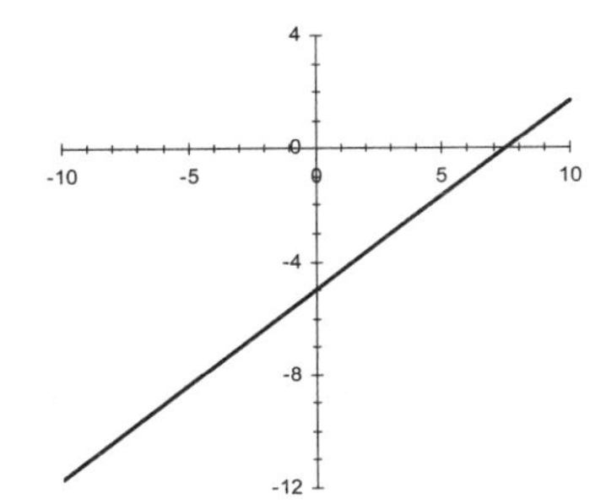

11

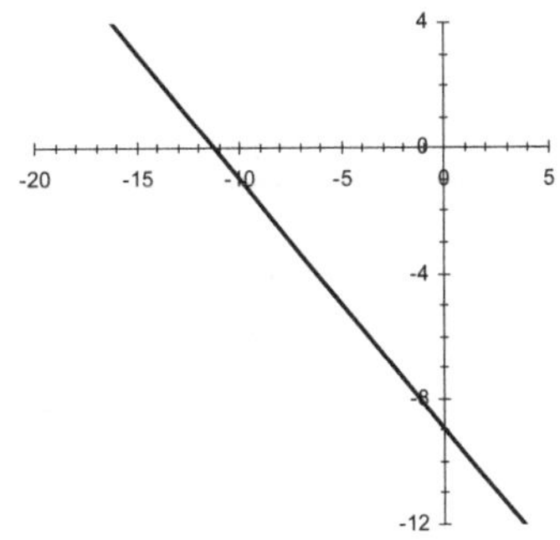

12.

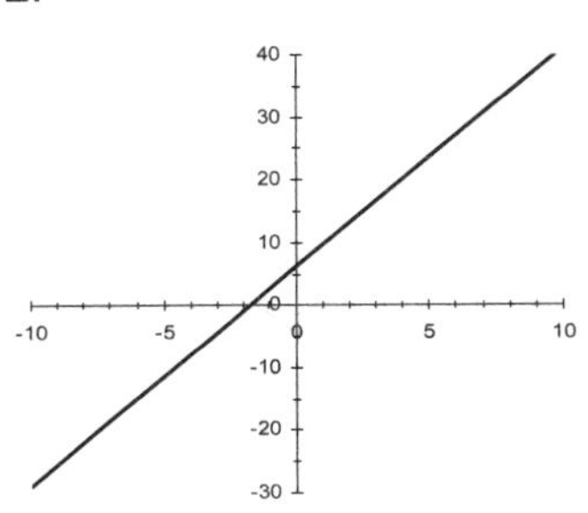

13.

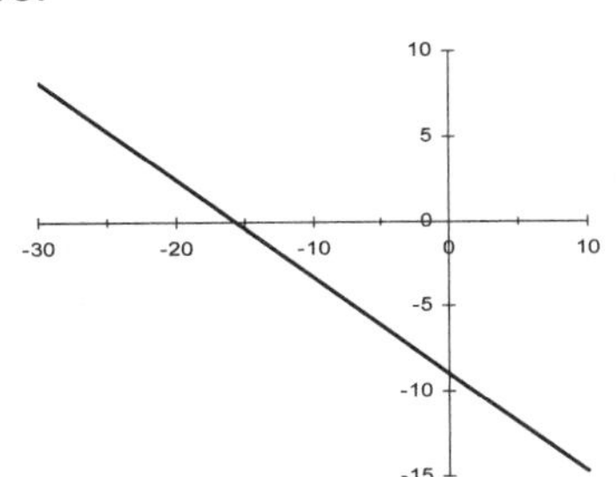

14.

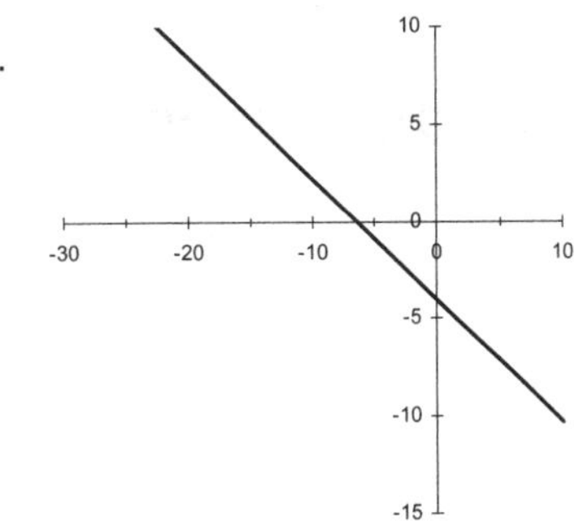

15.

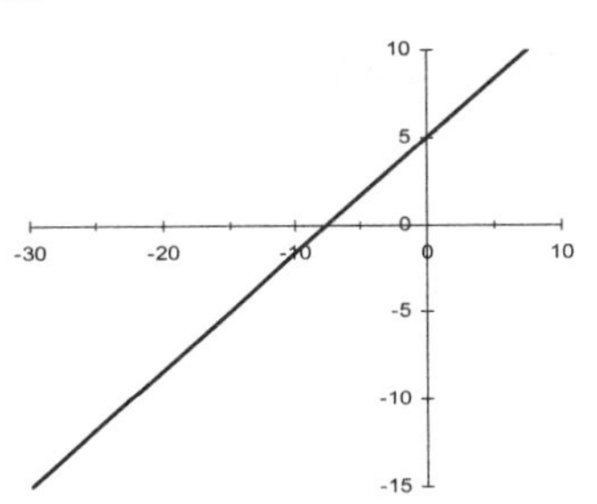

16.

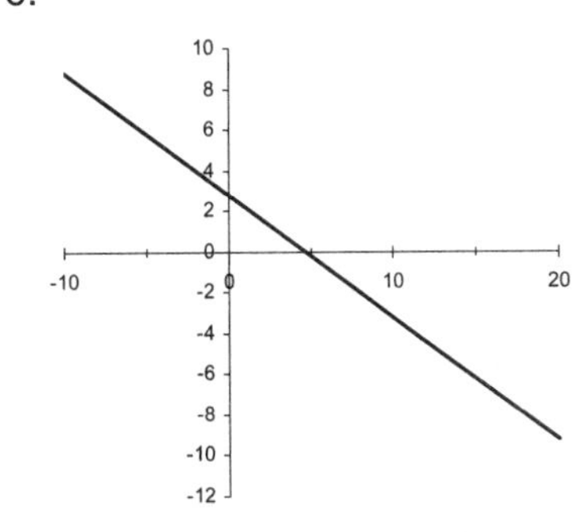

17.

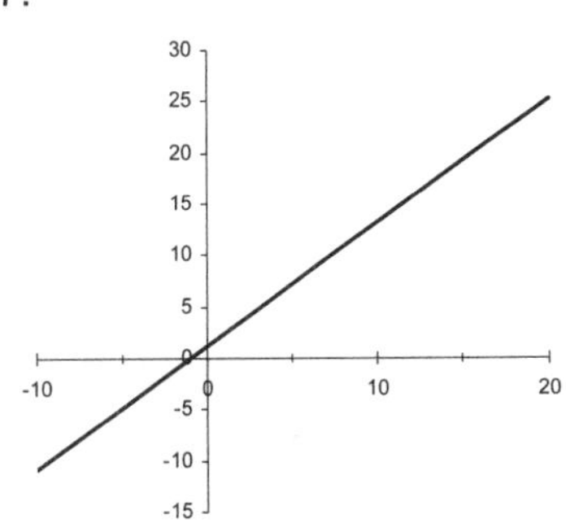

18.

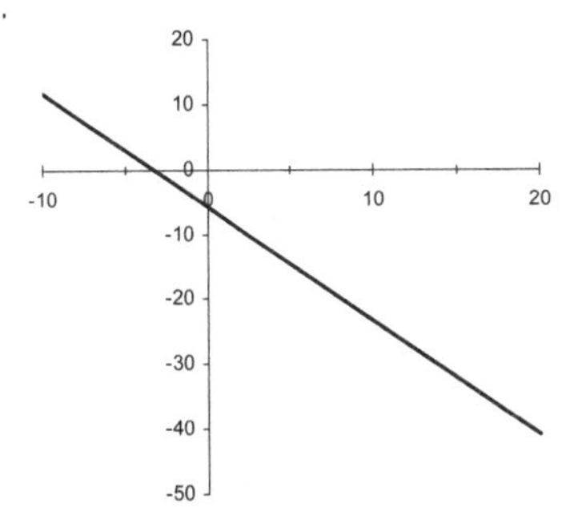

19.

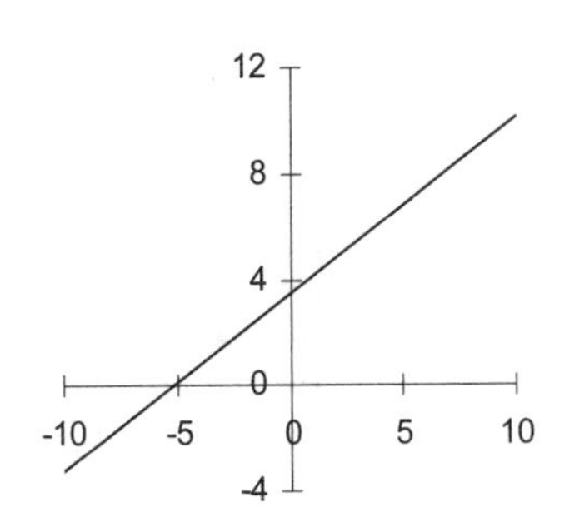

20.

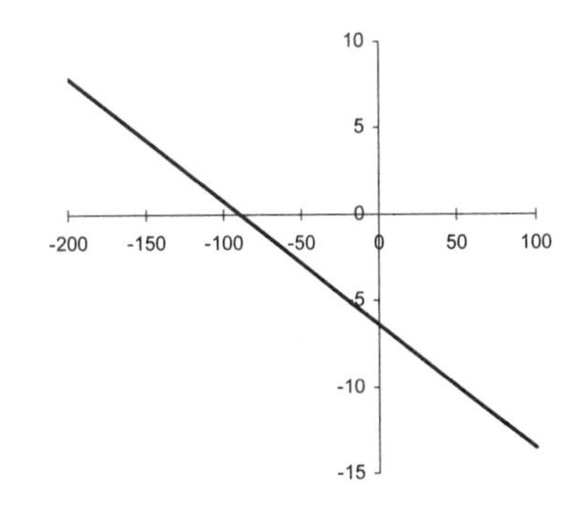

21.

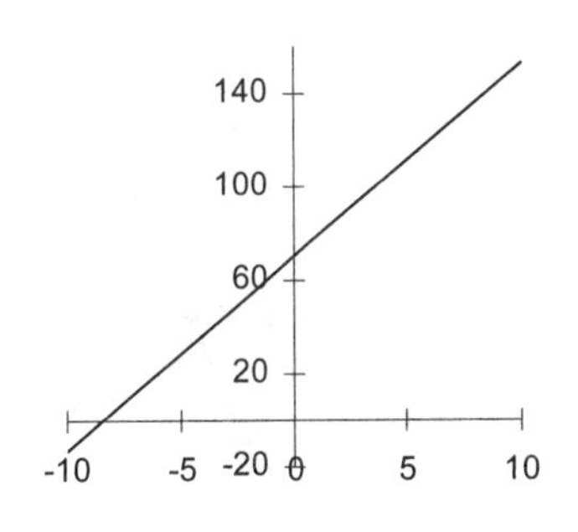

22.

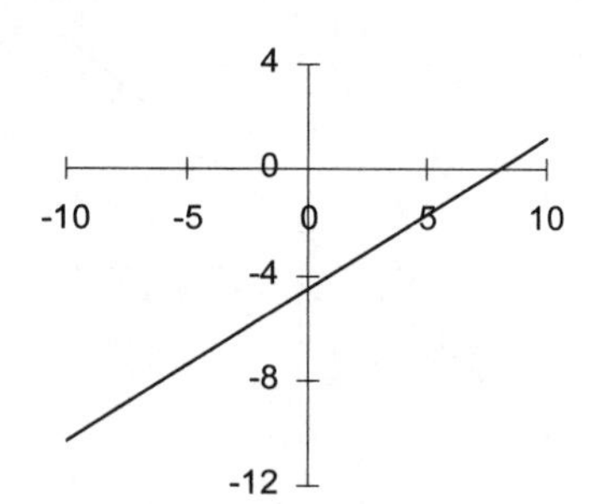

23

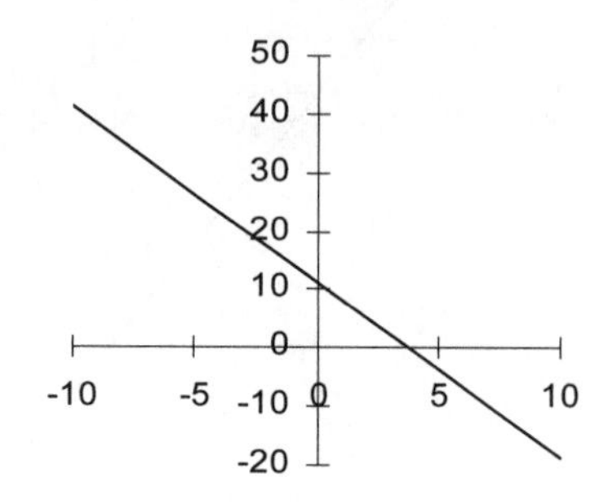

24.

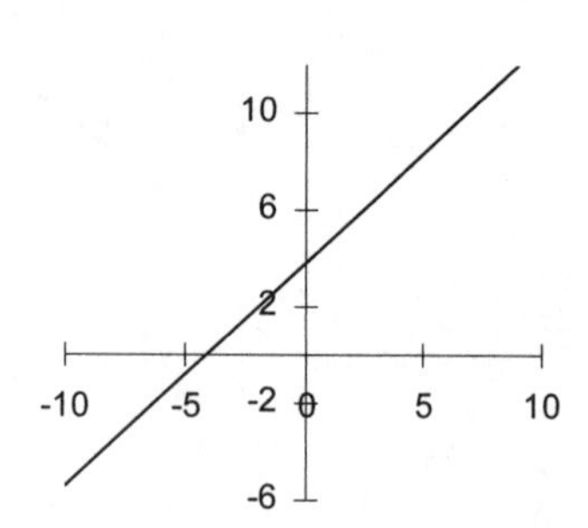

Graphing Lines By Plotting Intercepts, Drill and Practice page 420

1.

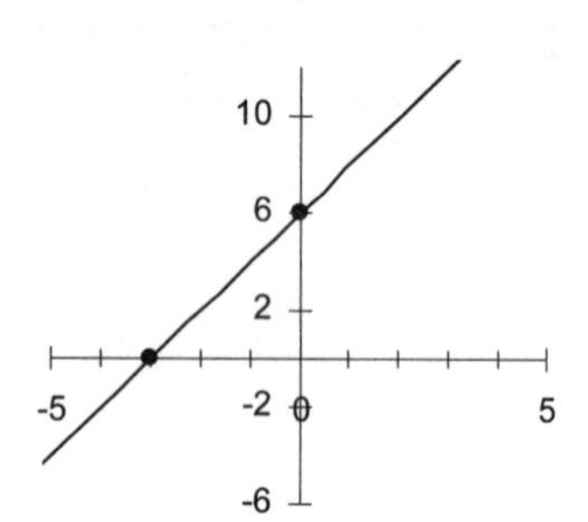

2.

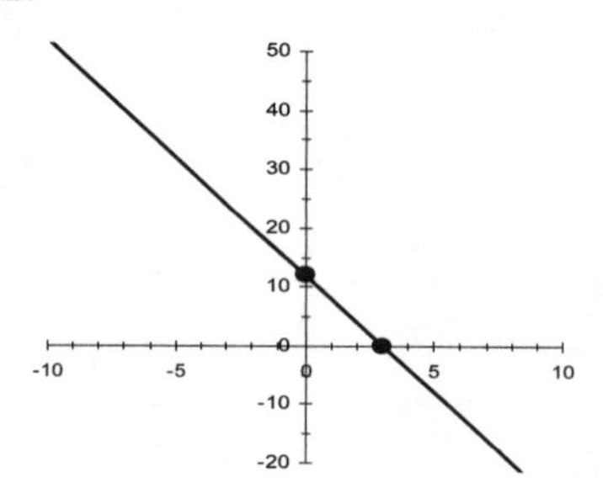

3.

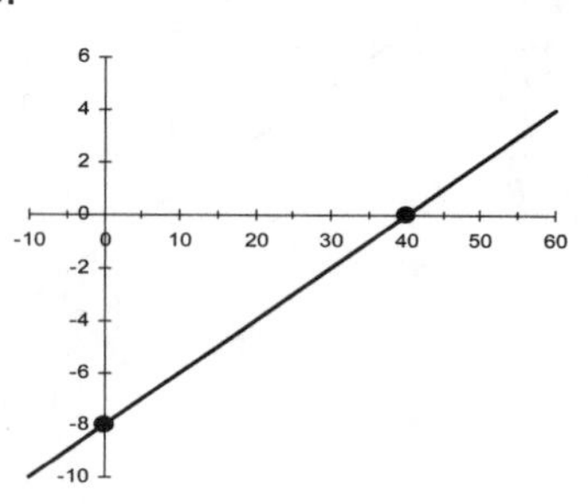

4.

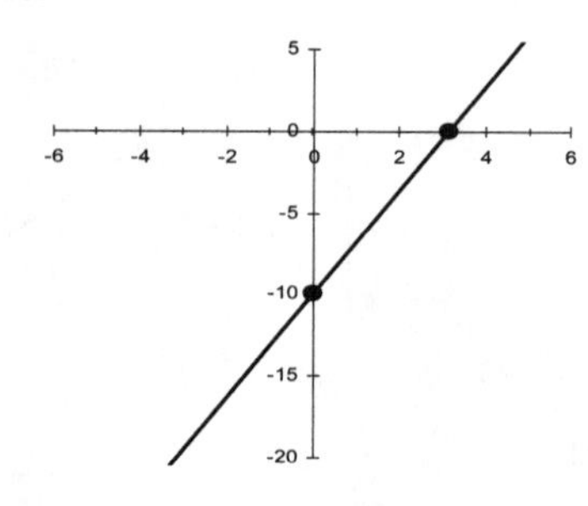

5.

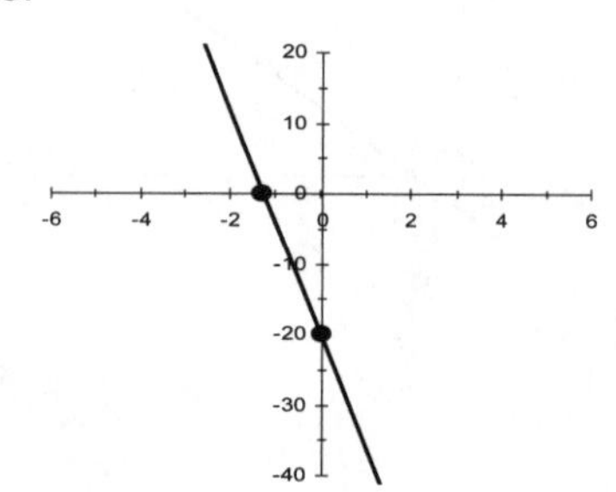

6.

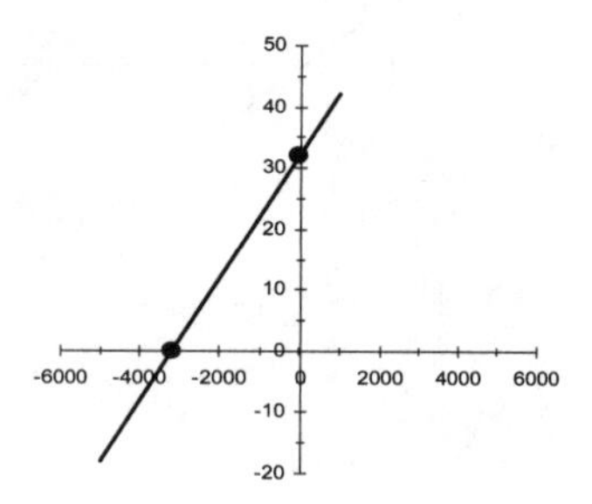

7.

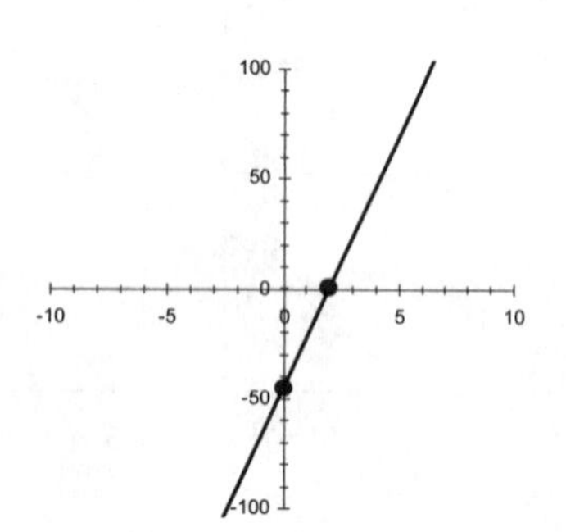

8.

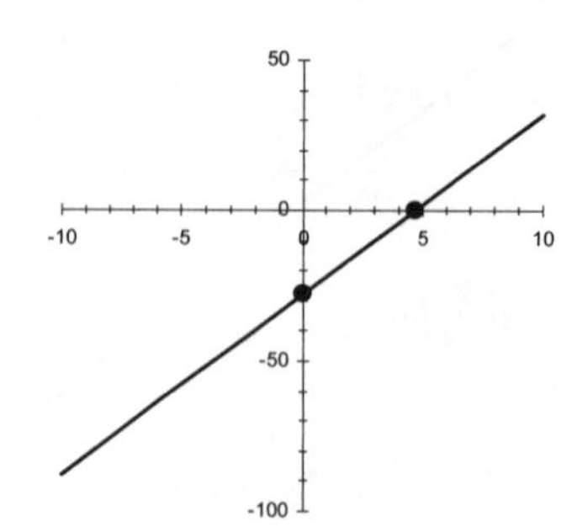

9.

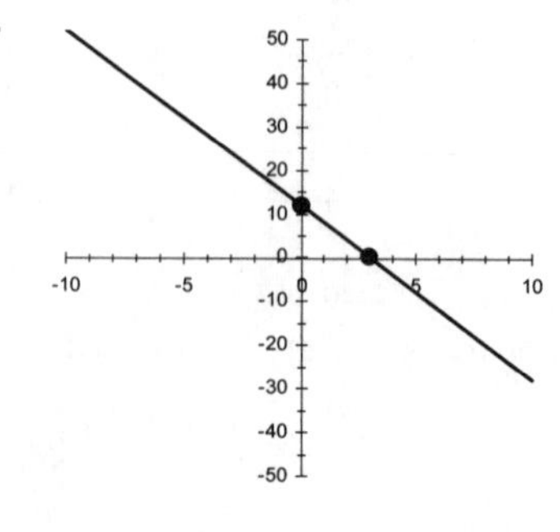

10.

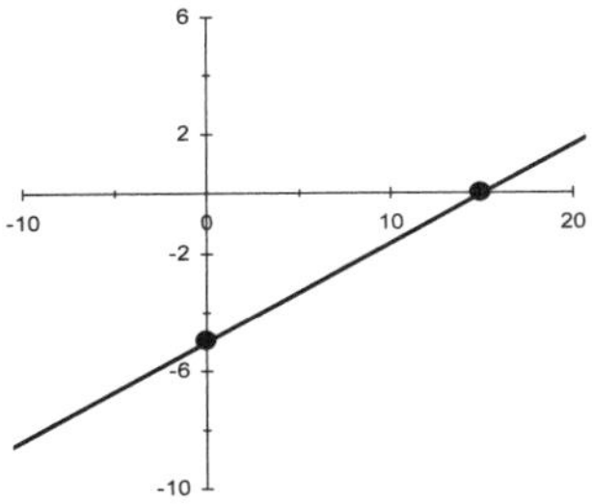

11.

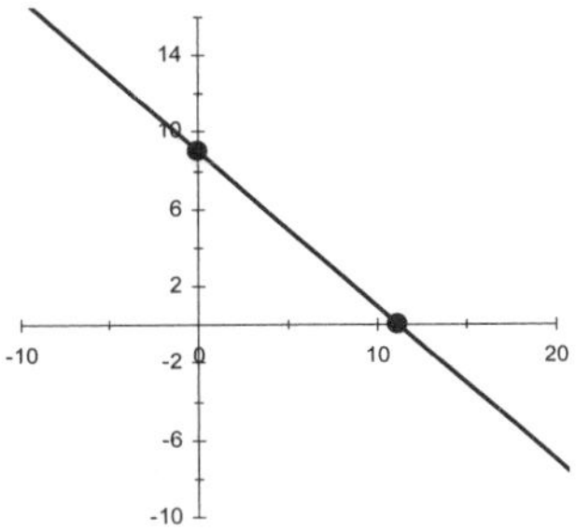

12.

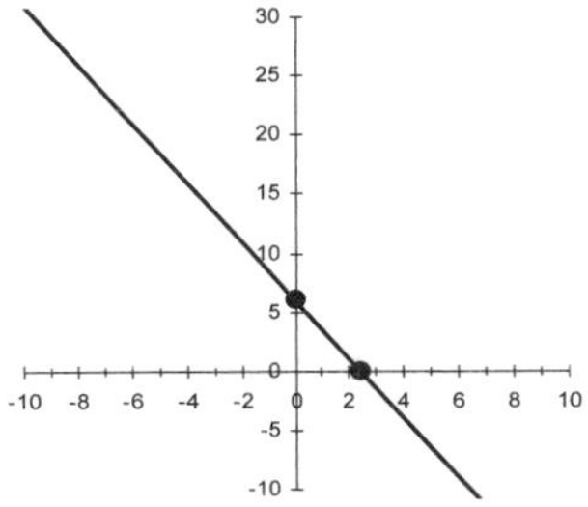

13.

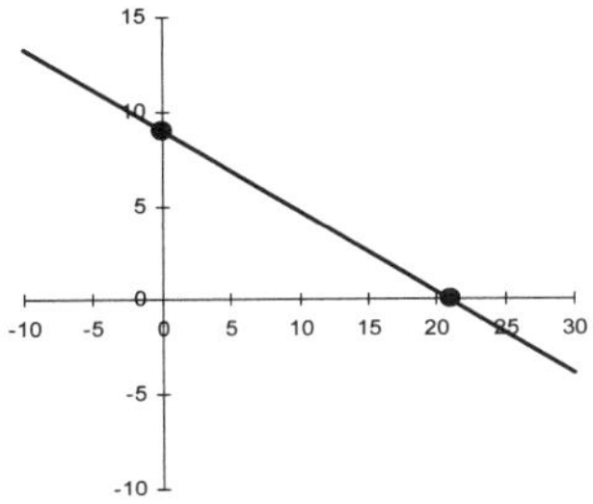

14.

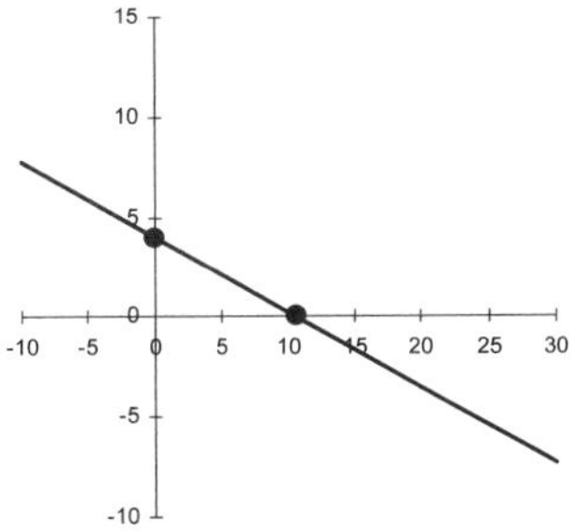

15.

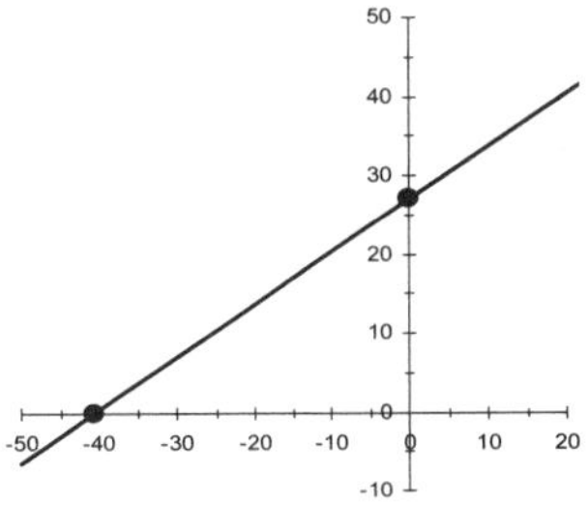

16.

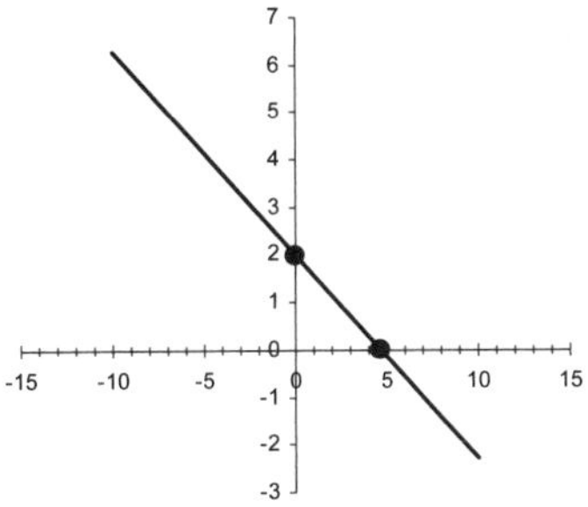

17.

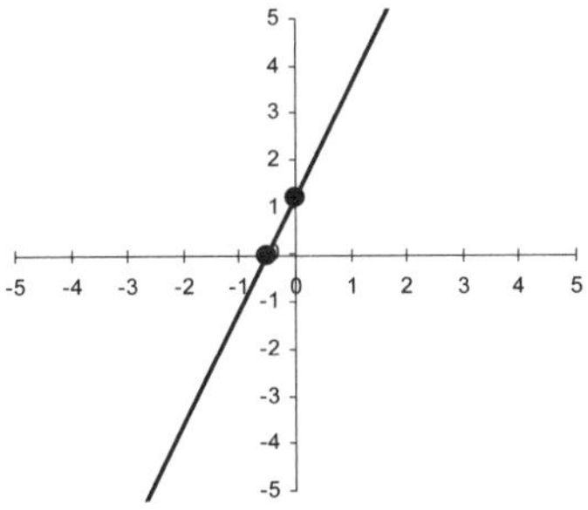

18.

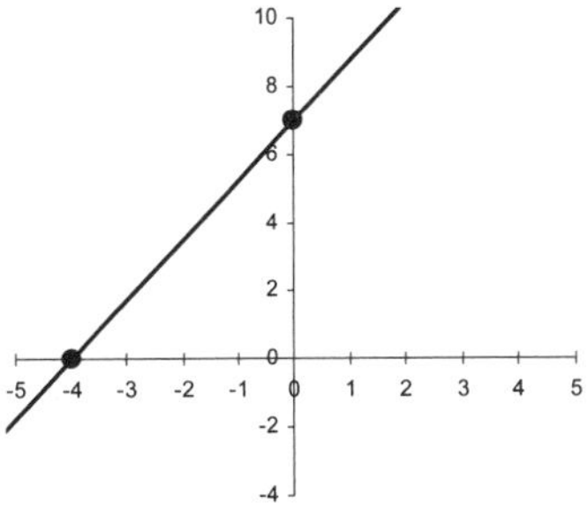

19.

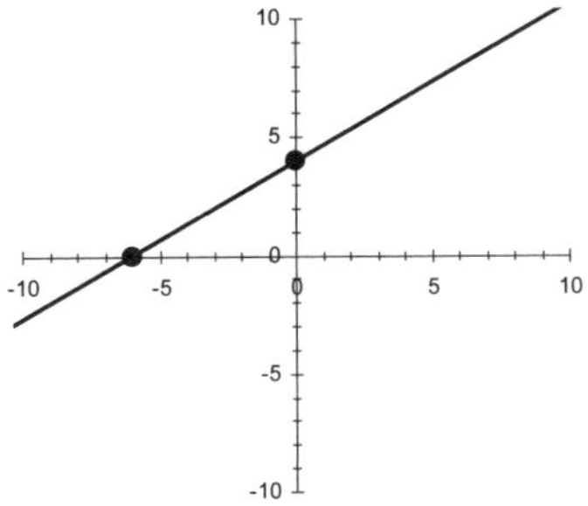

20.

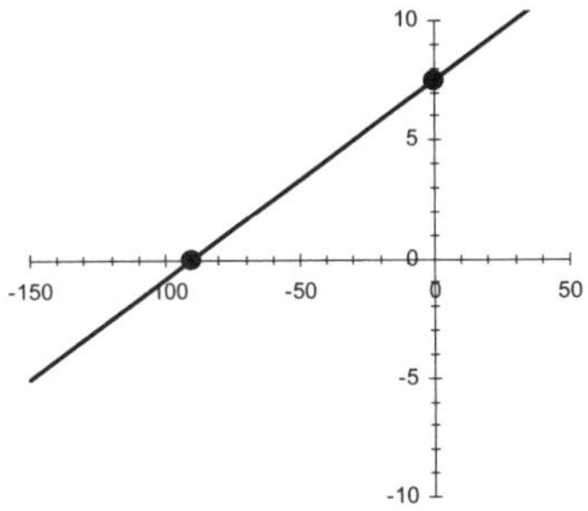

21.

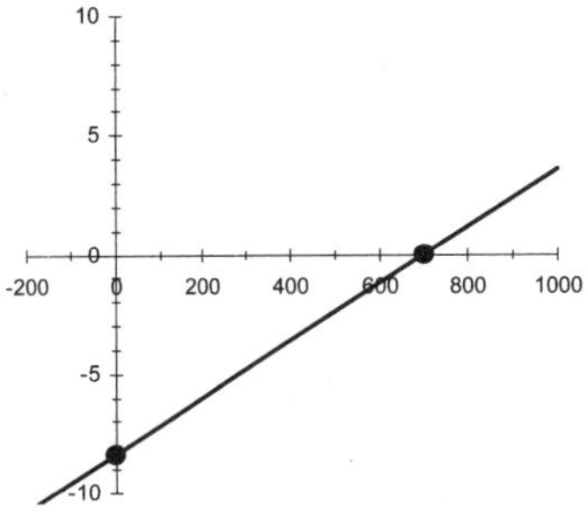

22.

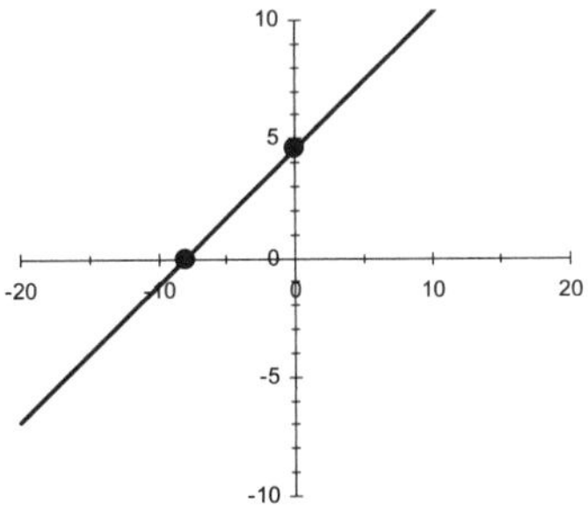

23.

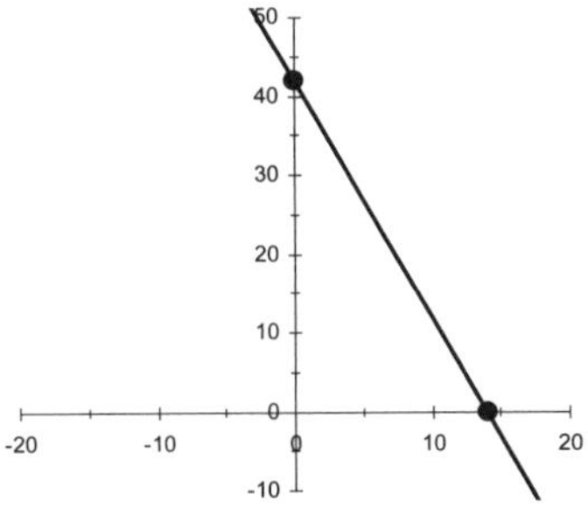

24.

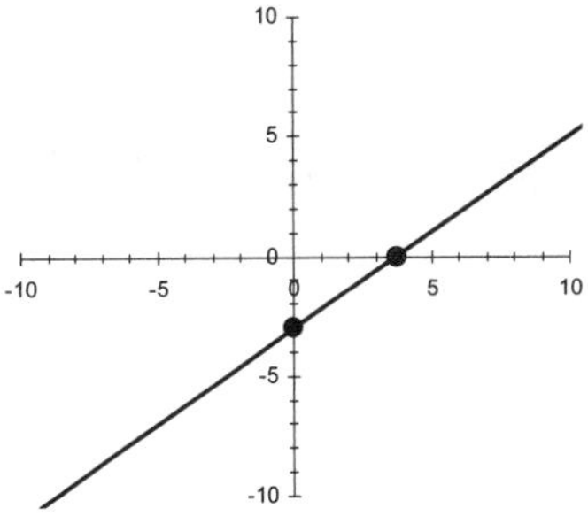

25.

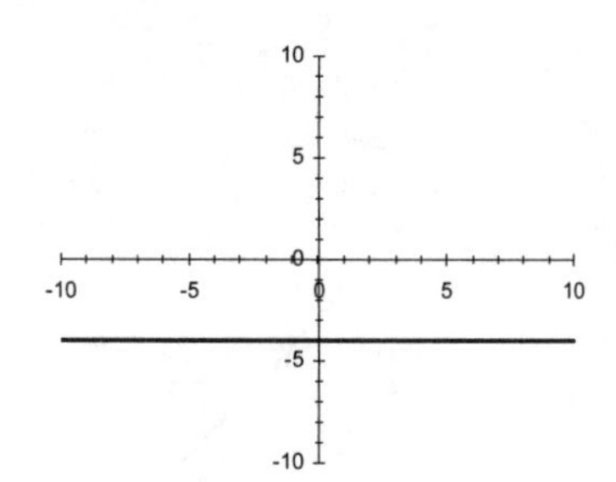

26.

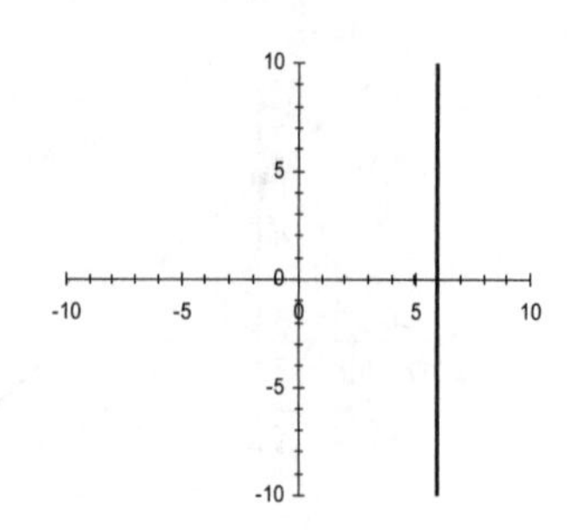

27.

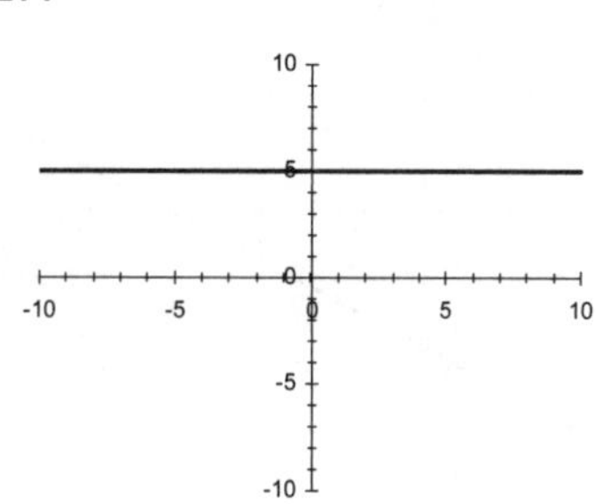

28.

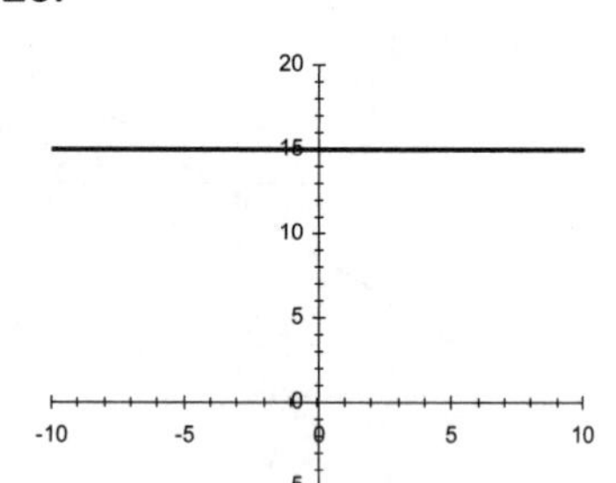

29.

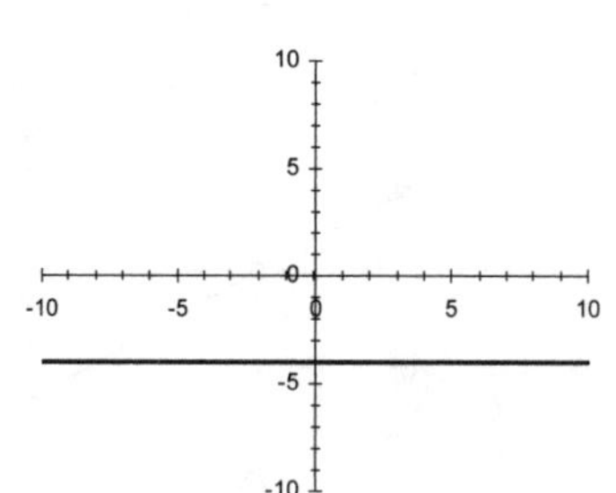

30.

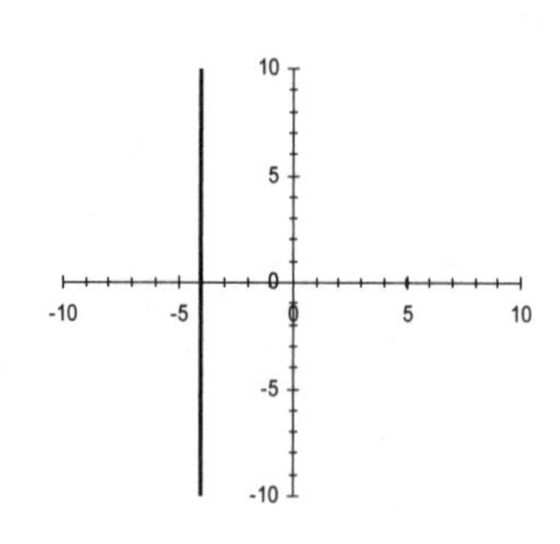

31.

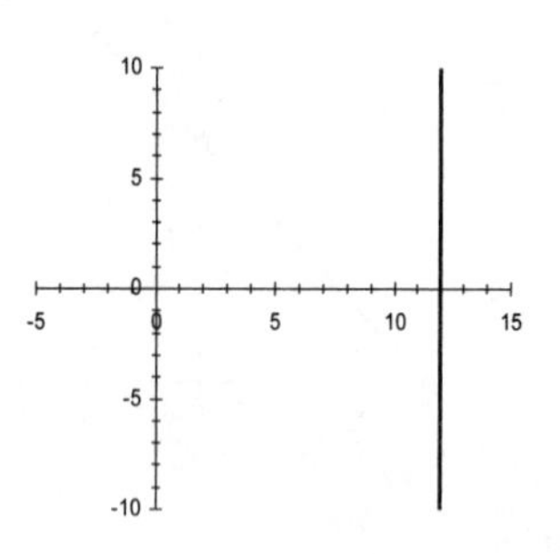

32.

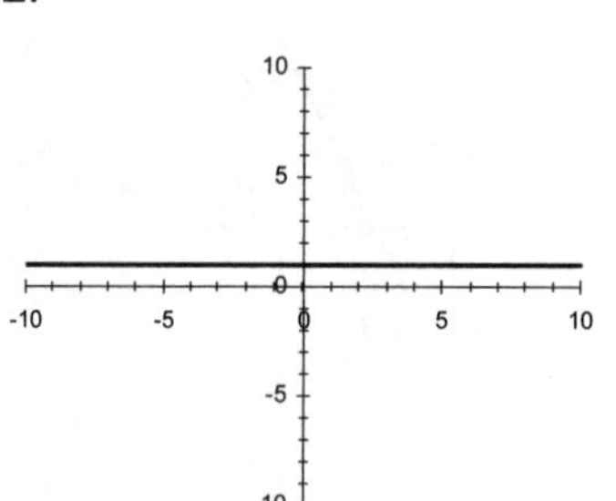

33.

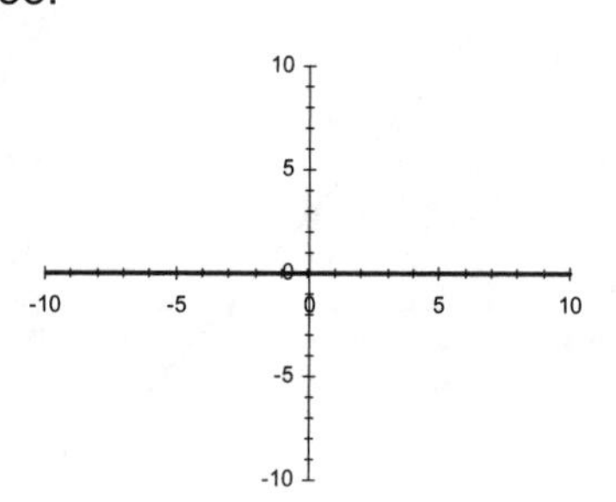

Slope, Drill and Practice page 421

1. m = -0.0909
2. m = -10
3. m = 2.5
4. undefined
5. m = 1
6. m = 0
7. m = 0.6593
8. m = 0.38
9. m = 0.9398
10. m = 0
11. m = 0.6389
12. m = 2.5
13. m = 3.2, (0, -10)
14. m = -16, (0. -20)
15. m = 0.01, (0, 32)
16. m = 23, (0, -45)
17. m = 6, (0, -28)
18. m = -4, (0, 12)
19. $m = \frac{1}{3}$, (0, -5)
20. $m = \frac{-4}{5}$, (0, 9)
21. $m = \frac{-5}{2}$, (0, 6)

Properties of Exponents, Drill and Practice page 422

1. x^7
2. $\frac{1}{x}$
3. $3x^3$
4. $\frac{1}{x}$
5. $7x^8$
6. $5x^2$
7. $81x^8$
8. $25x^6$
9. $81x^{20}$
10. $16x^{10}$
11. $7{,}776x^{15}$
12. $\frac{25}{x^6}$

13. $\frac{4}{x^3}$ 14. $\frac{2}{x}$ 15. $\frac{21}{x^7}$ 16. $\frac{2x^4}{3}$ 17. $\frac{2}{5x^4}$ 18. $\frac{x^5}{7}$

19. $\frac{x^2}{4}$ 20. $5x^2$ 21. 3 22. $\frac{1}{8x^4}$ 23. $\frac{x^3}{2}$ 24. $\frac{3}{x^3}$

25. $\frac{3}{2x^2}$ 26. $\frac{x^2}{4}$ 27. $\frac{x}{7}$ 28. $\frac{1}{16x^8}$ 29. $\frac{-x^{15}}{8}$ 30. $\frac{1}{9x^4}$

31. $\frac{x^3}{7}$ 32. $\frac{x^{21}}{27}$ 33. $\frac{1}{216x^6}$ 34. $\frac{16}{x^{12}}$ 35. $\frac{27x^6}{125}$ 36. $\frac{625x^8}{1{,}296}$

37. $\frac{49}{9x^6}$ 38. $\frac{125x^3}{216}$ 39. $\frac{16x^4}{25}$ 40. 1 41. $120x^7y^4$ 42. $6x^4y^4$

43. $27x^6y^{12}$ 44. $625x^{12}y^8$ 45. $512x^6y^8$ 46. $\frac{3x^2}{y}$ 47. $\frac{27}{8x^6y^6}$ 48. $\frac{9y^{12}}{25x^{10}}$

Introduction to Algebraic Fractions, Drill and Practice page 423

1. $\frac{x}{2}$ 2. $-3x^2$ 3. 6 4. $\frac{1}{7x^2}$ 5. $\frac{x^5}{8}$ 6. $\frac{-7}{x^2}$

7. $\frac{1}{3x^2y}$ 8. $\frac{2y}{x}$ 9. $\frac{xy^3}{5}$ 10. $\frac{1}{15}$ 11. $\frac{3}{4}$ 12. $\frac{5}{4}$

13. $\frac{8}{75}$ 14. $\frac{9}{x^3}$ 15. $9x^2$ 16. $\frac{48}{x^4}$ 17. $\frac{6}{x^2}$ 18. $\frac{9}{10x}$

19. $\frac{2}{3x^2}$ 20. $\frac{6}{x}$ 21. $\frac{8x^3}{3}$ 22. x^2 23. 2 24. $\frac{2}{x^2}$

25. $9x^2$ 26. $\frac{2}{9x^2}$ 27. $\frac{56x}{3}$ 28. $\frac{15}{x}$ 29. 5 30. $\frac{8}{15x}$

31. $\frac{12}{y}$ 32. $\frac{4y^2}{3x}$ 33. $\frac{2y^2}{x}$ 34. $\frac{3x^5}{5y^3}$ 35. $\frac{3x^6}{y^3}$ 36. $\frac{2x}{3y}$

Adding and Subtracting Algebraic Fractions, Drill and Practice page 424

1. $\frac{11}{5}$ 2. $\frac{1}{3}$ 3. 1 4. $\frac{-1}{x}$ 5. $\frac{3}{x}$ 6. $\frac{4}{3x^2}$

7. $\frac{7}{18}$ 8. $\frac{9}{8}$ 9. $\frac{5}{36}$ 10. $\frac{x}{12}$ 11. $\frac{17x}{8}$ 12. $\frac{-13x}{36}$

13. $\frac{3x+5}{x^2}$ 14. $\frac{7}{4x}$ 15. $\frac{25-12x^2}{40x}$ 16. $\frac{35+6y^2}{60y^3}$

17. $\frac{6-15m^2}{48m^3}$ or $\frac{2-5m^2}{18m^3}$ 18. $\frac{3y^2-2y}{42}$ 19. $\frac{8w}{27}$

20. $\frac{25+27x}{60x^2}$ 21. $\frac{75z+4}{80z^3}$ 22. $\frac{2+3x^2}{x^2}$ 23. $\frac{7w^3-4}{w^3}$

24. $\frac{7x^3-5}{15x^2}$ 25. $\frac{3x-29}{18}$ 26. $\frac{21+x}{6x}$ 27. $\frac{28y^2-20y+45}{80y}$

28. $\frac{w^3+11w^2-36}{9w^3}$ 29. $\frac{3y-14}{20y}$ 30. $\frac{5x^2-31x+16}{120x}$

Solving Equations with Fractions, Drill and Practice page 425

1. x = 13.5 2. x = 2 3. x = 8 4. x = 0.1667 5. x = -0.125 6. x = 1.5

7. x = -0.6 8. x = 1.2 9. x = -2 10. x = 4.8 11. x = 12.25 12. x = 20.4

13. x = 3 14. x = 3.667 15. x = 0.6522 16. x = -12.38 17. x = -3 18. x = 4.625

19. x = -6 20. x = -13 21. x = 8.25 22. x = 1.2 23. x = 0.3763 24. x = 1.5

Introduction to Quadratics, Drill and Practice page 426

1. $2x^2+8x-13$ 2. $-x^2+9$ 3. $-7x^2-4x+11$ 4. $-2x^2-20x+37$

5. $17x^2-13x-34$ 6. $14x^2-3x-42$ 7. $x^2+8x-17$ 8. $-9x^2+36x-33$

9. $6x^2+23x-32$ 10. $3x^2-10x$ 11. x^2+4x+3 12. $x^2+8x+12$

13. $x^2+12x+32$ 14. $x^2+16x+63$ 15. $2x^2+19x+35$ 16. $3x^2+19x+20$

17. x^2-6x+8 18. $x^2-9x+18$ 19. $5x^2-36x+7$ 20. $15x^2-46x+35$

21. $x^2-5x-14$ 22. x^2-81 23. $4x^2-1$ 24. $42x^2-27x-24$

25. $x^2+8x+16$ 26. x^2+6x+9 27. x^2-4x+4 28. $25x^2-80x+64$

29. $9x^2+54x+81$ 30. $x^2-22x+121$

The Quadratic Formula, Drill and Practice page 427

1. x = 3, -5 2. x = 0, 1.333 3. x = 4, 5

4. x = -2.873, 4.873 5. x = 4.303, 0.6972 6. x = -0.75, -2

7. x = -2.55, 2.55 8. x = 3, -1 9. x = -3, -3

10. x = 4, 4

11. x = -1.333, 0.75

12. x = -0.833, 1.2

13. No solution

14. No solution

Graphing Quadratics, Drill and Practice page 428

1.

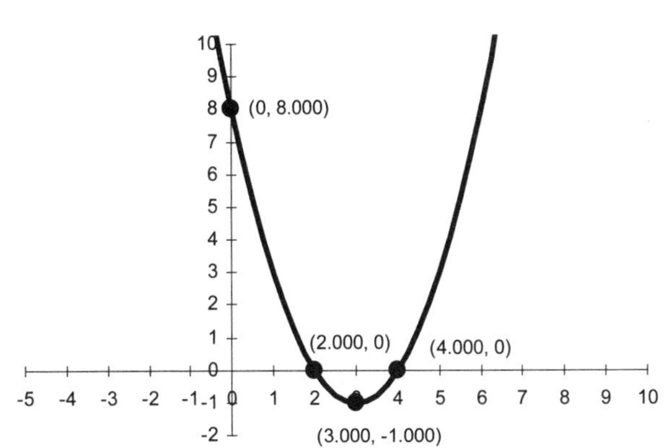

2.

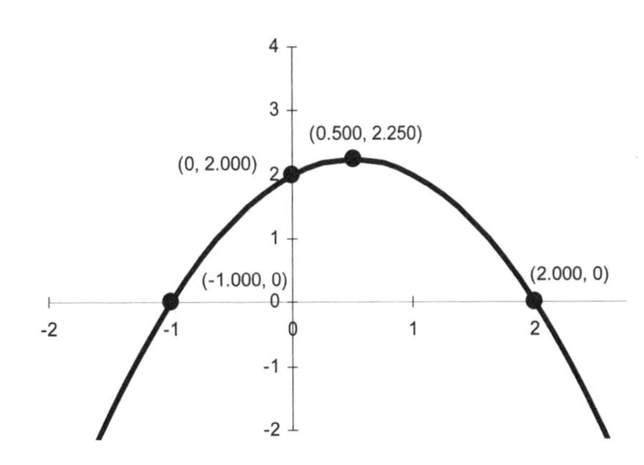

3.

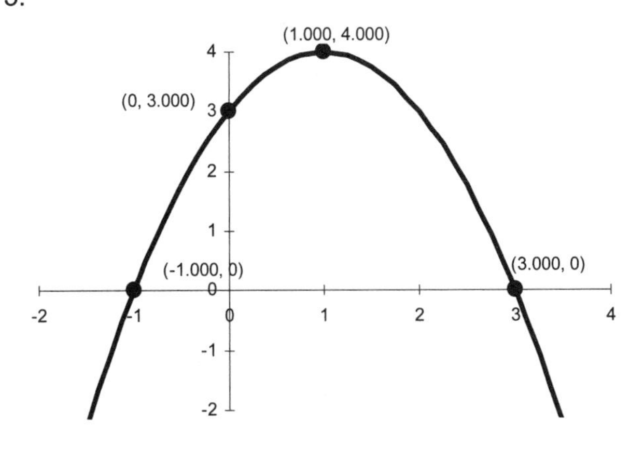

4.

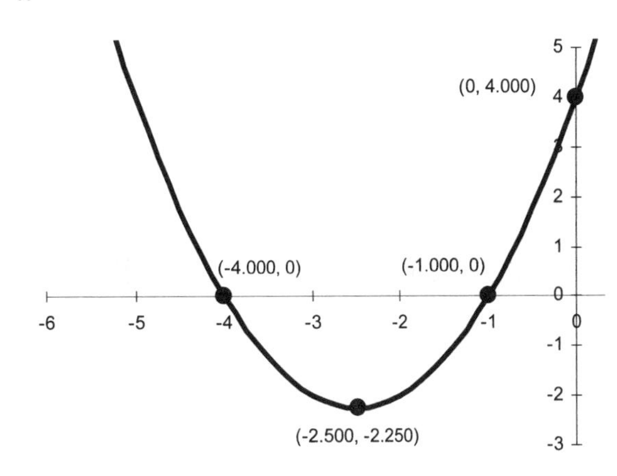

5.

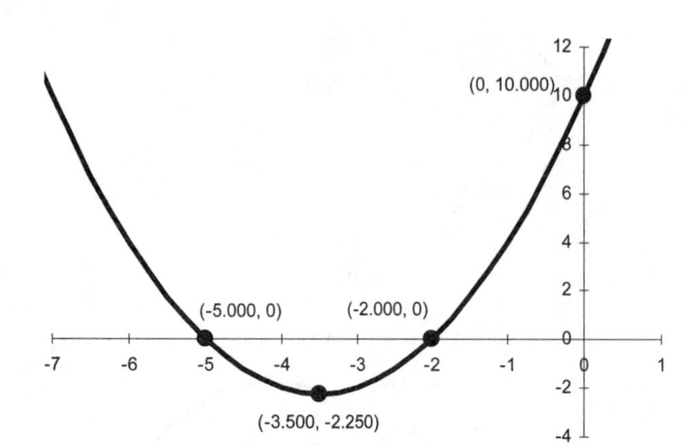

6.

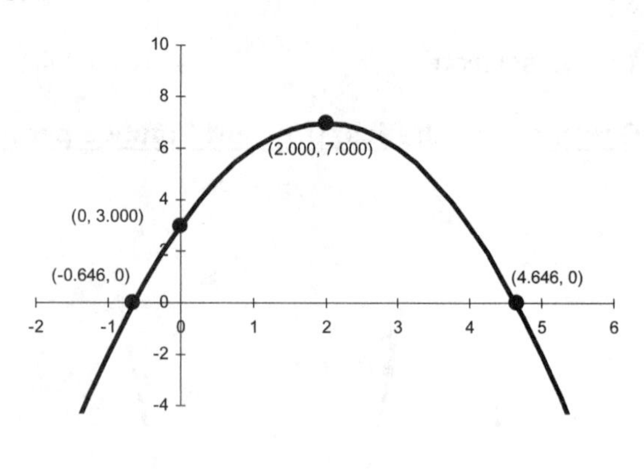

7.

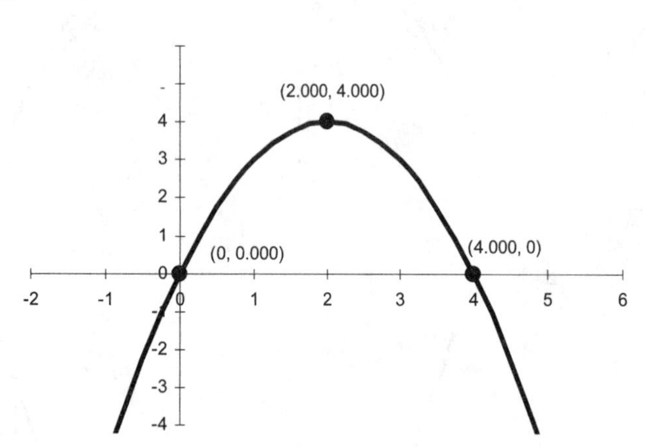

8.

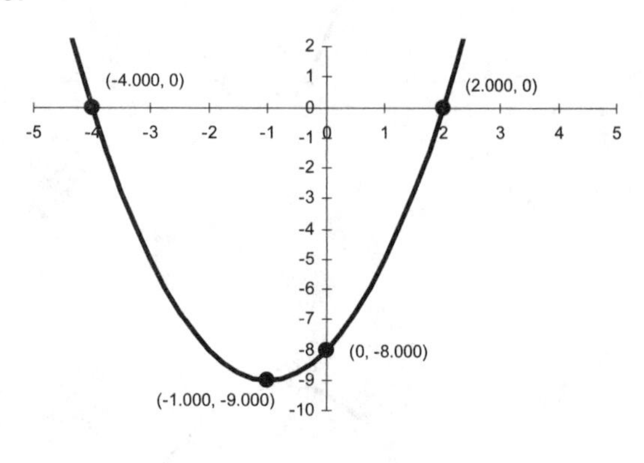

<u>Factoring, Drill and Practice page 429</u>

1. $3(x + 2)$
2. $6(3x - 2)$
3. $15(2x - 1)$
4. $7(6x - 1)$
5. $6x(4x - 3)$
6. $5x^2(5x^2 - 3)$
7. $3x(-5x^2 + 3)$
8. $2x(16 - 9x)$
9. $8x(5x - 2)$
10. $7x^2(-3x^2 + 7)$
11. $2x^3(3x^2 - 20)$
12. $x(-4x + 1)$
13. $(x + 6)(x + 1)$
14. $(x + 4)(x + 2)$
15. $(x - 5)(x + 8)$
16. $(x + 6)(x - 4)$
17. $(x - 5)(x - 3)$
18. $(x - 9)(x - 1)$
19. $(x - 3)(x - 3)$
20. $(x - 6)(x + 3)$
21. $(x - 6)(x + 5)$
22. $(x - 4)(x + 1)$
23. $(x - 5)(x + 10)$
24. $(x - 10)(x - 3)$
25. $(x - 7)(x - 2)$
26. $(x - 5)(x - 4)$
27. $(x - 8)(x + 7)$
28. $(x + 8)(x + 2)$
29. $3(x + 3)(x + 7)$
30. $2x(x + 6)(x + 1)$
31. $(x - 7)(x + 7)$
32. $(x + 6)(x - 6)$
33. $(x - 2)(x + 2)$
34. $(x - 1)(x + 1)$
35. $(x - 10)(x + 10)$
36. $(x - 11)(x + 11)$
37. $3(x - 5)(x + 5)$
38. $5(x - 3)(x + 3)$
39. $x(x - 4)(x + 4)$

Appendix A
Formal Rules for Adding and Subtracting Signed Numbers

Formal Approach to Addition and Subtraction

The formal approach to adding and subtracting signed numbers is for students who are uncomfortable with the intuitive explanation. Students do not need to understand both explanations. However, adding and subtracting signed numbers are basic skills that you must master in order to do well in Beginning Algebra.

To understand addition of signed numbers you first need to know two important concepts, the **number line** and **absolute value**.

Vocabulary: The **number line** is a graphical representation of numbers. Negative numbers are located to the left of zero while positive numbers are located to the right.

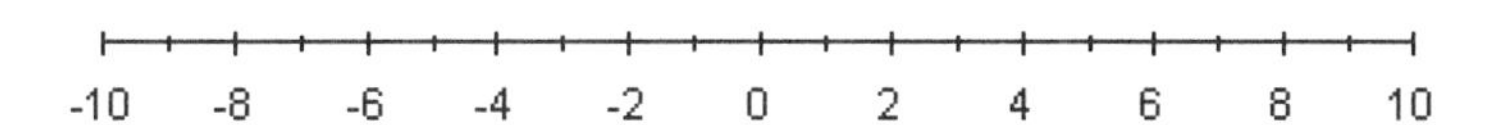

Example 3. Locate –5 on the number line.

Since the number is negative, move 5 units to the left of zero, starting from zero.

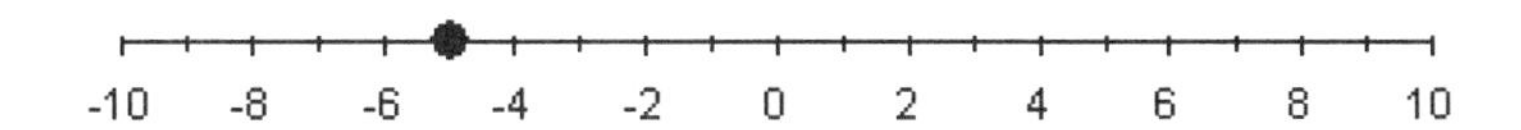

Example 4. Locate 8 on the number line.

Since the number is positive, move 8 units to the right of zero, starting from zero.

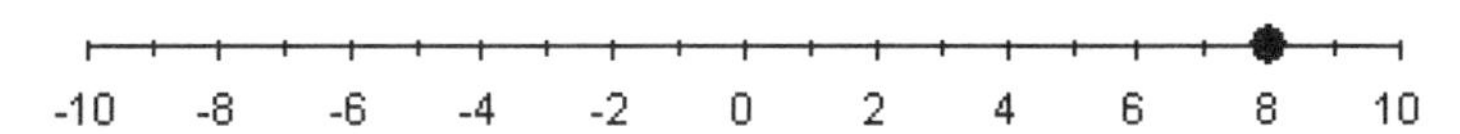

Vocabulary: The **absolute value** of a number is the distance from zero to the number on the number line. Since absolute value is distance, the **absolute value** of a number must be positive.

The **absolute value** of **b** number is denoted using the symbol $|b|$.

Example 5. $|-7|$ means:

> **Explanation:** The sign of the number gives the direction on the number line from zero and the absolute value of the number gives the distance.

The absolute value is the distance between zero and –7.

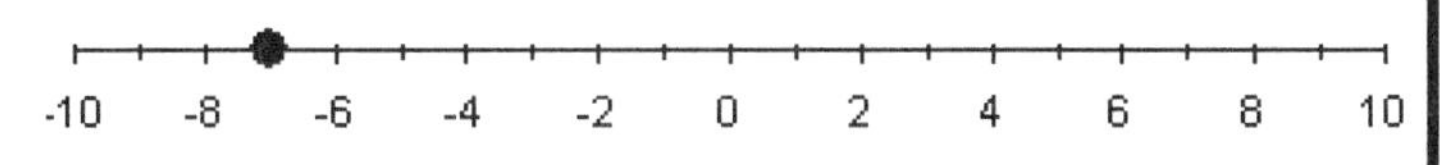

–7 is 7 units away from 0 on the number line, so $= |-7| = 7$.

The negative sign means move to the left from zero on the number line.

Addition on the Number Line

To add a + b on the number line:

1. Start at zero and move to **a**.
2. From **a** move **b** units to the left if **b** is negative or move b units to the right if **b** is positive.

Example 6. Add: 3 + 5

Start at zero and move 3 units to the right, then move 5 units to the right.

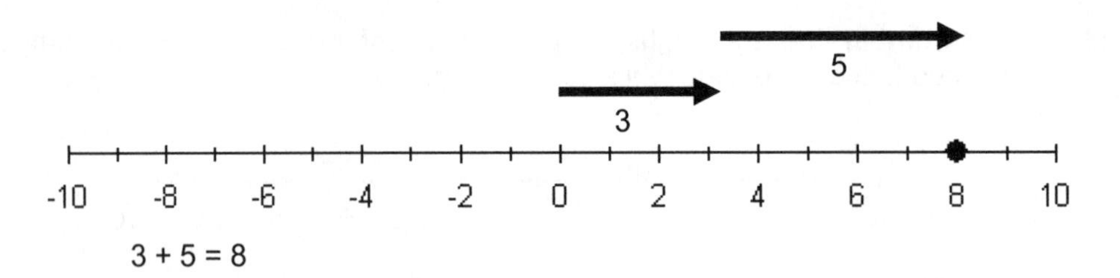

3 + 5 = 8

Example 7. Add: 4 + (–6)

Start at zero and move 4 units to the right, then move 6 units to the left.

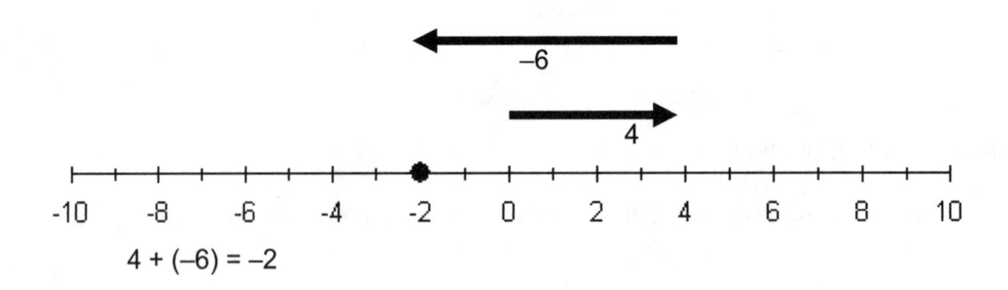

4 + (–6) = –2

Example 8. Add: (–2) + (–5)

Start at zero and move 2 units to the left, then move 5 units to the left.

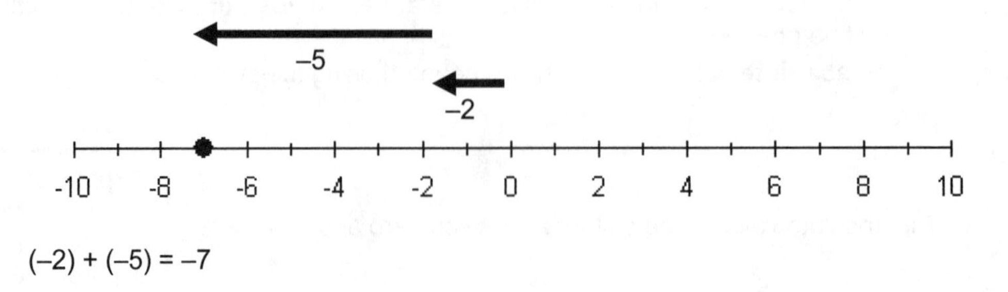

(–2) + (–5) = –7

Addition of Signed Numbers

Rules: Like signs: Add the absolute values of the numbers and use the common sign.

Unlike signs: Subtract the smaller absolute value from the larger and use the sign of the larger absolute value.

Example 9. Add: $-11 + (-4)$

Since both numbers have the same sign, add their absolute values,

$$|-11| + |-4| = 11 + 4 = 15.$$

Since both numbers are negative then the answer must be negative.

$$-11 + (-4) = -15$$

Example 10. Add: $-8 + 5$

Since the numbers have unlike signs, subtract the smaller absolute value from the larger,

$$|-8| - |5| = 8 - 5 = 3.$$

Since the negative number has the larger absolute value, the answer is negative.

$$-8 + 5 = -3$$

Example 11. Add: $9 + (-5) + 6 + (-3) + (-2)$

We can change the grouping and the order of the numbers; that is we can group all of the positive numbers together and all of the negative numbers together, and then add like signs.

$$9 + (-5) + 6 + (-3) + (-2) = 9 + 6 + (-5) + (-3) + (-2)$$

$$= 15 + (-10)$$

$$= 5$$

Study Tip: Make a note card with the rule for adding signed numbers. Review note cards at least twice a week as part of your homework routine.

Subtraction of Signed Numbers

Vocabulary: **Opposite numbers** are the same distance from zero on the number line but in opposite directions. They are also called **additive inverses** because their sum is zero.

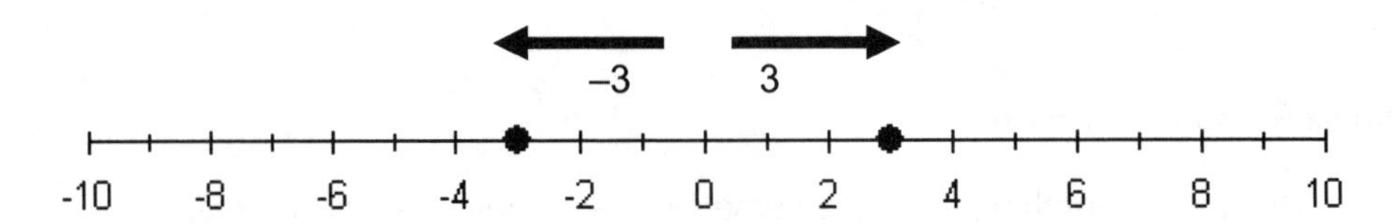

The opposite of –3 is 3. In mathematical notation, $-(-3) = 3$.

Example 12. Add $(-6) + 6$ on the number line.

Start at 0 and move 6 units to the left, then 6 units to the right.

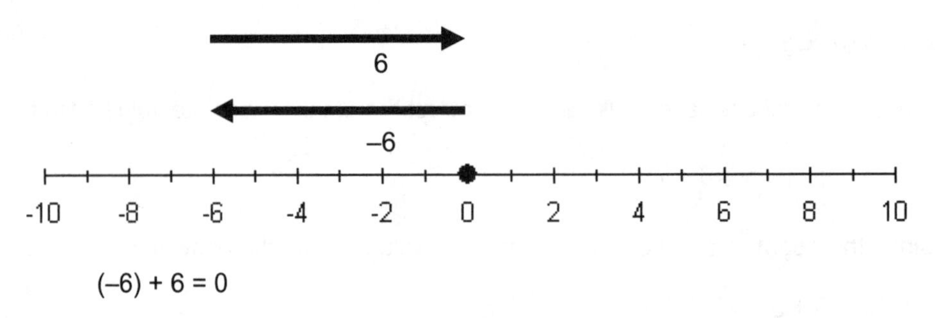

$(-6) + 6 = 0$

An important property of opposites, or additive identities, is that their sum is zero.

Rule: For any numbers **a** and **b**, $a - b = a + (-b)$.
To subtract, add the opposite (additive inverse) of the number being subtracted.

Example 13. Subtract: $4 - (-6)$
$= 4 + 6$ To subtract, add the opposite of –6 which is 6.
$= 10$

Example 14. Subtract: $-2 - 7$
$= -2 + (-7)$ To subtract, add the opposite of 7 which is –7.
$= -9$ Since the signs are like, add their absolute values. Since both numbers are negative the answer must be negative.

Example 15. Subtract: $8 - 12$
$= 8 + (-12)$ To subtract, add the opposite of 12, –12.
$= -4$ Since the signs are alike, subtract the smaller absolute value from the larger,

$$|-12| - |8| = 4.$$

Since the negative number has the larger absolute value, the answer is negative.

Study Tip: Make a note card with the rule for subtracting signed numbers.

Summary: Adding and subtracting signed numbers are basic skills that you must master in order to do well in Beginning Algebra. Go back and review the section entitled "Signed Numbers" on page one. Do the homework exercises starting on page 15 and on page 409.

Rules for adding signed numbers:

1. Like signs: Add the absolute values of the numbers and use the common sign.

2. Unlike signs: Subtract the smaller absolute value from the larger and use the sign of the larger absolute value.

Rule for subtracting numbers:

For any numbers **a**, and **b**, $a - b = a + (-b)$.
To subtract, add the opposite (additive inverse) of the number being subtracted

Weekly Cumulative Review Problems

Week One Review Problems

1. The bar graph below shows the annual profit and lose, in millions of dollars for the Blue Bell Publishing Company.

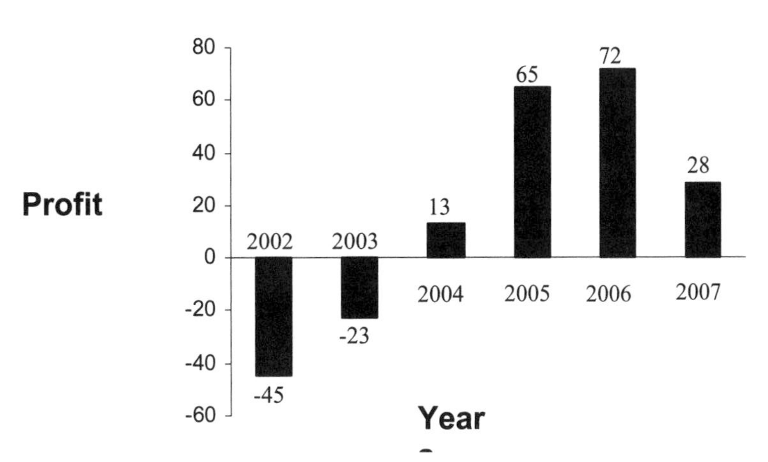

a. What is the difference between the profit in 2003 and 2002?

b. What is the difference between the profit in 2005 and 2002?

c. What is the difference between the profit in 2007 and 2006?

d. Determine the profit for the six years.

2. Duce Stanley wants to start a cabinet business. He spends $9,250 on supplies and plans to charge $575 a cabinet.

a. Complete the table below.

Cabinet	Calculation	Profit
10		
50		
c		

b. What is the equation that relates profit and number of cabinets made?

3. Simplify the algebraic expression.

a. $6x - 7 - 9x + 4$

b. $2x - 3(4x - 5)$

Week Two Review Problems

Solve each equation.

a. $6x - 11 = -112$

b. $-7x + 28 = 5x - 12$

c. $2(5-3x) = 85 - 2x$

d. $\frac{5x}{8} = 17$

e. $6(2 - 4x) + 10x = -8x + 21 - 6x$

Week Three Review Problems

1. Two companies offer you very similar jobs. CSI Company pays 6% commission on your sales plus $16,000 a year. Survivor Company B pays 13% commission on your sales.

   a. Complete the table below.

Company CSI

Sales	Calculation	Wages
100,000		
250,000		
s		

Company Survivor

Sales	Calculation	Wages
100,000		
250,000		
s		

   b. How much do you have to sell to earn the same amount in wages?

2. Rotor Ring Phone Company charges \$.45 per call and \$1.00 a minute after the first 5 minutes.

a. Create a table and find the formula for the cost of a phone call.

Minutes	Calculation	Cost
5		
15		
M		C

b. If it costs \$10.50, how long did you talk?

3. Solve for y

$3x + 2y = 11$

Week Four Review Problems

1. Professor Hunter computes his grades as follows:

   45% for the average of 4 tests
   20% for the average of homework assignments
   35% for the final exam

   a. Find Selena's average if she has a 93 test average, 88 homework average and a 99 final exam score.

   b. What does George Bush have to get on his final exam if he has a 68 test average, a 79 homework average, and he wants a 70 for the grade of the course?

2. The bookstore is having a 15% off sale.

   a. Complete the table below.

Cost	Calculation	Sales Price
15.00		
42.00		
c		

   b. If an item had a sales price of $65.85, what was the original cost of the item?

3. Describe each step.

	Step
$3x + 2(4x-1) = 4x - 3$	
$3x + 8x - 2 = 4x - 3$	______________
$11x - 2 = 4x - 3$	______________
$11x - 2 + 2 = 4x - 3 + 2$	______________
$11x = 4x - 1$	______________
$11x - 4x = 4x - 4x - 1$	______________
$7x = -1$	______________
$\frac{7x}{7} = \frac{-1}{7}$	______________
$x = -.1429$	______________

4. Find the mistake.

$$4(2x-5) = 3x + 7$$
$$8x - 20 = 3x + 7$$
$$8x - 20 + 20 = 3x + 7 + 20$$
$$8x = 3x + 27$$
$$8x + 3x = 3x + 3x + 27$$
$$11x = 27$$
$$\frac{11x}{11} = \frac{27}{11}$$
$$X = 2.\overline{45}$$

Week Five Review Problems

1. The graph below represents the annual rainfall that fell at Death Valley's Ranger Station.

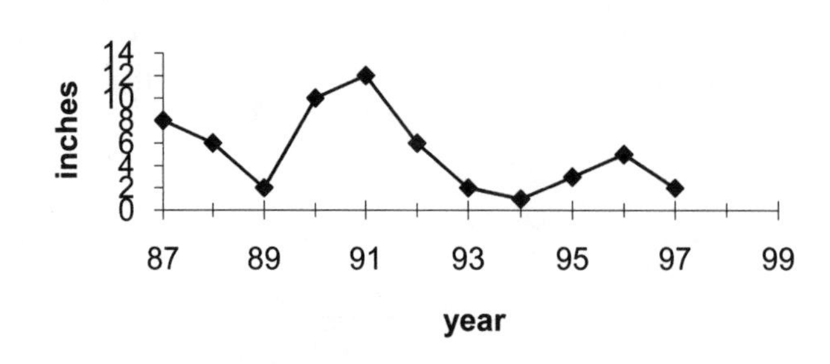

a. How much rainfall was there in 1987?

b. What year or years had 10 inches of rainfall?

c. What year had the most rainfall?

d. When did the greatest increase in annual rainfall occur?

2. Solve the following inequalities.

a. $11 - 3x \leq 53$

b. $2 \leq 7 + 2x \leq 15$

3. The Windless Surfing Company has determined its cost for making custom sails to be

$$C = 380 + 18S,$$

where C is the cost in dollars and S is the number of sails. If the cost can be higher than $4,000 but must be smaller than $11,000, how many sails can they make per week? (You must set up an inequality.)

Week Six Review Problems

1. An internet provider, Boundless Web, charges $12 per month plus 25 cents an hour.

   a. Complete the table below.

Hours	Calculation	Cost
20		
50		
100		
h		

   b. What is the equation that relates cost and hours?

   c. Use the results in Part a. to graph the equation in Part b. Choose an appropriate scale and only graph the portion that makes sense to the problem. Label the axes.

Hours	**Cost**	**Point (h, c)**
20		
50		
100		

2. Use the table to answer the following questions.

Year	**Number of Computers Sold**
1995	8.2 million
2000	13.5 million

   a. Find the average rate of change.

   b. Find the percent increase.

3. Find the x and y intercepts and graph the lines. Label your axis and choose an appropriate scale.

a. $y = 3x - 21$

b. $.04x - 18y = 7$

Week Seven Review Problems

1. You are trying to decide which phone company to chose for your business. Company Static will charge you $170 per month while Company Ringer will charge you $89 per month plus 18¢ per minute.

   a. Write an equation for the cost of making phone calls for each company.

   b. Use the equations to find when the two companies will cost you the same amount. Label this point on the graph you create below.

   c. Graph both equations on the same set of axis. Label your axis and choose an appropriate scale. Only graph the portion that is relevant to the problem.

   d. Use the graph to find when Static costs more than Ringer.

   e. Use the graph to find when Ringer costs more than Static.

   f. What do the c intercepts for both equations mean in terms of the problem?

   g. Find the slope of each line and explain what they mean in terms of the problem.

Week Eight Review Problems

1. There are 1400 bacteria initially present in a culture. The culture grows at a rate of 4% a day.

   a. Complete the table below.

Time	Calculation	Number of Bacteria
Initial Day		
1 Day Later		
2 Days Later		
3 Days Later		
n Days Later		

   b. Use the equation to find how many bacteria there will be in 30 days.

2. Assuming that the interest is compounded monthly, the formula below computes how much money will be in your account at sometime in the future.

$$FV = P(1 + i)^n$$

where FV is Future Value
P is amount invested
i is interest rate per month
n is the number of months

   a. A couple invests $2500 at an annual interest rate of 6%. How much money will they have after 10 years? (Hint: i = 0.06/12)

   b. How much money should you invest at an annual interest rate of 3% if you want $20,000 in 30 years? (Hint: i = 0.03/12)

Week Nine Review Problems

1. Use the following formula to answer the question below.

$$P = A\left[\frac{i}{1-(1+i)^{-n}}\right]$$

P is the monthly payment
A is the amount of the loan
n is the number of payments
i is the interest rate per month

Tom Ridge is borrowing $35,000 to buy a car. He takes out a 48 month car loan at an annual interest rate of 3%. Find Tom's monthly payments. (Hint: i= .03/12)

2. Simplify. Write with positive exponents only.

a. $x \cdot x^3$ b. $(5x^2)^4$ c. $\frac{16x}{4x^5}$

d. x^{-3} e. $8x^{-3}$

3. Write the number in Scientific Notation.

620,000,000

4. Write the number in Decimal Notation.

2.6×10^{-3}

Week Ten Review Problems

1. Perform the indicated operations.

a. $\frac{3x}{7y^2} \cdot \frac{49y^3}{6x^2}$

b. $\frac{5x}{3x^3} \div \frac{9x^2}{25}$

c. $\frac{4}{3x} + \frac{5}{15}$

d. $\frac{1}{2} - \frac{7}{x}$

2. Solve each equation.

a. $\frac{x}{3} + \frac{1}{2} = \frac{5}{6}$

b. $\frac{x-1}{3} - \frac{x-2}{2} = \frac{x+1}{6}$

3. Two students pool their money to buy raffle tickets from the MCCC Math Club. One student puts in $10 and the other student puts in $7, if they win $210, how should they divide their winnings?

Week Eleven Review Problems

1. Simplify the following:

   a. $x^2 + 2x + 3 - 2x^2 + 1$

   b. $2(x^2 - x + 1) - 2(x^2 - x - 1)$

2. Multiply:

   a. $(x - 3)(x + 5)$

   c. $(x + 4)^2$

3. A rocket is launched from the top of a cliff with an initial velocity of 320 feet per second. The height (in feet) of the rocket is given by the equation:

$$h = -16t^2 + 320t + 4800,$$

where t is the number of seconds the rocket is in the air.
Find the height of the rocket for

a. $t = 0$

b. $t = 5$

c. $t = 8$

d. $t = 10$

e. $t = 15$

f. $t = 30$

g. According to the calculations above, when will the rocket reach its maximum height?

h. According to the calculations above, estimate when the rocket hits the ground?

i. Graph the points a through f.

Week Twelve Review Problems

1. State the quadratic formula.

2. If the revenue function is given by: $R = 5x^2 - 20x$

   and the Cost function is given by: $C = 7x^2 - 50x + 100$.

   a. Find the profit equation.

   b. Find the break even points.

   c. Find the values for x that will give a profit of 12.

Week Thirteen Review Problems

1. State the formula for the x coordinate of the vertex

2. Deadly Toy Company makes BB guns. The cost of making *x* hundred BB guns per month is

$$C = .3x^2 - 65x + 150$$

and the revenue from selling *x* BB guns per month is

$$R = -.7x^2 + 25x.$$

C and R are in thousands of dollars.

a. Find the equation for profit. (Profit = Revenue - Cost)

b. Graph the profit equation. Explain what the vertex, x intercepts, p intercept mean in terms of making BB guns. Make sure you label the axis and use an appropriate scale.

d. Suppose the company needs to make $1,000,000 in profit (P = 1,000). Graph this line on the graph above and find where the line intersects the graph of the quadratic. Explain what the answers mean.

3. Factor

a. $3x^2 + 6x$

b. $x^2 + 12x + 20$

c. $x^2 - 49$

How to Use the TI-30X IIS Calculator

The following pages contain Power Point slides that accompany the CD that comes with the book. Learning how to use a calculator effectively is an important skill for MAT 011 students.

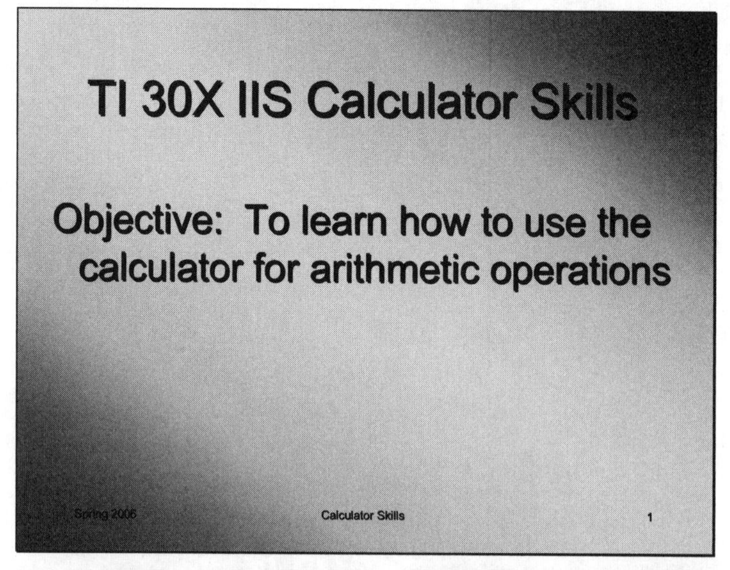

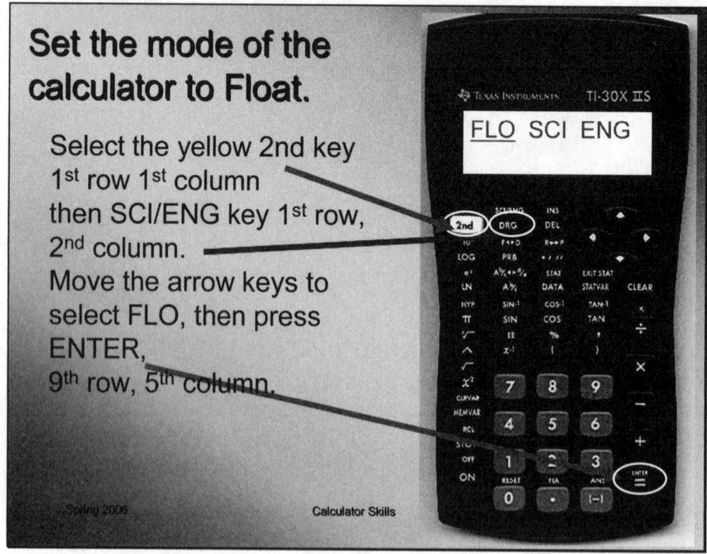

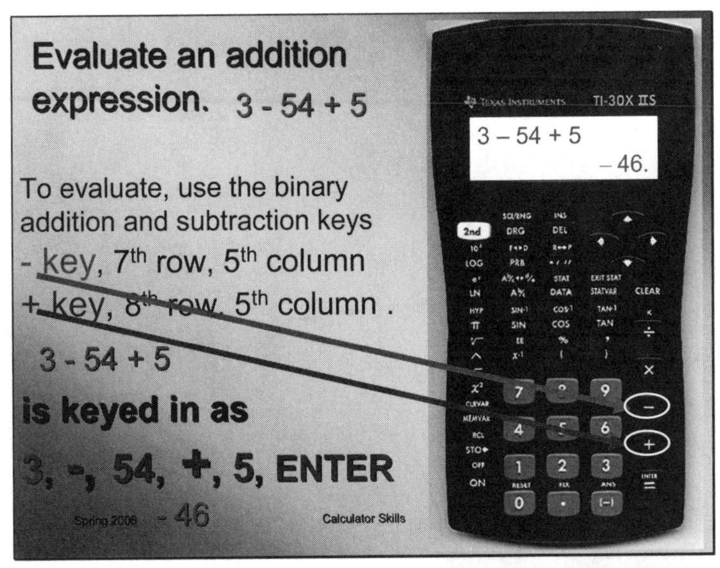

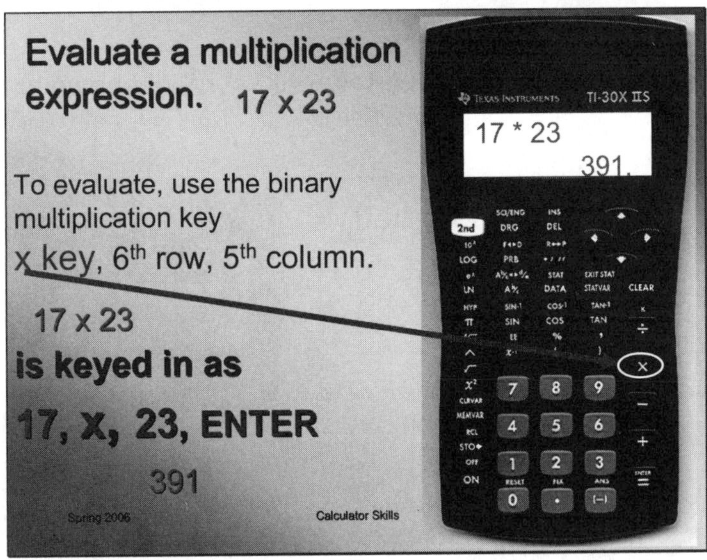

Note that the key symbol is marked x, but * symbol shows in the display.

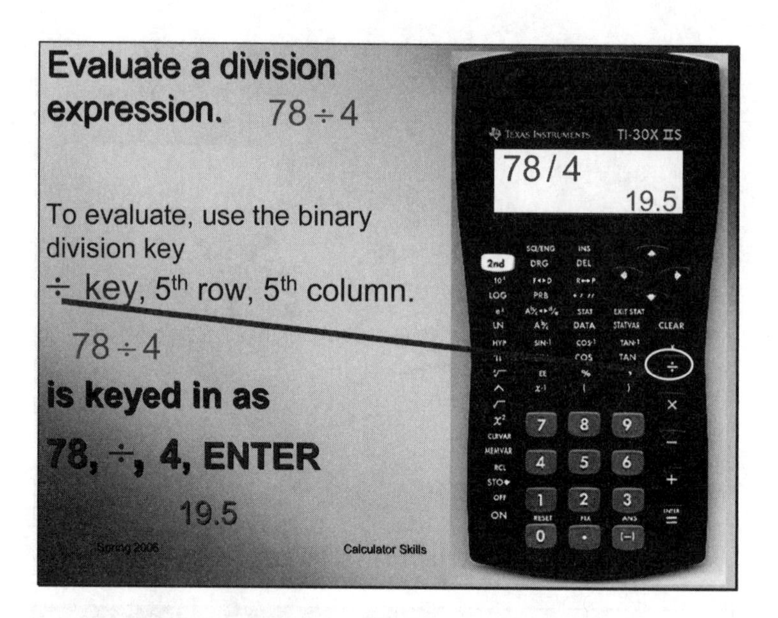

Note that the key symbol is marked ÷, but / symbol shows in the display.

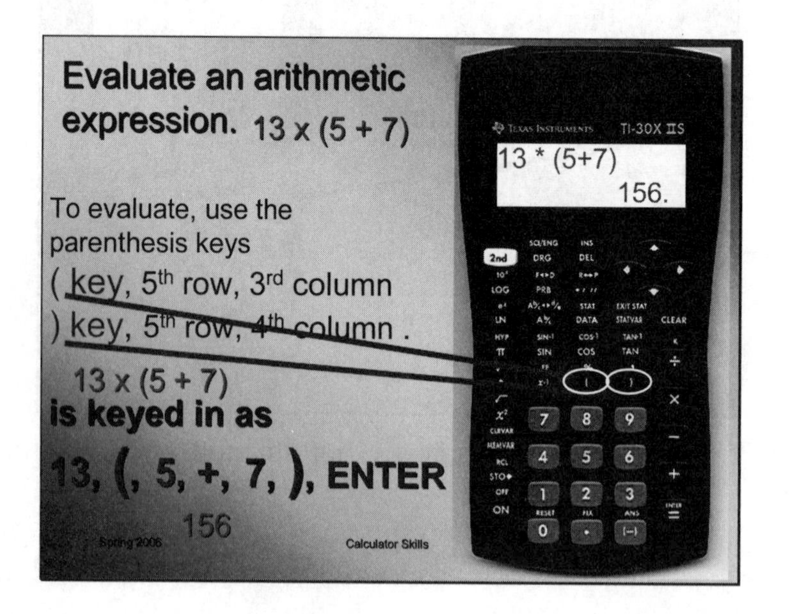

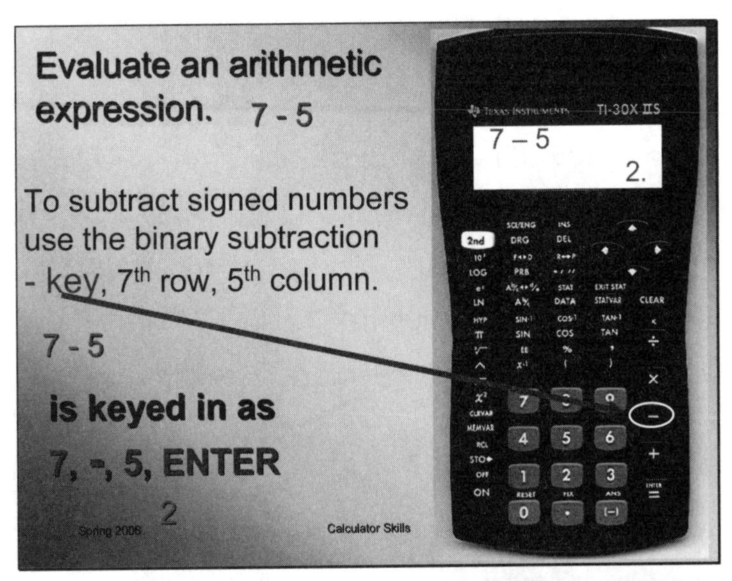
Evaluate an arithmetic expression. 7 - 5
To subtract signed numbers use the binary subtraction - key, 7th row, 5th column.
7 - 5
is keyed in as
7, -, 5, ENTER
2
Spring 2006
Calculator Skills
TEXAS INSTRUMENTS
TI-30X IIS
7 – 5
2.

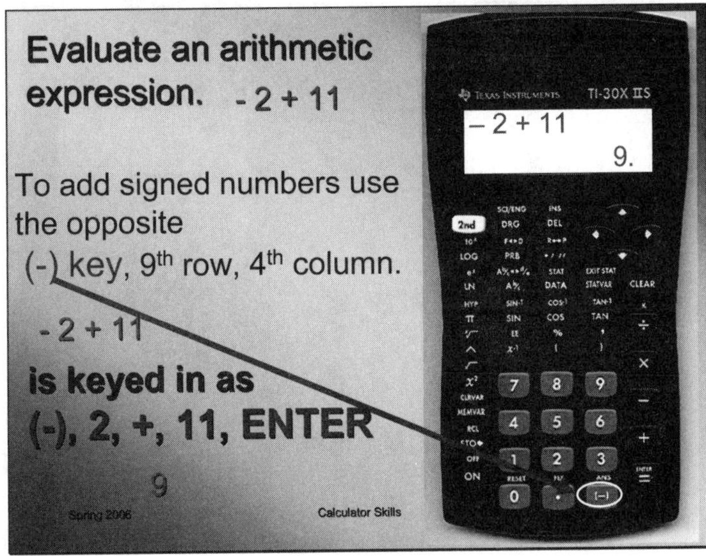
Evaluate an arithmetic expression. - 2 + 11
To add signed numbers use the opposite (-) key, 9th row, 4th column.
- 2 + 11
is keyed in as
(-), 2, +, 11, ENTER
9
Spring 2006
Calculator Skills
TEXAS INSTRUMENTS
TI-30X IIS
– 2 + 11
9.

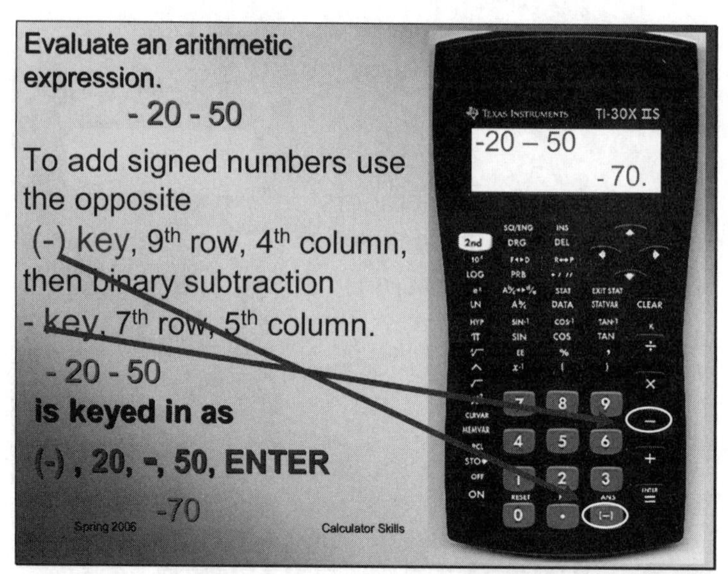
Evaluate an arithmetic expression.
- 20 - 50
To add signed numbers use the opposite
(-) key, 9th row, 4th column, then binary subtraction
- key, 7th row, 5th column.
- 20 - 50
is keyed in as
(-) , 20, -, 50, ENTER
-70
Spring 2006
Calculator Skills
TEXAS INSTRUMENTS
TI-30X IIS
-20 – 50
- 70.

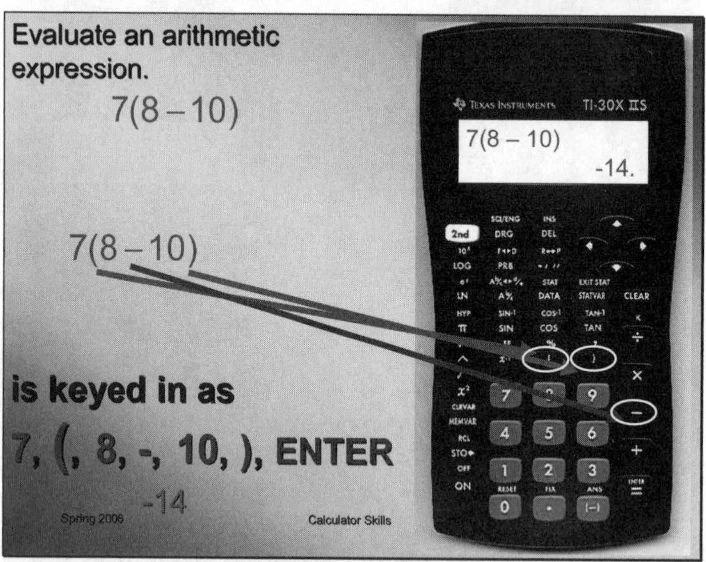
Evaluate an arithmetic expression.
7(8 – 10)
7(8 – 10)
is keyed in as
7, (, 8, -, 10,), ENTER
-14
Spring 2006
Calculator Skills
TEXAS INSTRUMENTS
TI-30X IIS
7(8 – 10)
-14.

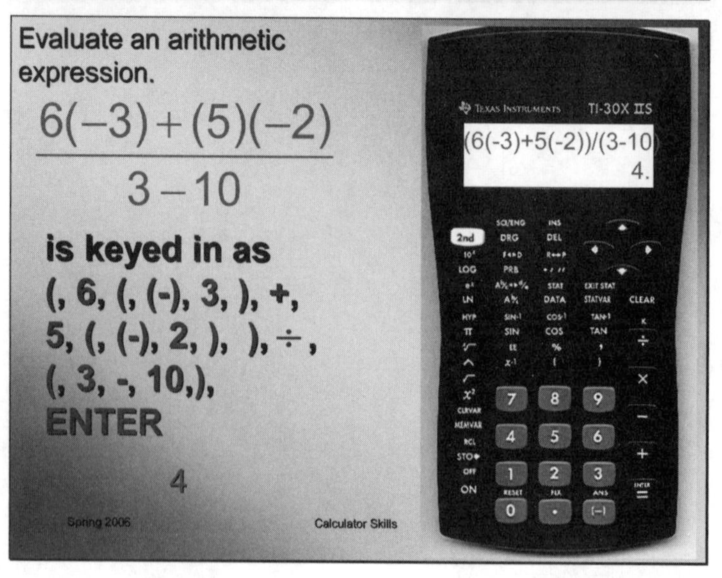
Evaluate an arithmetic expression.
(6(–3) + (5)(–2)) / (3 – 10)
is keyed in as
(, 6, (, (-), 3,), +,
5, (, (-), 2,),), ÷,
(, 3, -, 10,),
ENTER
4
Spring 2006
Calculator Skills
TEXAS INSTRUMENTS
TI-30X IIS
(6(-3)+5(-2))/(3-10)
4.

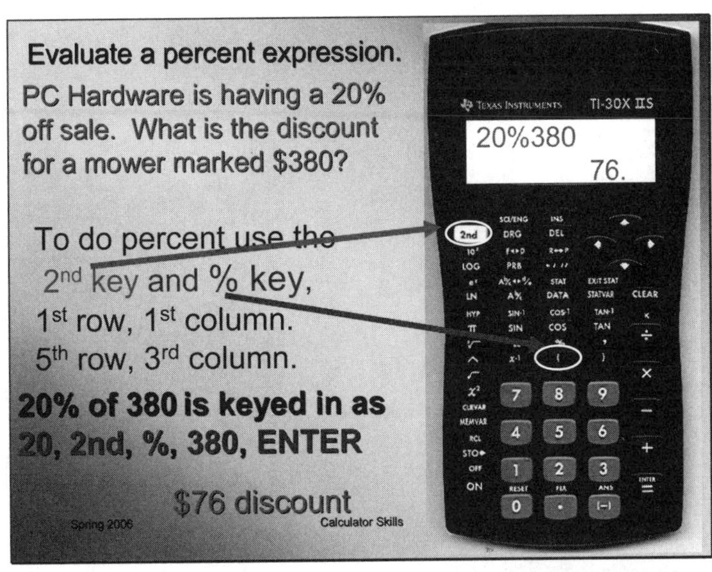
Evaluate a percent expression.
PC Hardware is having a 20% off sale. What is the discount for a mower marked $380?
To do percent use the 2nd key and % key,
1st row, 1st column.
5th row, 3rd column.
20% of 380 is keyed in as
20, 2nd, %, 380, ENTER
$76 discount
Spring 2006
Calculator Skills
TEXAS INSTRUMENTS
TI-30X IIS
20%380
76.

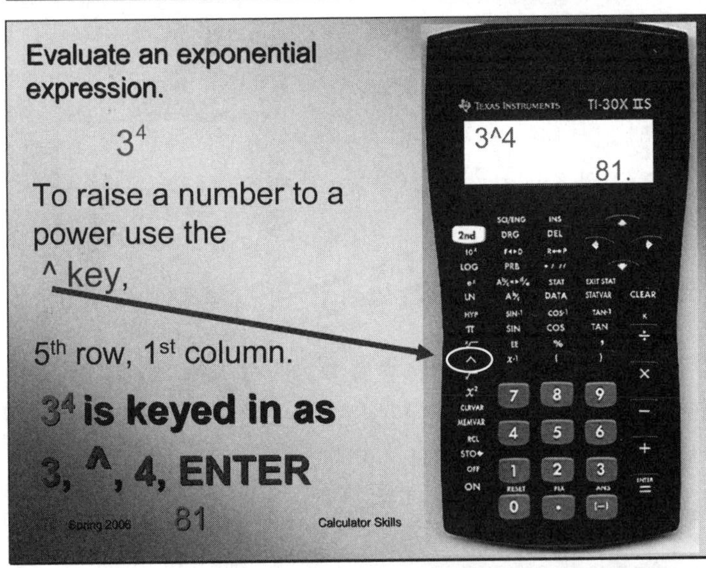
Evaluate an exponential expression.
3^4
To raise a number to a power use the
^ key,
5th row, 1st column.
3^4 is keyed in as
3, ^, 4, ENTER
81
Spring 2006
Calculator Skills
TEXAS INSTRUMENTS
TI-30X IIS
3^4
81.

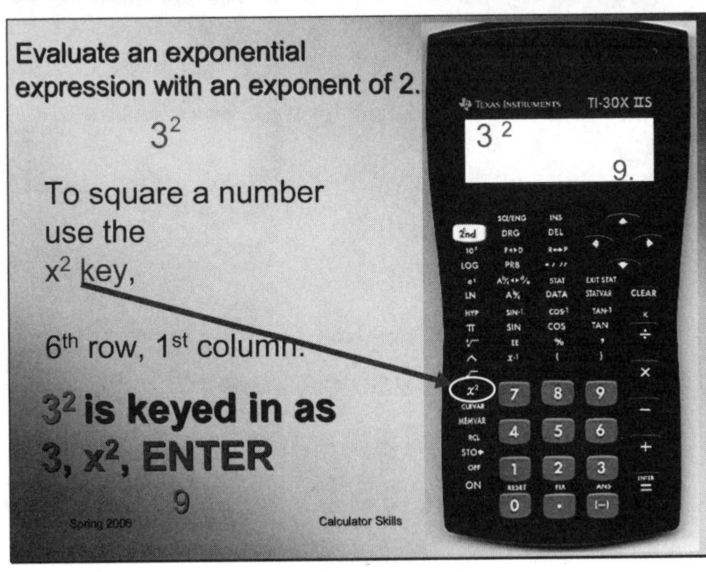
Evaluate an exponential expression with an exponent of 2.
3^2
To square a number use the
x^2 key,
6th row, 1st column.
3^2 is keyed in as
3, x^2, ENTER
9
Spring 2006
Calculator Skills
TEXAS INSTRUMENTS
TI-30X IIS
3 2
9.

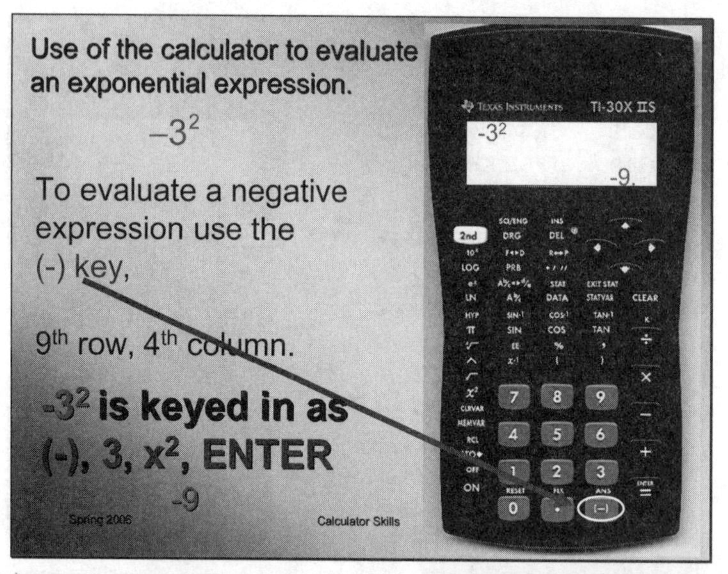
Use of the calculator to evaluate an exponential expression.
−3²
To evaluate a negative expression use the (-) key,
9th row, 4th column.
-3² is keyed in as
(-), 3, x², ENTER
-9
Spring 2006
Calculator Skills
TEXAS INSTRUMENTS
TI-30X IIS
-3²
-9.

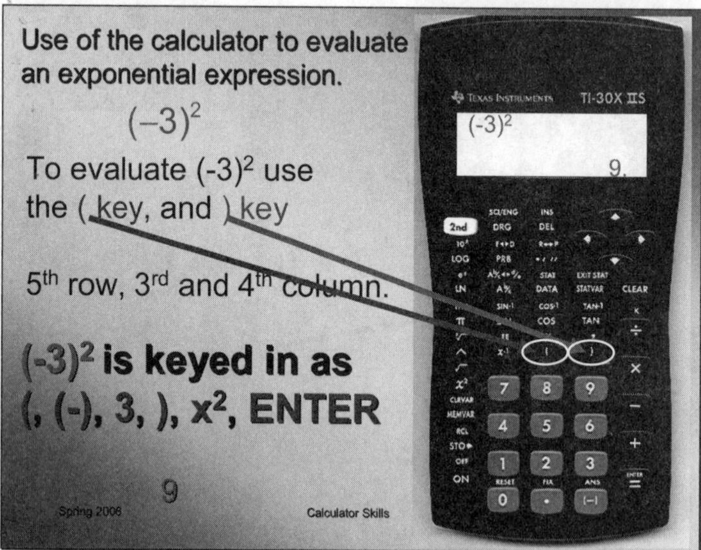
Use of the calculator to evaluate an exponential expression.
(−3)²
To evaluate (-3)² use the (key, and) key
5th row, 3rd and 4th column.
(-3)² is keyed in as
(, (-), 3,), x², ENTER
9
Spring 2006
Calculator Skills
TEXAS INSTRUMENTS
TI-30X IIS
(-3)²
9.

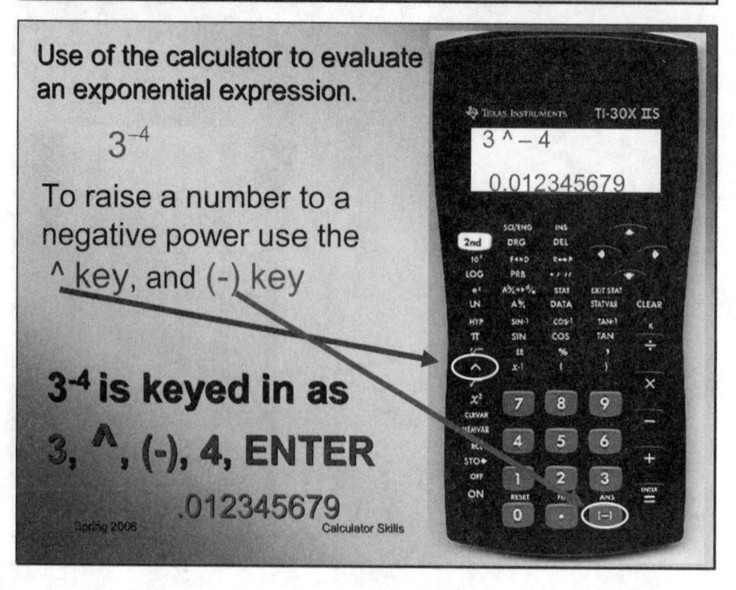
Use of the calculator to evaluate an exponential expression.
3⁻⁴
To raise a number to a negative power use the ^ key, and (-) key
3⁻⁴ is keyed in as
3, ^, (-), 4, ENTER
.012345679
Spring 2006
Calculator Skills
TEXAS INSTRUMENTS
TI-30X IIS
3 ^ – 4
0.012345679

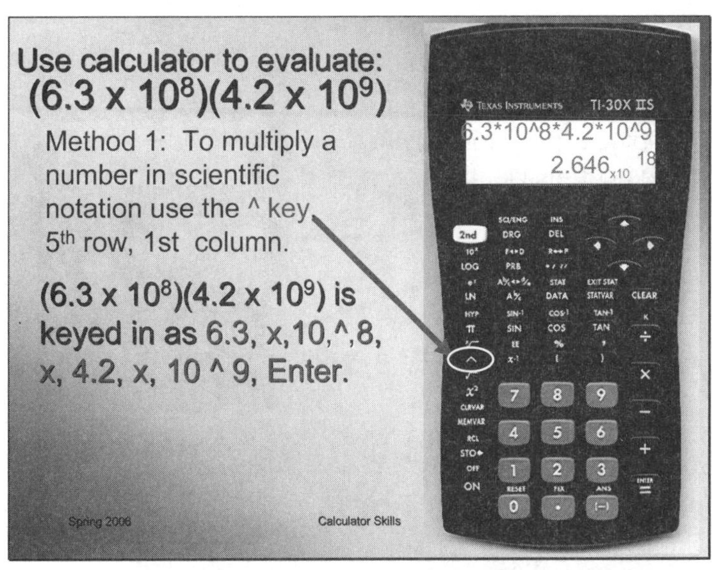

Use calculator to evaluate:
(6.3 x 10⁸)(4.2 x 10⁹)
Method 1: To multiply a number in scientific notation use the ^ key, 5th row, 1st column.
(6.3 x 10⁸)(4.2 x 10⁹) is keyed in as 6.3, x,10,^,8, x, 4.2, x, 10 ^ 9, Enter.
Spring 2006
Calculator Skills
TEXAS INSTRUMENTS TI-30X IIS
6.3*10^8*4.2*10^9
2.646x10 18

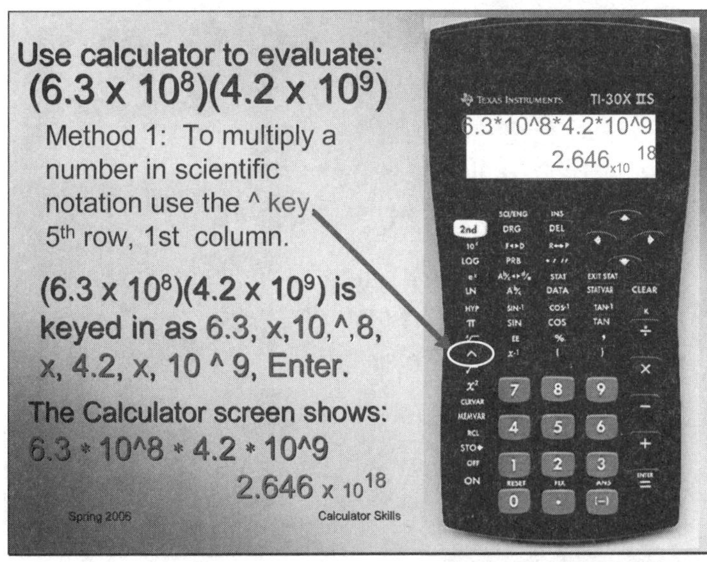

Use calculator to evaluate:
(6.3 x 10⁸)(4.2 x 10⁹)
Method 1: To multiply a number in scientific notation use the ^ key, 5th row, 1st column.
(6.3 x 10⁸)(4.2 x 10⁹) is keyed in as 6.3, x,10,^,8, x, 4.2, x, 10 ^ 9, Enter.
The Calculator screen shows:
6.3 * 10^8 * 4.2 * 10^9
2.646 x 10¹⁸
Spring 2006
Calculator Skills
TEXAS INSTRUMENTS TI-30X IIS
6.3*10^8*4.2*10^9
2.646x10 18

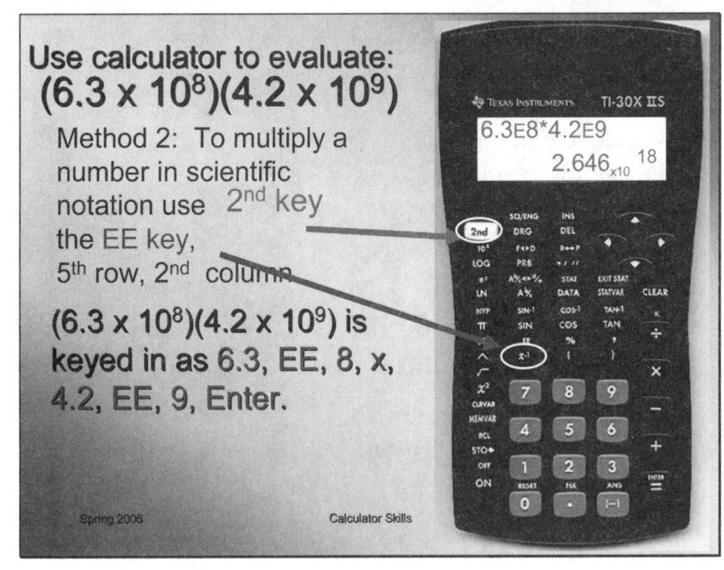

Use calculator to evaluate:
(6.3 x 10⁸)(4.2 x 10⁹)
Method 2: To multiply a number in scientific notation use 2nd key the EE key, 5th row, 2nd column
(6.3 x 10⁸)(4.2 x 10⁹) is keyed in as 6.3, EE, 8, x, 4.2, EE, 9, Enter.
Spring 2006
Calculator Skills
TEXAS INSTRUMENTS TI-30X IIS
6.3E8*4.2E9
2.646x10 18

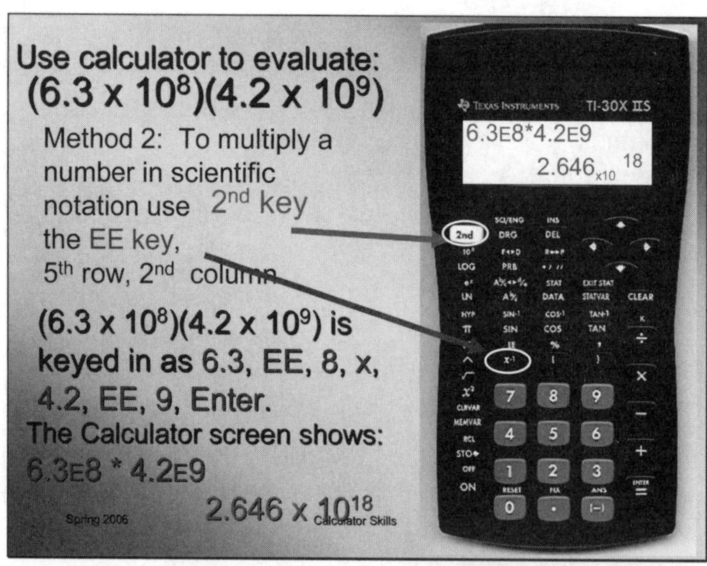
Use calculator to evaluate:
(6.3 x 10^8)(4.2 x 10^9)
Method 2: To multiply a number in scientific notation use the EE key, 5th row, 2nd column
2nd key
(6.3 x 10^8)(4.2 x 10^9) is keyed in as 6.3, EE, 8, x, 4.2, EE, 9, Enter.
The Calculator screen shows:
6.3E8 * 4.2E9
2.646 x 10^18
Spring 2006
Calculator Skills
TEXAS INSTRUMENTS TI-30X IIS
6.3E8*4.2E9
2.646x10 18

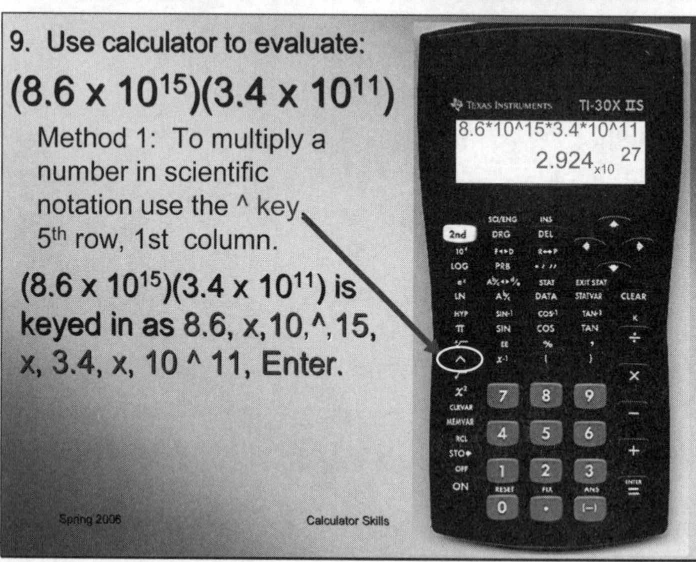
9. Use calculator to evaluate:
(8.6 x 10^15)(3.4 x 10^11)
Method 1: To multiply a number in scientific notation use the ^ key, 5th row, 1st column.
(8.6 x 10^15)(3.4 x 10^11) is keyed in as 8.6, x,10,^,15, x, 3.4, x, 10 ^ 11, Enter.
Spring 2006
Calculator Skills
TEXAS INSTRUMENTS TI-30X IIS
8.6*10^15*3.4*10^11
2.924x10 27

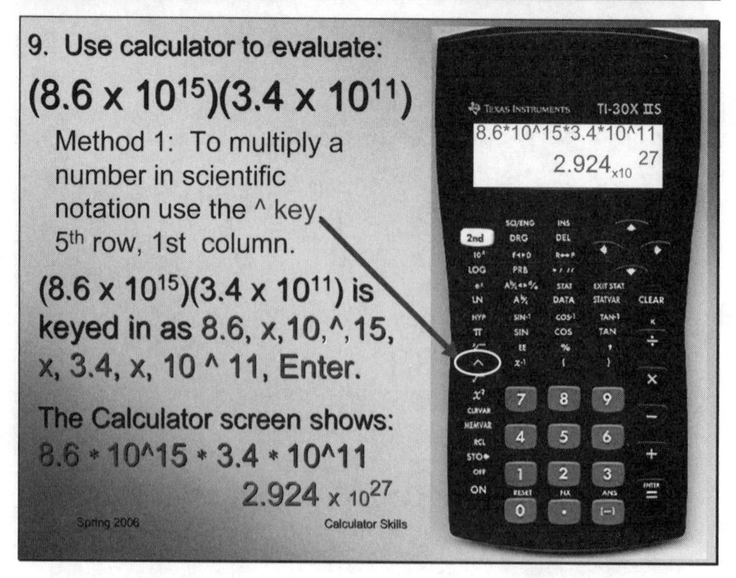
9. Use calculator to evaluate:
(8.6 x 10^15)(3.4 x 10^11)
Method 1: To multiply a number in scientific notation use the ^ key, 5th row, 1st column.
(8.6 x 10^15)(3.4 x 10^11) is keyed in as 8.6, x,10,^,15, x, 3.4, x, 10 ^ 11, Enter.
The Calculator screen shows:
8.6 * 10^15 * 3.4 * 10^11
2.924 x 10^27
Spring 2006
Calculator Skills
TEXAS INSTRUMENTS TI-30X IIS
8.6*10^15*3.4*10^11
2.924x10 27

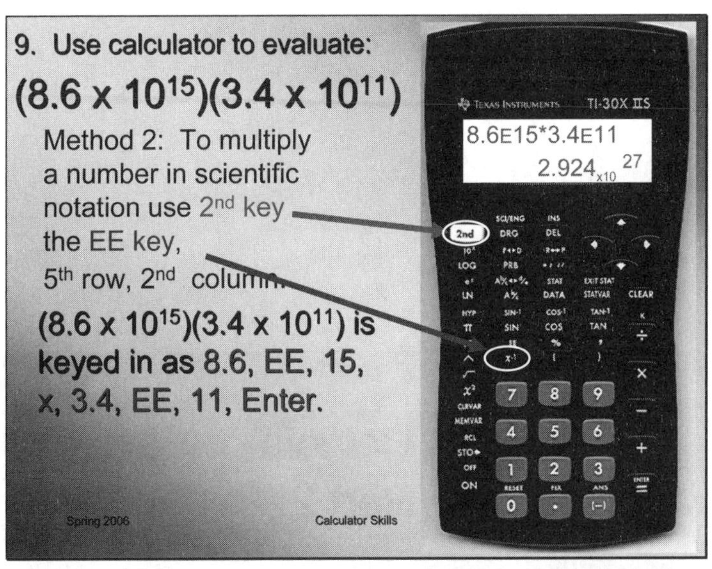
9. Use calculator to evaluate:
(8.6 x 10^15)(3.4 x 10^11)
Method 2: To multiply a number in scientific notation use 2nd key the EE key, 5th row, 2nd column.
(8.6 x 10^15)(3.4 x 10^11) is keyed in as 8.6, EE, 15, x, 3.4, EE, 11, Enter.
8.6E15*3.4E11
2.924x10 27
Spring 2006
Calculator Skills

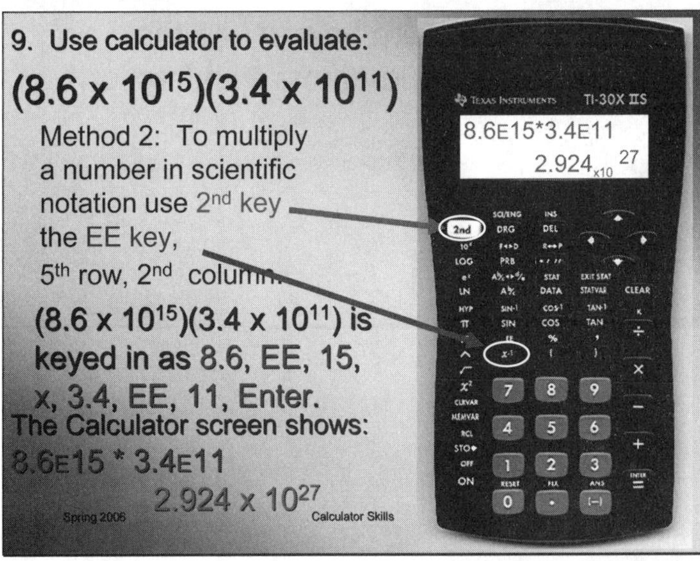
9. Use calculator to evaluate:
(8.6 x 10^15)(3.4 x 10^11)
Method 2: To multiply a number in scientific notation use 2nd key the EE key, 5th row, 2nd column.
(8.6 x 10^15)(3.4 x 10^11) is keyed in as 8.6, EE, 15, x, 3.4, EE, 11, Enter.
The Calculator screen shows:
8.6E15 * 3.4E11
2.924 x 10^27
8.6E15*3.4E11
2.924x10 27
Spring 2006
Calculator Skills

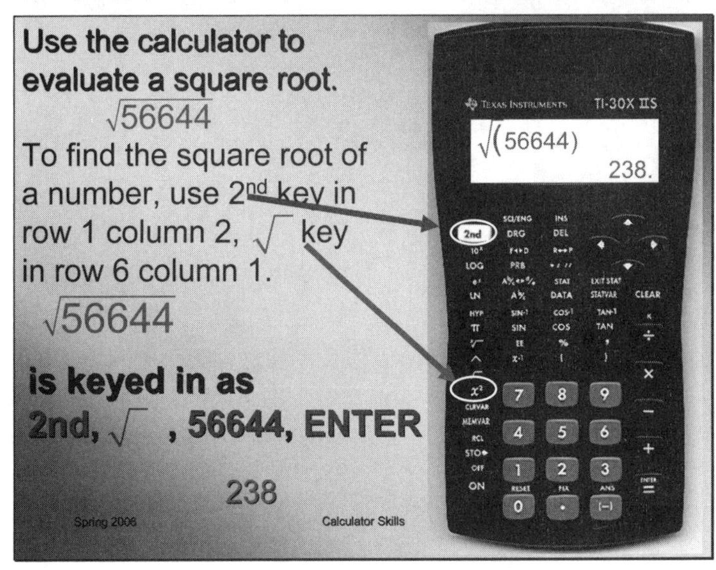
Use the calculator to evaluate a square root.
√56644
To find the square root of a number, use 2nd key in row 1 column 2, √ key in row 6 column 1.
√56644
is keyed in as
2nd, √ , 56644, ENTER
238
√(56644)
238.
Spring 2006
Calculator Skills

TI 30X IIS Calculator Skills, Part 2

Objective: To learn how to use the calculator for operations with fractions.

Spring, 2006 Calculator Skills 1

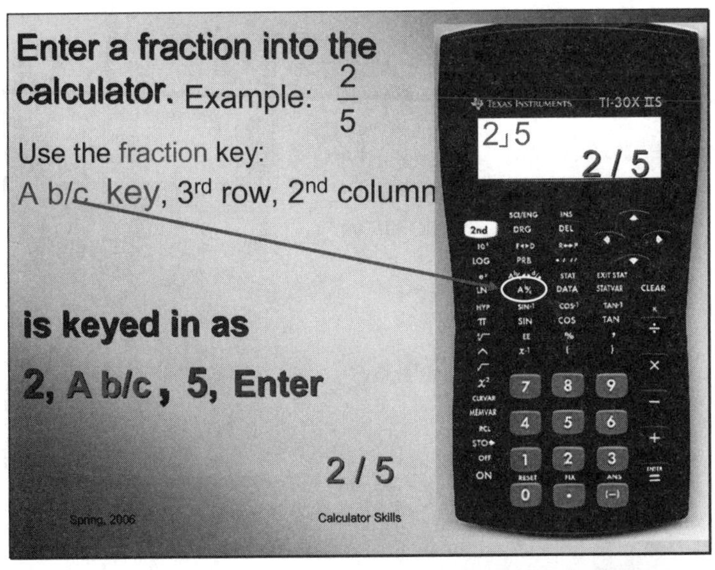
Enter a fraction into the calculator. Example: 2/5
Use the fraction key:
A b/c key, 3rd row, 2nd column
is keyed in as
2, A b/c, 5, Enter
2 / 5
Spring, 2006
Calculator Skills
TEXAS INSTRUMENTS TI-30X IIS

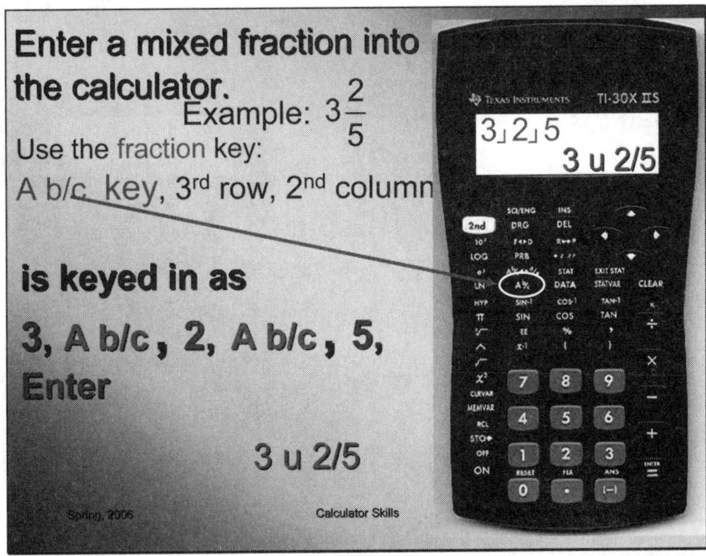
Enter a mixed fraction into the calculator.
Example: 3 2/5
Use the fraction key:
A b/c key, 3rd row, 2nd column
is keyed in as
3, A b/c, 2, A b/c, 5, Enter
3 u 2/5
Spring, 2006
Calculator Skills
TEXAS INSTRUMENTS TI-30X IIS

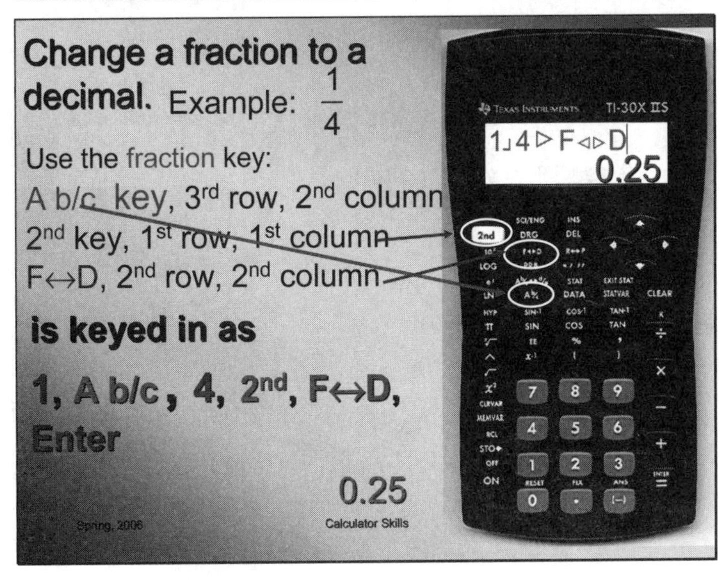
Change a fraction to a decimal. Example: 1/4
Use the fraction key:
A b/c key, 3rd row, 2nd column
2nd key, 1st row, 1st column
F↔D, 2nd row, 2nd column
is keyed in as
1, A b/c, 4, 2nd, F↔D, Enter
0.25
Spring, 2006
Calculator Skills
TEXAS INSTRUMENTS TI-30X IIS

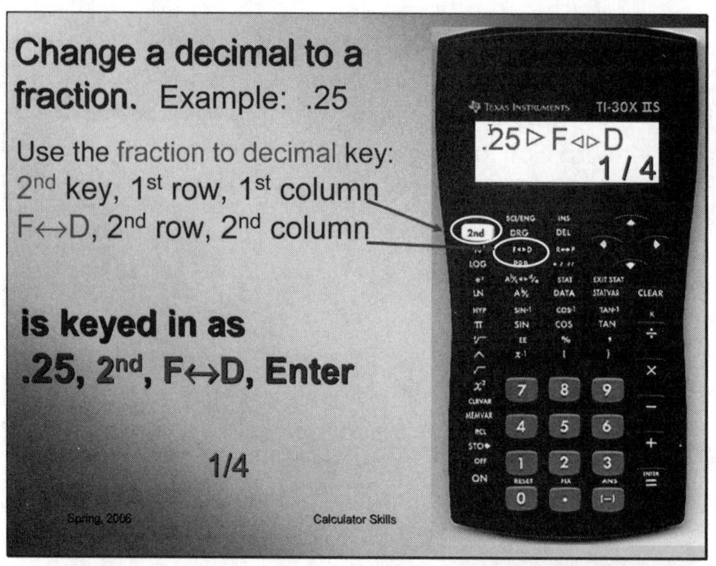
Change a decimal to a fraction. Example: .25
Use the fraction to decimal key:
2nd key, 1st row, 1st column
F↔D, 2nd row, 2nd column
is keyed in as
.25, 2nd, F↔D, Enter
1/4
Spring, 2006
Calculator Skills
TEXAS INSTRUMENTS TI-30X IIS
.25 ▷ F◁▷D
1 / 4

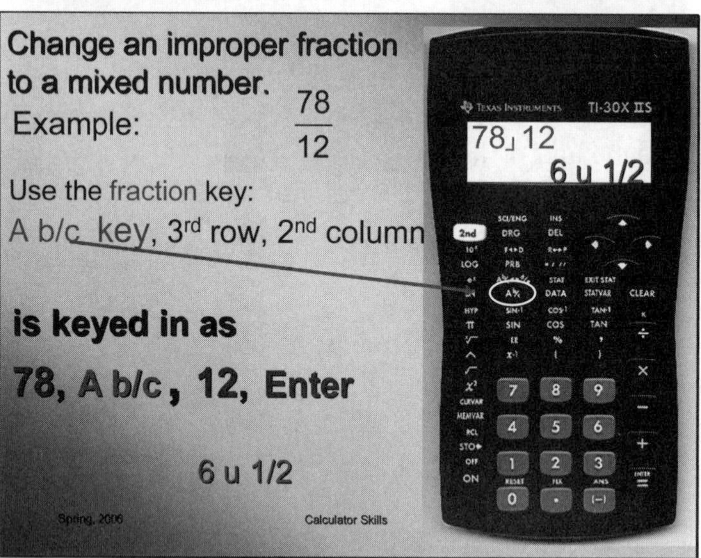
Change an improper fraction to a mixed number.
Example: 78/12
Use the fraction key:
A b/c key, 3rd row, 2nd column
is keyed in as
78, A b/c, 12, Enter
6 u 1/2
Spring, 2006
Calculator Skills
TEXAS INSTRUMENTS TI-30X IIS
78⌋12
6 u 1/2

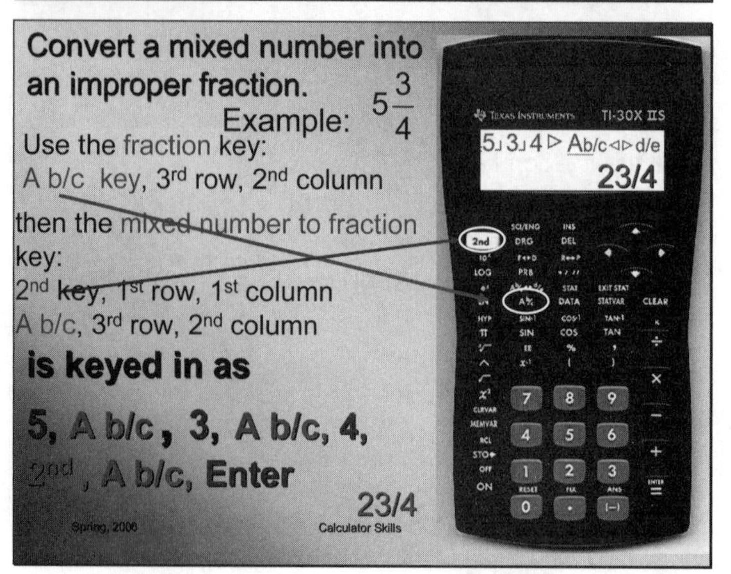
Convert a mixed number into an improper fraction.
Example: 5 3/4
Use the fraction key:
A b/c key, 3rd row, 2nd column
then the mixed number to fraction key:
2nd key, 1st row, 1st column
A b/c, 3rd row, 2nd column
is keyed in as
5, A b/c, 3, A b/c, 4,
2nd, A b/c, Enter
23/4
Spring, 2006
Calculator Skills
TEXAS INSTRUMENTS TI-30X IIS
5⌋3⌋4 ▷ Ab/c◁▷d/e
23/4